The Hackensack Water Works

By Clifford W. Zink

"Water promises to be to the twenty-first century what oil was to the twentieth century: the precious commodity that determines the wealth of nations."

—*Fortune* magazine

THE WATER WORKS
CONSERVANCY, INC.

The Water Works Conservancy, Inc.
Oradell, New Jersey

The Water Works Conservancy, Inc.
P.O. Box 714
Oradell, NJ 07649-2520
Telephone: 201-967-0133 Fax: 201-967-7517
www.hwwc.org

The New Jersey Historical Commission, a division of Cultural Affairs in the
Department of State, provided Research and Publication Grants in support of
this book.

Project Management, Jacket Design, and Typesetting in Times New Roman
by Argosy, Waltham, MA

An application for a Library of Congress Control Number has been submitted.

ISBN: 0-9746433-0-0

First Edition
This book was printed in Korea on acid-free paper.

Jacket Art
Front Cover
Color photos:
  left, Stairway detail from No. 7 Allis-Chalmers pumping engine, 1999. Chip Renner;
  center, No. 7 Allis-Chalmers pumping engine, c. 1996 (Plate 19). Jeff Wells;
  center right, "Hackensack Water Works, New Milford, N.J.," 1906 (Plate 2). Frank Vierling;
  far right, Pumping station and filtration house, 1997 (Plate 13). Dave Frieder
Illustrations:
  left, Overlay from "General Drawing, 18 Million Gallon Pumping Engine, Hackensack
  Water Company," 1901 (Figure 185). Water Works Conservancy;
  center, Detail from "Hackensack Water Company, New Milford, N.J., Engine House,"
  1882 (Figure 5). United Water Resources;
  center right, Illustration adapted from 1911 engine house entrance, west façade, c. 1988
  (Plate 14). Gerry Weinstein;
  far right, Illustration adapted from Coagulation basin, c. 1960 (Figure 167). United
  Water Resources
Back Cover
Hackensack Water Works, c. 1968. United Water Resources

Dedication

To all the people who founded, designed, built, managed, and
operated the Hackensack Water Works over a 108-year period,
and to all the men and women who have contributed their time,
efforts, and resources to preserving this American Treasure.

Table of Contents

Acknowledgements

Several organizations and numerous individuals have made essential contributions to the creation of this book.

The Water Works Conservancy has maintained a steadfast commitment to publishing this book. Maggie Harrer, the president and a founder of the Conservancy, has labored tirelessly for a decade to develop a broad appreciation of the remarkable history of the Hackensack Water Works, also known as the New Milford Plant, and its marvelous potential for preservation. Maggie's enthusiasm, creativity, generosity, determination, perseverance, and tireless efforts have inspired many people, including several Conservancy members who have generously contributed their efforts and resources toward the research and production of this book.

The New Jersey Historical Commission awarded research and publication grants to the Water Works Conservancy in support of much of the research, the oral history interviews, the writing, and the printing. Mary Murrin, the program officer at the Commission, provided steady encouragement and sound advice throughout the application and reporting process.

United Water Resources, the successor corporation to the Hackensack Water Company and a subsidiary of Suez, graciously provided access to historic resources that were essential for the production of this book. Several United Water employees provided exceptional help in the research stage. Many other current and former employees who worked at the New Milford Plant and who share a special reverence for its role in the development of modern water supply and purification have contributed considerably to this history. At the United Water offices, located in Harrington Park on a northern bank of the Oradell Reservoir, Rich Henning kindly arranged access to historic files, including documents and photographs of the development of the water works. Kevin Doell cordially assisted with the initial review of these files before he was called up for reserve duty in the spring of 2002. Rick Lane subsequently helped in the detailed research phase with equal cordiality, and his perseverance uncovered several important early documents. At the United Water engineering office at the Haworth Pumping Station, Jeanne Walker untiringly helped in accessing and copying the extensive collection of original drawings depicting the design and development of the water works. Tim Grud at Haworth contributed to this effort as well. Jack O'Hara at Haworth began his career at the New Milford Plant and enthusiastically shared his knowledge and appreciation of its operation. Jim Scherer at the Hackensack Yard provided access to pumpage records for the New Milford Plant.

Conservancy members and Oradell residents Linda and Nick Besink contributed enormously to the oral history research for this book. Linda cheerfully and efficiently organized the interviews and oversaw their transcriptions. Nick generously contributed his professional expertise and the use of his equipment to videotape the interviews in residential settings and at the water works, and he also scanned several historic images for the book. Reed Gidez also generously contributed his professional expertise and equipment for several of the interviews, and he provided copies of video images. Jeff and Bonnie Wells, members of the Conservancy, and Maggie Harrer and Rick Henly graciously contributed the use of their Oradell homes for the six primary interviews. Miles Kuchar and his son Jeff Kuchar assisted with the August 2002 interview and photo shoot at the plant. Cynthia J. Maissen of Teaneck professionally transcribed the interviews with precision and clarity.

Four former employees and two individuals long associated with the Hackensack Water Company graciously shared their experiences and knowledge of the New Milford Plant and the water industry in oral history interviews recorded on videotape: George Haskew of Hillsdale, an engineer and former president; Barry Schwartz of Hillsdale, a chemist and former supervisor of water treatment; Jim Flynn of Paramus, a former watch engineer; and Pat Hoffman of Park Ridge, a former laboratory technician. Pat's interview includes personal recollections of her husband Dan Hoffman, the former superintendent of the New Milford Plant, who died in 2000. Of the two individuals associated with the plant, Ted Hoffman of Paramus (no relation to Pat and Dan) shared his recollections of the many years when his father, Frank Hoffman, worked as a machinist at the New Milford Plant; and Miles Kuchar of Montvale shared his memories of the plant over several decades through his work as a contractor on numerous company projects at New Milford and other sites. Three former employees also shared their recollections: MaryFrances Schwartz started with the water company as a laboratory technician and eventually married Barry Schwartz; Jesse Jones started as a laborer and rose through the ranks in a variety of jobs around the plant; Fred Schelhas worked for the company for 34 years in several positions at the New Milford Plant, including foreman, assistant to Dan Hoffman, and assistant plant manager. Frank Vierling, the Oradell historian, shared his recollections of visiting the plant as a young boy growing up in Oradell. These vivid accounts of the water works in the second half of the twentieth century will only become more valuable with time.

Several photographers generously contributed their efforts to carefully document the beauty of the water works, often under difficult conditions. Conservancy members Dave Frieder of New Milford and Chip Renner of Rochelle Park have devoted countless hours to photographing the water works and to processing their images, which they shared graciously through multiple requests. Their legacy is a marvelous record of the decommissioned plant that significantly enhances this book and will serve many other purposes in the future. Conservancy member Jeff Wells of Oradell provided color photographs of the engine house, and his associate Jaime Laga helped document the plant and collect digital images. Two professional photographers provided their special expertise: James Hogan, a freelance photographer from Ireland, captured the oral history interviewees at the water works, and Ron Jautz, a freelance photographer from New York, captured portrait images of the interior and exterior of the plant.

Several individuals graciously provided historic images that augment the documentation of the water works in the United Water archives. Robert Von Autenreich, of Buck, Seifert & Jost of Norwood, which has provided decades of engineering services to the water company, shared several historic photographs of the New Milford Plant from his company's files. Frank Vierling shared numerous images from the marvelous collection of Oradell photographs that he has assembled, and he tirelessly assisted with numerous requests to scan many of these images for the book. Frank also obtained copies of postcard images kindly provided by William Berdan and Alice Berdan. Drawings by John Bowie Associates and photographs by A. Pierce Bounds from the "New Milford Plant of the Hackensack Water Company, Historic Structures Report, 1998" are used with permission of the Bergen County Division of Cultural and Historic Affairs.

Ed Smyk, the Passaic County historian, graciously provided access to the Passaic Valley Water Commission, where Ethel Senst kindly provided historic information and a tour of the Commission's pumping station and filtration plant at Little Falls. Ed also provided a timely introduction to Marinus De Nooyer, a 104-year-old former commissioner who assembled a museum at the Little Falls plant that the Commission subsequently named after him.

Gerry Weinstein generously shared his photographs of the New Milford Plant when it was still operating as well as drawings of early pumping engines from his collection, the Archive of Industry. Conrad Milster of Pratt Institute provided information on historic steam sites and graciously shared his extensive knowledge of steam technology. Frank Vopasek provided access to historic New Milford documents and shared photographs of steam technology from his collection. Larry Mostar, the Assistant Treatment Superintendent of the Cincinnati Department of Water Works, provided copies of early documents depicting the design of the Cincinnati Water Works and George Warren Fuller's experimental research on which it was based. Jennifer Metz provided information about the Grand Rapids Filtration Plant, designed by Hering & Fuller in 1911. Barry Schwartz, Jeff Carbeck, and Carol Litchfield provided explanations of some of the science on which filtration is based. Barry shared historic documents that are key resources in understanding early water analysis and purification efforts at the Hackensack Water Company. Paul Shopp provided information on historic resources.

Within the Bergen County administration, Art Cummings provided access to the water works on several occasions, and Janet Strom of the Division of Cultural and Historic Affairs provided access to materials in the county archives.

Robie Lange, a historian of technology at the National Park Service's National Landmark Program, provided wise counsel on assessing the water work's national significance and encouraged its interpretation for the public. Eric DeLony, chief of the Historic American Engineering Record at the National Park Service, provided a detailed report on the McNeil Street Pumping Station in Shreveport, Louisiana, as well as encouragement for this book. Margaret Newman, of Holt and Morgan Architects of Princeton, kindly shared historic images and information from the firm's research on the Weehawken Water Tower. Mark Magyar boosted the efforts on this book by publishing with great care a summary of the water works in *New Jersey Heritage* in the spring of 2002.

Several sources contain essential information on the water works that has been instrumental in producing this book. Adrian Leiby's *The Hackensack Water Company 1869–1969*, published by the Bergen County Historical Society in 1969, is an invaluable resource on the Hackensack Water Company's first 100 years, as seen from the perspective of an amateur historian and company officer. More recent historical studies have contributed significantly to understanding the development of the water works: "Historical Study and Evaluation of the New Milford Filtration Plant and Pumping Station," by Elise Baranowski, Gerald Weinstein, Nancy Gibbs, and Edward Lenik of Sheffield Archaeological Consultants (1991); "New Milford Plant of the Hackensack Water Company," National Register Nomination by Albin Rothe of Rothe Architects-Planners (1996); and "The New Milford Plant of the Hackensack Water Company, Historic Structures Report," by John Bowie Associates, Historical Architects, in association with Jane Mork Gibson, Industrial Historian (1998). Jane, who is an historian of the Fairmount Water Works in Philadelphia, graciously shared research and her knowledge of the early history of water purification in America.

Bob Griffin of Englewood, a past president of the Bergen County Historical Society, provided access to historic materials in the BCHS library as well as steady encouragement and sound advice.

At Argosy, Robb Kneebone, Alex Bilsky, and Adriana Lavergne have provided professional guidance throughout the book production process, and Carol Noble's editing of the manuscript improved it significantly. Frank Vierling graciously reviewed the text and contributed many comments that improved its historic accuracy. Ruth Van Wagoner also kindly contributed helpful comments.

My wife, Emily Davis Croll, contributed beyond measure with her unwavering support, encouragement, and counsel. My children, Alexander and Julianna, contributed their forbearance on many occasions.

To all these individuals I extend my sincere gratitude for their contributions toward the completion of this book.

Clifford Zink
Princeton, New Jersey
May 2003

Preface

One of the Great Pioneering Plants

"no city can grow beyond the possibilities of its water supply"

Water supply and quality are becoming major concerns around the world. Conflicting interests make increasing demands on shrinking supplies, and existing and projected shortages have become political issues. Water contamination plagues growing populations in many areas, including those with plenty of water. With few practical solutions to these challenges, many people are predicting that water will become the critical issue of the twenty-first century.

Most Americans take clean water for granted today, but a century ago the country struggled to supply its growing population with running water and to protect residents from deadly waterborne diseases like typhoid. In the nineteenth century America was growing faster than anyone had imagined. Canals, railroads, and the Civil War created vast opportunities to develop land and harvest natural resources, and Americans leapt at them. Waves of immigrants pushed natural population growth into double digits. Cities burst their boundaries and suburbs overran rural farmland. Soon Americans had to confront the fundamental reality of history: water controls growth. As one observer noted, "No city can grow beyond the possibilities of its water supply, as the water supply limits increase in population."[1]

These struggles were prominent in northeastern New Jersey as it changed in the second half of the nineteenth century from villages and farms to cities, towns, and suburbs. The growth of Bergen and Hudson counties and the development of the Hackensack Water Company to meet the regional demand for water paralleled similar progressions in many parts of the United States in the late nineteenth and early twentieth centuries. The first challenge was physical: collecting, storing, and pumping water to homes, businesses, and public places. The second challenge was environmental: providing clean and safe water for drinking, cooking, bathing, and manufacturing. The quest for purified water and the protection of watersheds were some of the first environmental efforts in New Jersey and in the country.

The people who started and developed the Hackensack Water Company rose to the challenge. Their efforts often placed the water company and its water works in the forefront of the national quest to develop safe and pure municipal water supplies. The history of the Hackensack Water Works is the story of the dedicated directors, officers, managers, employees, contractors, and consultants who shared this mission. Water people have historically given their best efforts to this work, typically putting their personal lives aside to ensure the continuity and safety of water supplies.

Most historic sites are readily understandable, such as the homes of famous people like Thomas Jefferson, monuments of nation building like Ellis Island, and the memorials of great struggles such as Gettysburg. By comparison, historic industrial sites are typically inaccessible and unknown. The processes that took place in them are often technical, their scale and design are unfamiliar, and their historic significance can be difficult to understand.

This book began with the desire to understand the Hackensack Water Works in Oradell, New Jersey—how it started and developed, what went on there, why it looks like it does, who made it work, and why it is nationally significant. In the spring of 2002 the Water Works Conservancy obtained a grant from the New Jersey Historical Commission to research these questions beyond the existing documentation and to present the story of the Hackensack Water Works in a book that would help illuminate its remarkable place in New Jersey and American history.

Part I tells the story of the Hackensack Water Works, also known as the New Milford Plant of the Hackensack Water Company, from its inception in 1882 through the end of World War II. The story of its development is contained in the words, drawings, and images of the people who created, designed, built, and operated it, and in scientific publications of the period. Most of the historic documents directly relating to the water works are in the archives of United Water Resources, the successor to the Hackensack Water Company. Other period documents can be found in libraries, particularly in the professional journals of the era.

Part I draws on the work of Adrian Leiby, a director of the Hackensack Water Company and an amateur historian of Bergen County. Leiby chronicled much of the company's history in his 1969 book, *The Hackensack Water Company 1869–1969*. A graduate of Hackensack High School, Middlebury College, and Columbia Law School, Leiby was a director of the Hackensack Water Company for over thirty years and its secretary for many of them. He was an officer of the Bergen County Historical Society and the author of several books on the history of Dutch New Jersey, including "The Revolutionary War in the Hackensack Valley" and "The Early Dutch and Swedish Settlers of New Jersey." He was a resident of Bergenfield and a partner of the New York law firm LeBoeuf, Lam, Leiby, and MacRae. Leiby's interesting book presents an inside story of the Hackensack Water Company with many fine illustrations and intriguing anecdotes.

Part II tells the postwar story of the Hackensack Water Works, largely through the oral histories of people who worked there. In the summer of 2002 the Water Works Conservancy conducted interviews and collected the reminiscences of former employees and relatives, and of people who had memorable experiences at the water works. The history of operating and improving the water works in the second half of the twentieth century is told in compelling words by six individuals interviewed for this book: Jim Flynn, George Haskew, Pat Hoffman, Ted Hoffman, Miles Kuchar, and Barry Schwartz. Two former employees, MaryFrances Schwartz and Jesse Jones, and Frank Vierling, the Oradell historian and a borough native, also shared their remembrances of the water works for this book. The interviews and reminiscences provide firsthand descriptions of working for the company, operating the filtration plant and the pumping station, analyzing water quality, and growing up around the water works.

All together, these rich sources present the story of the dedicated efforts and pioneering spirit that provided pure water for a large portion of New Jersey's population. Some of the country's leading engineers developed innovations that made the Hackensack Water Works a model of water works engineering. The filtration plant represents a milestone in the development of the American system of mechanical filtration that enabled cities and towns to deliver purified water on a large scale for the first time. As Adrian Leiby wrote in 1969, "Standard texts on water supply engineering now refer to the New Milford Plant, along with Louisville, Kentucky, and Little Falls, New Jersey, as one of the great pioneering plants in the field, one of the plants which laid the groundwork for most of the later filter plants in the nation."[2]

Today the Hackensack Water Works represents the development of modern water supply in its critical period of growth. It occupies most of historic Van Buskirk Island in Oradell at the tidal head of the Hackensack River in Bergen County. The water works contains a steam powered pumping station that the water company first erected in 1882 and expanded five times over thirty years, and a filtration plant that the water company opened in 1905 and expanded twice in fifty years. Although the water company added electric pumps in the 1950s, it continued its steam operation until closing the plant in 1990. Most of the complex predates World War I, and its site, buildings, and equipment are remarkably intact.[3]

In 1993 United Water Resources, the successor corporation to the Hackensack Water Company, donated the New Milford Plant to the citizens of Bergen County. In 1996 Preservation New Jersey designated the site one of New Jersey's "10 Most Endangered Historic Sites." That year, concerned citizens in Bergen County, led by Maggie Harrer, a resident of Oradell, formed a coalition to preserve the Hackensack Water Works for cultural and educational purposes. In 1999 the coalition incorporated the Water Works Conservancy. In 2000 Save America's Treasures, a public/private coalition between the White House Millennium Council, the National Park Service and the National Trust for Historic Preservation "dedicated to identifying and rescuing the enduring symbols of American tradition that define us as a nation," designated the Hackensack Water Works as an "American Treasure." In 2001 the water works was listed on the New Jersey and National Registers of Historic Places, and Preservation New Jersey and the National Trust for Historic Preservation formed the Statewide and National Coalition to Save the Water Works. In 2002 the National Trust for Historic Preservation included the site as one of the "11 Most Endangered National Historic Places" and the History Channel aired nationally a preservation documentary, "Save Our History," that included the site. Despite its sparkling history, the future of the Hackensack Water Works remains cloudy as many issues affecting its preservation and adaptive reuse remain unresolved.

Hackensack Water Works Time Line

1867 Charles H. Voorhis of Hackensack charters the Cherry Hill Water & Gas Company to supply water to Hackensack.

1869 Garrett Ackerman of Hackensack charters the Hackensack Water Company.

1873 Charles H. Voorhis acquires controlling interest in the Hackensack Water Company and merges it with the Cherry Hill Water & Gas Company.

Bacot & Ward of Jersey City design and build the Cherry Hill Reservoir and distribution lines to deliver water to Hackensack.

1874 Water service begins in Hackensack, population 4,500, at a rate of approximately 750,000 gallons per week.

1879 Hackensack Water Company placed in receivership.

1880 Bacot & Ward acquire Hackensack Water Company assets and create the Hackensack Water Company Reorganized, with William S. Banta as president and R. C. Bacot as treasurer.

1881 Reorganized company contracts in September with Hoboken, population 30,000, to supply water starting on November 1, 1882.

1882 New directors elected: Robert de Forest, of the Central Railroad of New Jersey, and president of the Metropolitan Museum of Art, New York; Julian Kane of Elizabethtown Water, Elizabeth, New Jersey; W. W. Shippen, executor of the Stevens' Estate in Hoboken; and Daniel Runkle of the Warren Foundry and Machine Company in Phillipsburg, New Jersey.

Purchase of 11-acre Van Buskirk Island in New Milford for $50,000 in December.

Charles B. Brush of Spielmann & Brush, Civil Engineers, of Hoboken, hired as chief engineer and superintendent.

Construction of engine house and coal shed/boiler house begins at New Milford, with pump No. 1, a 6-million-gallon Worthington steam pumping engine, and laying of 20-inch main from New Milford to Weehawken along New Jersey & New York Railroad.

Beginning of water service to Hoboken in November at a rate of 3.8 MGD.

1883 Construction of Weehawken Reservoir No. 1, for storage of 15 million gallons, and 175-foot-high water tower with 150,000-gallon tank; opening of Weehawken office.

1884 Installation of pump No. 2, a 4-million-gallon Worthington steam pumping engine.

1885 Robert de Forest elected president.

1886 Construction of first additions to the engine house and boiler house.

1887 Professor Albert Ripley Leeds of Stevens Institute in Hoboken begins recording monthly water analysis of Hackensack water.

1888 Construction of 24-inch main from New Milford to Ridgefield via Englewood.

1891 Construction of 12-inch main from the West Shore Railroad at Weehawken to Edgewater along River Road.

Construction of second addition to engine house with pump No. 3, a 10-million-gallon Worthington steam pumping engine.

1894   The Borough of Delford is incorporated with boundaries including Van Buskirk Island, formerly in the village of New Milford.

1898   D. W. French appointed superintendent.

Construction of new boiler house with four boilers east of the engine house.

Construction of third addition to the engine house with Nos. 5 and 6 pumps, VTE pumping engines manufactured by Edward P. Allis Company of Milwaukee, rated at 12 MGD and 18 MGD, respectively.

1900   Report by Allen Hazen on feasibility of filtration at New Milford pumping station, recommending sand filtration.

Purchase of Spring Valley Water Works and Supply Company, established in 1893 by real estate developer J. P. Lespiasse to supply the village of Spring Valley.

1901   Purchase of Veldran's Mill and land along Hackensack River for the Oradell Reservoir in December.

1902   Construction begins on Oradell Reservoir for storage of 250 million gallons.

Construction begins on Weehawken Reservoir No. 2, for storage of 69 million gallons.

East Jersey Water Company opens the Little Falls Filtration Plant in September, the first large-scale mechanical filtration plant designed to the specifications of George Warren Fuller, supervising engineer.

1903   Hering & Fuller, the New York engineering firm of George Warren Fuller and Rudolph Hering, report on feasibility of filtration at New Milford pumping station in February, recommending a mechanical filtration plant.

Construction begins on Woodcliff Lake Reservoir on Pascack Creek for storing 800 million gallons.

Construction begins on mechanical filtration plant designed by Hering & Fuller.

1904   Construction of New Durham relay pumping station in Hudson County.

1905   Filtration plant placed in service, the second large-scale mechanical filtration plant, with eight filters rated at 24 MGD, and a water quality laboratory for daily analysis of raw and filtered water. George R. Spalding hired as supervisor of water treatment.

1906   Construction of addition to boiler house with two boilers.

1908   First use of chlorine treatment for disinfecting water, in Jersey City.

1909   Chlorine treatment started at New Milford filtration plant.

1911   Construction of fourth addition to engine house with three VTE steam pumping engines manufactured by Allis-Chalmers Company: No. 7, rated at 20 MGD, and Nos. 8 and 9, rated at 7.5 MGD.

Construction begins to enlarge Oradell Reservoir to a storage capacity of 1.6 billion gallons.

1912   Construction of filter house extension with eight additional filters, for a total capacity of 48 MGD.

Spring Valley service territory extended to Hudson River to serve Piermont, Grandview, and Orangetown.

1915   No. 3 pump, a 36-MGD Allis-Chalmers centrifugal steam pumping engine, installed in 1886 engine house.

1917   Water supplied to Camp Merritt in Dumont, an embarkation point for 42,000 World War I troops.

1918   Construction of circular chimney at northeast corner of 1906 boiler house.

1920   Delford changes its name to Oradell.

1921 Construction begins on concrete dam and expansion of Oradell Reservoir for storage of 2.3 billion gallons.

1923 Water supply contract with Hoboken ends.

1926 Nicholas S. Hill elected president.

1927 Holland Tunnel opens.

1928 Construction begins to enlarge Oradell Reservoir for storage of 2.85 billion gallons.

1929 George Spalding oversees development of powdered activated carbon treatment for taste and odor control at New Milford.

No. 10 pump, a 30-MGD centrifugal steam turbine manufactured by the DeLaval Turbine Company, installed in 1911 engine house.

1932 George Washington Bridge completed, linking Bergen County with Manhattan.

Land in Old Tappan purchased for future reservoir.

1934 Water quality laboratory quadrupled at New Milford to meet new testing requirements; Paul Tamer becomes first chief chemist.

1936 Henry L. de Forest elected president.

1937 Lincoln Tunnel opens.

1941 Installation of No. 11 pump in 1891 engine house and No. 12 pump in 1911 engine house, both centrifugal turbine pumps manufactured by the Worthington Company and rated at 20 MGD and 10 MGD, respectively.

1943 Water supplied to Camp Shanks in Orangeburg, Rockland County, New York, an embarkation camp during World War II.

1945 Water treatment process adds the application of ammonia.

1950 George H. Buck elected president; Peter Pallo appointed superintendent of water treatment.

1954 Construction of substation on Van Buskirk Island for electrification of New Milford Plant.

1955 Construction of filter house extension with six additional filters, bringing capacity of the filtration plant to approximately 70 million gallons.

1956 Installation of No. 13 pump in the 1911 engine house, a centrifugal pump rated at 30 MGD and manufactured by the DeLaval Turbine Company, the site's first electric pump.

Acquisition of Monsey Water Corporation system in Rockland County.

1957 Opening of De Forest Lake Reservoir with a storage capacity of 5 billion gallons in Rockland County.

1958 Acquisition of Montvale Water System.

1959 Installation of No. 14 pump, a DeLaval electric centrifugal rated at 30 MGD.

1961 Beginning of five-year drought—the worst on record.

1964 Haworth Plant opened with a projected capacity of 50 MGD.

Acquisition of Franklin Lakes and Bogota water systems.

Construction of 5-million-gallon pumping and filtration plant at De Forest Lake.

1965 Acquisition of Haverstraw water system.

1967 Lake Tappan Reservoir opens with a storage capacity of 3.5 billion gallons.

1970 Construction of 9.1-million gallon Alpine elevated tank, one of the largest of its kind.

1972 Acquisition of Upper Nyack water system.

Construction of Ridgefield storage tanks, with a capacity of 5 million gallons.

1973   Walter T. Lucking elected president.

1974   Mastodon bones discovered in Oradell Reservoir.

1975   Water quality laboratory doubled in size to meet new drinking water regulations.

1976   Construction of raw water engine house south of New Milford Avenue, on site of 1882–1886 boiler house and coal shed, with two electric pumps rated at 45 million gallons each.

1979   Robert A. Gerber, who had been with the company since 1961, becomes president.

1980   Research on ozone purification process begins.

1981   Construction begins on the Oradell Aqueduct to bring Passaic basin water to the Oradell Reservoir, the first phase of the Wanaque South Project, which will be the water company's first major supply source outside the Hackensack basin.

1983   Hackensack Water Company reorganizes and forms United Water Resources.

1984   Water quality laboratory expanded in a prefabricated building adjacent to the filtration house for advanced analytical equipment needed to meet expanded regulations for drinking water.

1985   Expansion begins on Haworth Plant for ozone purification process.

        Construction begins on the Monkeville Dam and Reservoir, with a projected storage capacity of 7 billion gallons for the Wanaque South Project.

1987   Seventy-eight-inch main completed to connect Haworth Plant to the hub of the distribution system at New Milford Plant.

        Wanaque South Project opens, increasing capacity by 40 MGD to ensure sufficient water supply into the twenty-first century.

1988   George M. Haskew elected president.

1989   Dedication of the Haworth Water Treatment Plant, hailed by many as the most advanced in the world.

1990   Pumping and water treatment terminated at New Milford on May 31.

1991   Water quality laboratory moved to a new building at the Haworth Plant.

1993   New Milford Plant donated to Bergen County with $1 million stewardship fund.

1996   Preservation New Jersey designates New Milford Plant as one of the state's ten Most Endangered Sites.

1997   Water Works Conservancy formed by Oradell and regional residents to preserve the water works.

2000   New Milford Plant designated as an official site of the Save America's Treasures Program at the U.S. Department of the Interior, a coalition among the White House Millennium Council, the National Park Service, and the National Trust for Historic Preservation.

2001   New Milford Plant entered into the New Jersey and National Registers of Historic Places.

2002   National Trust for Historic Preservation designates New Milford Plant as one of America's 11 Most Endangered National Historic Places.

2003   New Jersey Department of Environmental Protection confirms the New Jersey Historic Sites Council's resolution requiring Bergen County to develop a Preservation Plan to guide the public stewardship of the Hackensack Water Works.

Glossary

Air scour—The process of blowing air up through the sand to loosen filtering residue prior to the backwashing of the 1905–1912 filters with filtered water. Also called *air scrub*.

Alum—Sulphate of alumina, a natural chemical used for treating water to coagulate suspended particles.

Boiler house—A building at the pumping station that housed boilers for producing steam to power the pumping engines and other machinery.

Chemical house— See *coagulant house*.

Clear well—A covered reservoir for holding filtered water before it is pumped into the distribution system, located in the basement of the filtration house. Also called a *filtered water reservoir*.

Coagulant—See *flocculant*.

Coagulant house— South end of the filtration plant; the four-story central tower contains tanks for mixing alum and soda solutions for chemical treatment of the water in the coagulation basin, and the two-story wings contain laboratories, machinery, and storage space. Also called *chemical house* or *head house*.

Coagulation basin— Formed by excavation and embankments, the basin held 12 million gallons of water for chemical treatment with a coagulant and the subsequent settling of coagulated particles. Also called *cog basin*, *co-ag basin*, *settling basin*, and *sedimentation basin*.

Conduit—A large duct for conducting water made of reinforced concrete.

Controller—Valve mechanism for regulating the filtration rate of water through a filter and into a clear well.

Cross-compound engine—A steam engine that uses a single blast of steam successively in two cylinders of small and large sizes to increase efficiency.

Drinking water—Water that has been filtered and purified with chemical treatments; the water that consumers receive through the distribution system. Also called *filtered water*.

Effluent—Water that comes out of something, such as filtered water from a filter.

Engine house—A building containing pumps, engines, and motors for pumping water.

Filter—A concrete tank with a filtering medium of sand and gravel and devices for screening and collecting filtered water at the bottom.

Filter gallery—The raised, central portion of the filter house that runs between the filters and contains the operating tables for controlling the filtering and backwashing processes. Also called *operating gallery* and *operating floor*.

Filter house—The portion of the filtration house north of the coagulant house that contains the filters, the operating gallery, and the pipe gallery.

Filtered water—See *drinking water*.

Filtered water reservoir—See *clear well*.

Filtration house—The building containing the filter house and the coagulant house.

Filtration plant—All the buildings, structures, machinery, and piping necessary to filter water: the filtration house, coagulation basin, gate house, wash water tank, equalization basin (modern), and underground piping. Also called *purification works*.

Flocc—A precipitate that forms and sinks to the bottom of the coagulation basin when a chemical flocculant is applied to water.

Flocculant—A chemical applied in a solution to raw water to coagulate particles for settling, commonly sulphate of alumina or alum. Also called *coagulant*.

Gate house—A small building containing chambers and piping for controlling the flow of water into and out of the coagulation basin and the application of flocculants and other treatment chemicals.

Head—Water pressure from gravity, measured in part by the amount of water accumulated above an outlet.

Head house—Same as the *coagulant house*; typically a one- or more story structure at one end of a building like a filtration plant.

Influent—Water going into a tank, basin, or filter.

Intake canal—A canal for conveying water from the intake reservoir to the engine house.

Intake reservoir—A pond filled from the Hackensack River that holds water for the pumping station; excess water flows to the river. Also called *intake pond* and *intake basin*.

Machinery room—On the ground floor of the east wing of the coagulation house; contains air compressors and pumps for backwashing the filters.

Mechanical filter—A filter with layers of sand and gravel that uses stirring devices or air scour to agitate the filtering media in conjunction with backwashing by water up through the filter drain.

MGD—Millions of gallons per day.

Monolith—A structure made from a continuous pour of concrete, such as a filter.

Operating floor—See *filter gallery*.

Operating table—A cabinet with a table top containing various switching devices for controlling the flow of water through a filter and the backwashing process.

Pumping station—Consisted historically of a boiler house where steam was produced; an engine house where steam engines pumped the water, and all the necessary piping. A modern pumping station typically has an engine house powered by electric motors.

Purification works—See *filtration plant*.

Raw water—Untreated water taken from a source like a river, well, or reservoir.

Reciprocating engine—An engine with a piston that moves back and forth in a horizontal cylinder or up and down in a vertical cylinder.

Sedimentation basin—See *coagulation basin*.

Settled water—Water taken from the upper half of a coagulation or settling basin after the flocculant has settled coagulated particles to the bottom. Also called *treated water*.

Settling basin—See *coagulation basin*.

Suction well—A small reservoir from which pumps suck water. The 1882 and 1898 engine house sections have interior suction wells, while the 1911 section has one on the exterior.

Tastes and odors—The tastes and odors in potable water measured by industry standards.

Traveling crane—An overhead crane that rolls along steel rails supported on steels posts; used for installing and maintaining equipment.

Treated water—See *settled water*.

VTE—A vertical triple expansion steam engine that uses one blast of steam three times in three different cylinders of increasing size to maximize the use of the steam.

Wash water—Filtered water used to backwash filters.

Wash water tank—A tank for holding filtered water that is used in backwashing filters.

Water wheel—A wheel powered by pressurized water that operates machinery, as in the Pelton water wheels originally installed in the machinery room and in the coagulation basin.

Part I

The Sparkling Purity of the Product

This first part of the history of the Hackensack Water Works begins with the founding of the Hackensack Water Company in 1869 and continues through World War II. The abundance of historic resources from this era contributes substantially to our understanding of the national significance of the Hackensack Water Works and our appreciation of the many capable people who dedicated themselves to meeting the water supply and water quality challenges within the Hackensack Valley as it developed from farmland into a densely populated region.

One of the sources is Adrian Leiby's centennial history of the Hackensack Water Company published in 1969, in which he illuminated the social, political and financial circumstances surrounding its formation in 1869 and its early years through corporate minutes, newspaper accounts, and anecdotes of the period. The remarkable collection of drawings, photographs, ledgers, reports, and publications within the United Water Resources archives sheds considerably more light on the water company's development of its water works on Van Buskirk Island at the head of the navigable portion of the Hackensack River and its expansion eight times in the ensuing decades. Professional journals of the late nineteenth and early twentieth centuries add a compelling perspective and absorbing details on the landmark role of the Hackensack Water Works within the development of modern water supply and purification.

Architectural and engineering drawings of the Hackensack Water Works from 1882, 1886, 1891, 1898, 1904, 1906, 1911, 1912, and 1953 document how exceptionally talented engineers met the on-going challenges of providing increasing amounts of safe and pure water to an ever-growing population. In addition to handsomely illustrating their innovative technical solutions, the drawings show the engineers' aesthetic aspirations and those of the directors who recognized that the buildings represented the water company's prominent public role as a private supplier of municipal water.

Historic photographs provide complementary views of the evolution of the water works over the decades, including the gradual transition from steam pumping engines to electric pumps and the increasing importance of water quality. They also present intriguing and tantalizing images of some of the many people involved with the water works, whether they were key individuals engaged in design and management or the typically anonymous workers who kept the pumps and purification equipment running around the clock. Many photographs also reveal portions of the water works landscape as the site evolved from a basic pumping station to an integrated pumping and purification complex.

Ledgers and reports from the turn of the twentieth century, when suppliers all over the country were struggling with an increasing demand for water amidst a growing public concern about its quality, provide eloquent and revealing analyses of the conditions of Hackensack River water, and of the supply and quality challenges faced by the Hackensack Water Company. Albert Leeds' *Water Analysis* ledger (1887–1900) presents an extraordinarily detailed account of early scientific efforts to document and understand factors affecting water quality. Several reports on the Hackensack watershed provide the rationale for the water company's purchase of watershed land and the construction of the series of impounding reservoirs along the river that today store many billions of gallons of water for customers in Bergen County in New Jersey and Rockland County in New York. Reports by the era's foremost sanitary engineers, Allen Hazen (1900) and Hering & Fuller

(1903), document the water purification debate between the leading proponent of the slow sand system of filtration, and the principal developers of the new system of rapid sand or mechanical filtration. The Hering & Fuller report specifies the rationale for the water company's construction of its filtration plant, which today is the nation's oldest example of mechanical filtration on a large scale and a landmark of innovative American engineering.

A series of pamphlets published by the Hackensack Water Company beginning in 1906 illustrates the growth of its facilities over six decades to meet the ever-increasing demand for pure water. *The Hackensack Water Company Filtration Plant* of 1906 illustrates and describes the water company's state-of-the-art efforts to purify water and to scientifically monitor its quality from the river to the faucet. The pamphlet also explains the water company's systematic efforts to protect the Hackensack watershed, a remarkably early example of environmental protection in New Jersey.

Engineering and scientific journals from the late nineteenth and early twentieth century present a fascinating national perspective on the development of modern water supply and the role of the Hackensack Water Company and its water works. Detailed and illustrated papers by Allen Hazen, George Warren Fuller, and other leaders in the emerging field of sanitary engineering enable us to understand from their own words the unprecedented challenges they faced and the remarkable creativity they employed to solve them. Peer reviews published in the journals alongside these reports enhance our understanding of this creativity and its impact on the design and operation of the Hackensack Water Works.

All these sources help us understand the remarkable buildings, structures, and machinery of the Hackensack Water Works that survives intact today as a monument on Van Buskirk Island to all the people who dedicated their efforts to bringing safe, pure municipal water to the Hackensack Valley.

Chapter 1

Give Our People a Good Supply of Water

With its easy access to Manhattan Island across the Hudson River, Bergen County became the early center of the Dutch settlement of New Jersey in the late seventeenth century and early eighteenth centuries. The fine timber stands and good soil in the Hackensack River valley contributed to the prosperity of the Dutch farmers who built frame and stone houses along the river and its tributaries.

The Hackensack River begins in the foothills near Pomona in Rockland County, New York, and flows through Bergen County into Newark Bay (see Color Plate 32). Railroad construction around the time of the Civil War stimulated considerable population growth in Bergen and a switch from agriculture to suburban development. With nearly 4,000 residents in 1869, the county seat of Hackensack was changing from a "complacent country village . . . to a cosmopolitan suburban town."[4]

In November 1869 an editor of the *Bergen County Democrat* wrote:

> *Hackensack is rapidly advancing in wealth and population in spite of old fogeyism; we have a superior quality of gas in our streets and we need pure water in our houses as well. We cannot get along with the supply furnished us from our superficial wells and cisterns; what we need is a broad, liberal and gushing supply permeating through our houses, and affording every family enough and to spare for bathing as well as culinary and drinking purposes. A good bath is a luxury which cannot be too highly appreciated, but it can be obtained but in few houses in Hacken-*
> *sack except at the expense of much toil and trouble. Let the . . . Water Company build their works and give our people a good supply of water, and it will pay from the start.*[5]

"a memorial to the introduction of water into town"

Adrian Leiby credited two prominent Bergen Dutch citizens with initiating parallel efforts to develop water service for Hackensack. Charles H. Voorhis was a lawyer, landowner, banker, and a prominent Republican who was born at the Voorhis homestead on Spring Valley Road in Paramus. In 1867 he chartered the Cherry Hill Water & Gas Company to supply water to Hackensack. Garret Ackerson was a businessman and banker, militia officer, and prominent Democrat who was born in Pascack. In 1869 he chartered the Hackensack Water Company for the same purpose.

The competition between these efforts discouraged investors from advancing the capital each firm needed to build a system. By 1873 public frustration with the lack of progress and a series of disastrous fires led *The Bergen Citizen* to proclaim, "The leading question agitating Hackensack at present is that of a water supply and everything pertaining to it is of interest." With his charter set to expire, Ackerson offered his company's stock at a public subscription in July 1873. To the consternation of Ackerson and his associates, Voorhis bought a controlling number of Hackensack Water Company shares and merged his Cherry Hill Water & Gas Company into it.[6]

With the competition removed, Voorhis hired Bacot & Ward of Jersey City to design and build a system to deliver Hackensack River water to customers in Hackensack who were willing to install the necessary piping in their buildings. Leiby described Bacot & Ward as "one of New Jersey's ablest engineering and construction firms" and R. C. Bacot as "the first of a long line of distinguished engineers that the Hackensack Water Company [was] proud to claim as its own." A descendent of Huguenots from South Carolina, Bacot was instrumental in the development of Jersey City and served several terms in the New Jersey Assembly.[7]

Despite the financial panic that gripped the country near the end of 1873, Voorhis pressed on and acquired a portion of John Zabriskie's farm on Cherry Hill, on the east side of the Hackensack River near New Bridge, for the Cherry Hill Reservoir, which he had first contemplated back in 1867. Over the winter, laborers for Bacot & Ward dug miles of trenches by hand, and laid iron and wooden pipes in them along Main, Essex, and other streets in Hackensack. During the spring and summer they built the 3-million-gallon reservoir of brick and earth and completed connections to customers' service lines. Bacot & Ward installed a small pumping station to pump the river water into the reservoir, which was about 75 feet higher in elevation than Hackensack. The water company operated the pump as needed to keep the water level high enough to maintain the required gravity pressure for customers and fire hydrants.[8]

On October 21, 1874, the Hackensack Water Company initiated service with a "water celebration" that included a parade of a dozen brass bands and firemen's groups. *The Bergen Citizen* reported that Voorhis "presented to the citizens of Hackensack the handsome fountain on the Public Green as a memorial to the introduction of water into town." Bacot & Ward donated the fountain (Figure 1), and in accepting it, J. J. Anderson, the president of the Hackensack Improvement Commission, proclaimed, "The people should feel proud of the water and grateful to the gentlemen who had initiated the enterprise."[9]

Despite this celebration, Hackensack, Bergen County, and the Hackensack Water Company faced darkening prospects as the economic downturn

Figure 1: "Fountain on the Green, Hackensack, N.J.," c. 1880. Bacot & Ward of Jersey City, the designers and builders of the Hackensack Water Company's first water supply system, donated a classical statue on the public green to celebrate the initiation of water service in Hackensack in 1874. William Berdan and Alice Berdan

that began in 1873 expanded around the country. While the water company would soon fall on hard times, Albert R. Leeds foretold its resurrection in a January 1875 article that appeared in *The New Jersey Citizen*. Leeds, a chemist and professor at the Stevens Institute of Technology in Hoboken, noted, "The Hackensack River could easily provide 20,000,000 gallons a day, enough to supply the City of Hoboken and provide thirty years growth." In the next two decades, both Hoboken and Leeds would play prominent roles in the development of the Hackensack Water Company.[10]

In the spring of 1875, the New Jersey Midland Railroad, one of the lines serving Hackensack, went bankrupt, along with many other businesses. By 1876 there were thousands of delinquent tax sales in Bergen County, and tumbling property values pinched large landowners, including Charles Voorhis. Financial problems mounted at his bank and at the water company, as more and more customers couldn't pay their bills and discontinued service. Despite these problems, Voorhis ran for Congress in 1878 and was elected. By the spring of 1879 the water company was unable to sell bonds and ran out of money to pay its creditors. As part of their payment for designing and building the water system, Bacot & Ward had accepted a large number of bonds, and in April 1879 they forced the Hackensack Water Company into receivership. In 1880 Bacot & Ward acquired the water company's assets and created a new company, called the Hackensack Water Company Reorganized, with R. C. Bacot as treasurer.[11]

The reorganization proved to be a major turning point in several ways. Bacot & Ward's Hudson County connections launched the reorganized water company as a supplier for multiple towns. This transition attracted investors who were prominent in the financial and political affairs of northeast New Jersey.

"the leading men in their fields"

In 1880 the city of Hoboken, located on the Hudson about 10 miles southeast of Hackensack, had a population of 30,000. Thanks to regular ferry service, Hoboken was growing rapidly as a bedroom community for people who worked in Manhattan, and it needed a new source of water, particularly since a drought that year worsened the water supply situation. The family of John Stevens, the steamship inventor and Camden & Amboy Railroad promoter, had incorporated the Hoboken Land and Improvement Company in 1838 after his death, and had extensive landholdings in the city. Leiby credited the Stevens as the "prime movers in bringing Hackensack Water to Hoboken." In June 1881, the *Bergen County Democrat* reported "that the Stevens' Estate had taken 300,000 of the stock of the Water Company, and that the prospect of enlarging the plant was good."[12]

In September 1881, Hoboken contracted with the Hackensack Water Company to begin supplying water to the city on November 1, 1882. To benefit its interests in Hoboken, the Stevens' Estate had specified that the water company supply the city at wholesale rates. When Hoboken residents enthusiastically confirmed the arrangement by referendum in early November 1881, Hackensack residents were also relieved, as "it meant that a new and enlarged plant would be constructed in the fresh water reaches of the river, and that sufficient capital would be provided to extend service throughout the town."[13]

After the referendum, the board reorganized, appointing several influential directors, including W. W. Shippen, the executor of the Stevens' Estate; Julian Kean, a member of the Elizabeth, New Jersey, family that controlled the Elizabethtown Water Company and was prominent in banking and state affairs dating back to William Livingston, the colonial governor; Daniel Runkle, whose family controlled the Warren Foundry and Machine Company of Phillipsburg, New Jersey, the firm that would supply miles of piping for the new system and continue supplying the water company for over two decades; and Robert de Forest, a prominent New York philanthropist, Wall Street lawyer, officer of the Central Railroad of New Jersey, and president of the Metropolitan Museum of Art (he and his wife donated the museum's American wing). As the primary owners, the Stevens, Kean, and de Forest families would control the water company for decades, and along the way provide much of the capital that fueled its dramatic expansion.

De Forest's appointment was particularly significant: he served on the board for forty-six years, forty-two of them as president, from 1885 to 1927. Under his guidance the Hackensack Water Company grew from a one-town pumping operation to a regional utility with exemplary distribution and water purification. De Forest's involvement in dozens of other business and philanthropic efforts in New York and New Jersey no doubt gave him a sense of the Hackensack Water Company's potential in the region and access to the finances and talent needed to realize it. When de Forest died in 1931, Jimmy Walker, the mayor of New York, noted that with all his achievements and contributions, "He remained in the background, modest and self-effacing." Leiby noted de Forest's "ability to seek out and attract the leading men in their fields for his enterprises," a precedent that the water company followed for over a century.[14]

With this influx of talent and resources, the water company established its home office in Hoboken and promptly began developing the facilities needed to supply Hoboken and to expand service in Hackensack. A few weeks after the Hoboken referendum, the water company acquired a parcel of land along the Hackensack River for $50,000. It included the western portion of what is now known as Van Buskirk Island, J. & H. Van Buskirk's gristmill at the southwestern corner of the island on the south side of Landing Road, now known as New Milford Avenue, a mill pond north of the road, and a smaller island slightly upriver (see Color Plate 1: "Map of Property conveyed to the Hackensack Water Company Reorganized, Dec. 28th, 1881"). Van Buskirk Island was at the head of navigation and brackish water on the river, and the sloops that sailed up the river tied up at the "old dock" along Landing Road. The island had been a mill site since before the Revolutionary War, first as a sawmill and later as a tannery, bleaching mill, button factory, and finally the gristmill (Figure 2). The mill was fed by a pond formed by a dam at the northwest corner of the island. This dam and a second dam further upstream, which fed an old millrace, kept salt water from advancing up the river. The New Jersey & New York Railroad ran along the west bank of the river and connected the site with Hackensack, providing a potential water line route as well as transportation for construction materials and operating supplies.

In January 1882, F. W. Jenkins devised an "Outline of Proposed General Arrangement" for the Hackensack Water Company's works on Van Buskirk Island (Figure 3). The plan called for a single building with 40-foot-square engine and boiler rooms and an adjacent 10-foot-square "Chimney 100 Ft. High." The design included two pumping engines that would draw water

Figure 2: J. & H. Van Buskirk's Mill. The nineteenth-century gristmill stood on the southwest corner of the island on Landing Road, now New Milford Avenue. This view is toward the southeast. Oradell Library

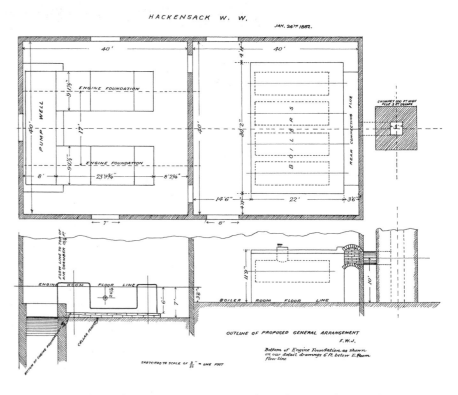

Figure 3: "Hackensack W. W. Jan. 24th 1882, Outline of Proposed General Arrangement, F.W.J." A note on the sheet refers to "our detail drawings," suggesting that additional drawings were done at the same time. United Water Resources

from a "Pump Well" in the engine room, and four boilers in the boiler room. Whether F. W. Jenkins was an engineer or a draftsman is unknown.

With resources from the Stevens' Estate and the de Forest and Kean families, the directors invested substantially in their new facilities. As they considered Jenkins' "Proposed General Arrangement," they must have been thinking of the future expansion of the works as well as the precedents and public image established by other water works. The designers of publicly owned facilities like the 1818 Fairmount Water Works in Philadelphia and the 1860 Louisville Water Works in Louisville, Kentucky, had employed neoclassical design to relate their buildings to the great engineering works of ancient Rome. While private water companies typically built utilitarian structures to house their pumping equipment, the Hackensack Water Company directors chose to erect distinguished buildings that were symbolic as well as functional.

"an inspiring engineer and an all-around gentleman"

Early in the development of the new facilities, the directors hired Charles Benjamin Brush as the company's first chief engineer (Figure 4). Brush was born in New York in 1848 and upon graduating from New York University as a civil engineer at the age of 19 in 1867, he went to work for the Engineer Corps on the Croton Aqueduct. In 1869, at the age of 21, he formed a partnership with Arthur Spielmann in Hoboken. During the next three decades, Brush rose to prominence in the engineering profession, becoming an instructor in engineering at New York University in 1874, a professor in 1888, and dean of the School of Engineering in 1895. The American Society of Civil Engineers (ASCE) elected Brush a director in 1888 and vice president in 1892.[15]

While Brush worked on railroads, trolleys, ferries, bridges, tunnels, buildings, and insurance atlases, he concentrated much of his career on water and

Figure 4: Hackensack Water Company Weehawken office, c. 1885. Chief Engineer Charles Benjamin Brush, seated at the desk on the right, supervised the development of the company's water supply system from 1882 to 1897. United Water Resources

sewerage: "As chief engineer, consultant, or managing director, he either built, remodeled, or enlarged water and sewerage systems in New Rochelle, Irvington, Highland Falls, Southampton, Far Rockaway, and Syracuse in New York; Plainfield, and the great Hackensack system in New Jersey; Lancaster and Easton, Pennsylvania; Alliance, Ohio; Kansas City, Missouri; Kansas City, Kansas; and Portsmouth, Suffolk, and Berkeley, Virginia." A fellow engineer characterized Brush as "an inspiring engineer . . . and an all-around gentleman," and his engineering reports as "models of terse English and convincing logic." Brush contributed over thirty articles to the *ASCE Transactions* on road construction, cable cars, electric streetcars, tunnels, building materials, and many aspects of water supply.[16]

Brush's experience, clients, and relationships made him an obvious choice for chief engineer for the reorganized water company. His clients included

7

the Hoboken Land and Improvement Company, controlled by the Stevens family; the Hoboken Ferry Company; the North Hudson County Railway Company; and many other organizations in Hudson and Bergen counties. Besides sharing an interest in railroads, Brush and Robert de Forest were prominent members of the Presbyterian Church in New York and both contributed to community improvement activities. Given his experience in water supply and his connections to the Stevens family and other interests in Hoboken, Brush probably helped analyze the potential for bringing Hackensack water to the city prior to the water company's reorganization.

Although the 1882 drawings of the "Hackensack Water Company, New Milford, N.J., Engine House" on the north side of New Milford Avenue and the "Coal Shed and Boiler House" on the south side were not signed or ini-

tialed, Adrian Leiby credited Charles Brush with the design of the buildings, citing the engine house as "a monument to his skill as an architect." Brush adhered to the original concept of 40-foot-square engine and boiler rooms, but he separated them into two buildings to allow for future expansion and to make the boiler operation more efficient. For the engine house, Brush specified a wide doorway facing west, a window bay facing south, windows on the east and north sides, and a hipped roof capped by a 20-foot-square "ventilating turret" (Figures 5, 6, and 7). Brush added a 60-foot by 40-foot coal shed to the east side of the boiler room, and he erected this combined "Coal Shed and Boiler House" on the south side of New Milford Avenue (Figure 8). The location facilitated the transfer of coal via hoppers that ran on a rail spur

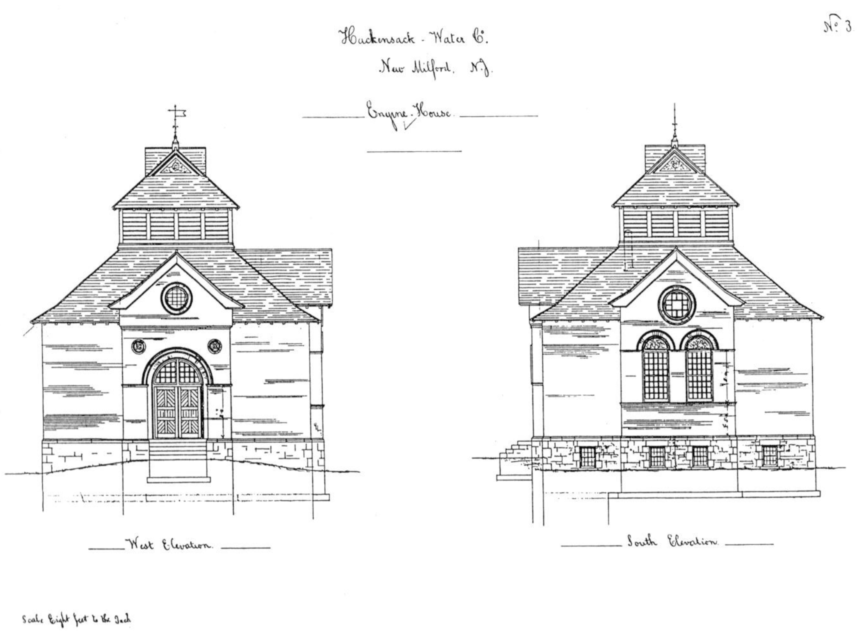

Figure 5: "Hackensack Water Company, New Milford, N.J., Engine House," south and west elevations. The design of the 1882 engine house included 16 in. brick walls, gables and hipped roofs, and copper-trimmed, slate roofing. United Water Resources

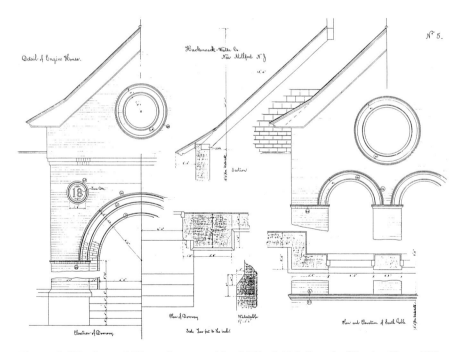

Figure 6: "Hackensack Water Company, New Milford, N.J., Detail of Engine House." The exterior design included circular terracotta medallions noting "1882" above the doorway, projecting roof eaves with molded rafter tails, and semicircular arches over the window and door openings in the industrial Romanesque style. United Water Resources

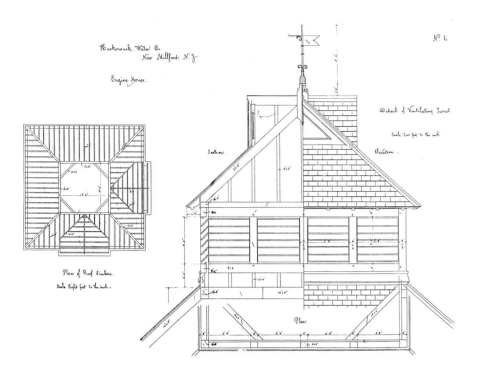

Figure 7: "Hackensack Water Company, New Milford, N.J., Engine House, Detail of Ventilating Turret." A fine example of intricate, late nineteenth-century carpentry, the turret originally had wooden louvers for open ventilation. The turret is capped by a weathervane on a kingpost at the peak. United Water Resources

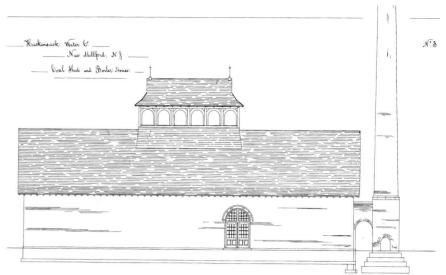

Figure 8: "Hackensack Water Company, New Milford, N.J., Coal Shed and Boiler House." An open cupola in the center of the roof ventilated the interior, and a 135-foot-high square chimney on the east end of the building provided a flue for the boilers. United Water Resources

over a trestle connecting the coal shed to the New Jersey & New York Railroad line on the west bank of the Hackensack River (see Figure 132).[17]

The semicircular arches over the window and door openings on the 1882 buildings were typical of the industrial Romanesque style popularized in the 1870s by noted Boston architect Henry Hobson Richardson. The water company continued to employ these details through four decades of construction on the site. The attractive design and massive construction of the original New Milford buildings presented the water company as a substantial enterprise committed to quality and a long-term investment.

"rapid progress is being made"

By the spring of 1882 fifty men were at work on the pumping station, and a local paper noted, "The walls of the buildings are being run up by a dozen bricklayers and concrete foundations [are being] laid for the building of the pumping engines." Workers simultaneously dug trenches by hand along the railroad line and laid 20-inch cast-iron pipe to bring the fresh water to Hackensack and Hoboken. In June the *American Contract Journal* reported, "Rapid progress is being made on the completion of the water-works for [Hackensack]," noting that "C. B. Brush of the firm of Spielmann & Brush, Civil Engineers, of Hoboken, is chief engineer and John F. Ward contractor." In July the water company hired D. W. Chase as superintendent of the new plant. Because the steam engines and boilers needed constant attention, the water company built houses just north of the engine house for Chase and the plant operators, with free rent constituting part of their pay (Figure 9).[18]

Figure 9: Hackensack Water Works, c. 1885. 1882 engine house, center; 1882 boiler house, right; storehouse, left; superintendent's house and worker's housing, behind storehouse; settling basin, left foreground; New Milford Avenue, right. Frank Vierling

Delivering water to Hackensack was difficult, but supplying Hoboken was an even greater challenge. Located on the Hudson River some 16 miles southeast of New Milford, Hoboken was too far away to supply with steady pressure. Brush devised a plan similar to Bacot & Ward's 1873 gravity supply from the Cherry Hill Reservoir to Hackensack. He designed a 15-million-gallon, brick-lined reservoir on Union Hill in Weehawken, a small town just north of Hoboken but located some 150 feet higher on top of the Palisades. The 20-inch main from New Milford fed the new brick reservoir, and from there the water flowed down to Hoboken. This was the company's first effort to deliver water at "high service." George Haskew, a former president of the water company, noted that "Any areas of higher elevation required additional pumping and storage at higher levels, hence the terminology 'high service.' Low service was considered to be the general gradient serving most of the system as pumped from the New Milford Plant." When the pumping station at New Milford began operating on November 1, 1882, "low service" Hackensack customers were pleased with the increase in pressure over the company's original gravity system, and "high service" Hoboken customers were delighted to have water for the first time in place of their old cisterns and wells.[20]

"the most important structure of its kind in the country"

Since Weehawken and the adjacent towns of Union Hill and West Hoboken were too close to the level of the reservoir for steady water pressure, Brush built an elevated tank next to the reservoir. Pumping engines forced

To collect the river water, Brush designed a 700-foot-long, 48-inch-wide brick conduit leading from the northwest corner of the island to a 110-foot-wide settling basin to the west of the engine house. The river water was often turbid, especially after spring rains, and this basin was the company's first effort to clarify it by allowing suspended particles to settle prior to pumping. The quality of the water was initially a low priority, given the pumping and distribution challenges, but it would soon command equal attention. From the sedimentation basin the water flowed though a 4-foot tunnel into a suction well in the engine house. To pump the water into the distribution mains, Brush installed a 6-million-gallon-per-day (MGD) duplex pumping engine manufactured by the Worthington Company in Harrison, New Jersey (Figure 10). In 1883 he installed a similar 4-MGD Worthington duplex pumping engine in Weehawken (Figure 11).[19]

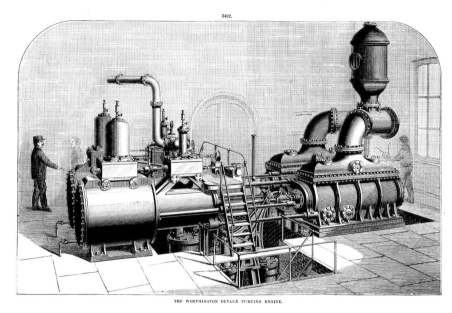

Figure 10: *"The Worthington Duplex Pumping Engine." With a pair of pistons powered by the successive high-pressure and low-pressure use of a single blast of steam, the horizontal engine maintained an even pumping pressure.* Appleton's Cyclopedia, *1880. Archive of Industry*

Figure 11: *The engine room at the Weehawken water tower, c. 1885. The 4-MGD Worthington duplex pumping engine in Weehawken was the same type the water company installed at New Milford in 1882. United Water Resources*

water into the supply mains for the three towns, and the excess flowed through a vertical pipe into the tank where the weight of the water provided a steady pressure in the mains. To work properly, the tank had to be about 150 feet high. With the elevation of Weehawken about 150 feet above high tide, the top of the tank tower would be some 300 feet above New York Harbor and, therefore, visible from Manhattan and the Hackensack Meadowlands.

Robert de Forest and the other directors saw the tower as an opportunity to further develop the company's public image. They hired the noted New York architect Frederick Clark Withers to design a substantial tower that would signify the company's presence in the region. A native of England, Withers was celebrated for his Victorian Gothic churches and public and institutional buildings in New York, Connecticut, Pennsylvania, and Washington, D.C. In the 1860s he had developed a partnership in New York with

Calvert Vaux and Frederick Law Olmstead, the superintendent of Central Park, to design buildings and structures in the park.

For the tower, Withers turned to the precedent of the "medieval guard tower," and allegedly borrowed details from the celebrated Palazzo Vecchio in Florence. His design "expressed the tower's function as a sentinel maintaining the efficiency of the water system" (Figures 12, 13, 14, and 15). John Ward, the Jersey City builder who had erected the pumping station for Charles Brush, helped Withers design the eight-story tower and then built it. To transfer the load of the 150,000-gallon tank to the tower's 24-inch-thick brick walls, Withers and Ward designed a series of Gothic arches that soar 30 feet over the seventh-story storeroom. Two stories of employees' quarters below the storeroom included living rooms, bedrooms, and water closets. The four lower stories contained the director's office, the engine room, a storeroom, and the boiler room within the stone foundation.[21]

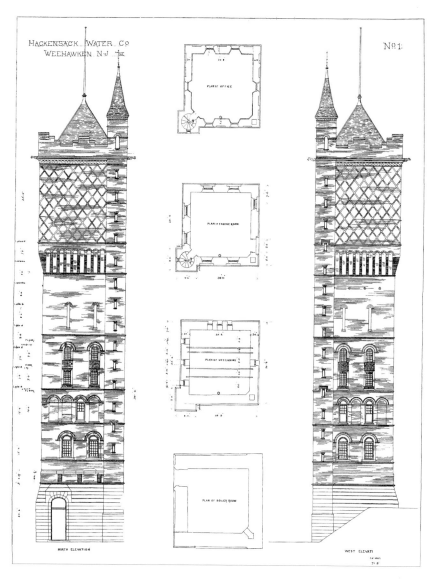

Figure 12: *"Hackensack Water Company, Weehawken, N.J." Frederick Clark Withers designed the 175-foot tower like a medieval guard tower and allegedly borrowed details from the Palazzo Vecchio in Florence. The exterior expressed the multiple functions within the building through various arrangements of arch-topped windows and brick detailing, including the corbelling and diamond patterns that signaled the presence of the 150,000-gallon water tank at the top. United Water Resources*

Figure 13: *"Water Tower, Hackensack Water Company, Weehawken, N.J." Withers' presentation drawing showed the elaborate tower as a single structure on the northwest corner of the Weehawken Reservoir. American Architect and Building News, Sept. 8, 1883*

Figure 14: The Weehawken water tower, c. 1885. Hailed as a bold design when built, the tower was the Hackensack Water Company's symbol for many years and today it is an historic landmark in Weehawken. United Water Resources

Figure 15: Park Avenue, Weehawken, c. 1900. The Hackensack Water Company's Weehawken facility included the reservoir, right, and the water tower and main office, center. United Water Resources

As a melding of architecture and engineering, the design succeeded brilliantly. *Engineering News* described the tower "as conspicuous both from its commanding position and architectural appearance and from the fact that it is the most important structure of its kind in the country." The story noted, "The use of Gothic arches in supporting a tank weighing, when full, 620 tons . . . though considered bold at the time when built has proved entirely stable." Along with the tower, the journal remarked that Withers' design of the nearby gate house "proves that in an artist's hand such a building need not be made a dull and repulsive feature in the landscape, as is too generally the case."[22]

The directors were no doubt pleased as well. In an 1885 cover feature on the tower, *Carpentry and Building* magazine noted, "Among the many conspicuous objects in the neighborhood of New York City is the High Service Tower of the Hackensack Water Company. It is so situated as to be seen from all the ferries plying the city and the Jersey shore, and also from the decks of excursion boats running on the Hudson and about the bay. The top of the tower projects far above the surrounding trees and its bright red is in marked contrast with the green of the foliage."[23]

Building the complicated tower was a major accomplishment for the water company, and its start of water service in Weehawken, Union Hill, and West Hoboken on September 14, 1883, was "an occasion of great rejoicing by the citizens, a feature of which was a grand parade, in which nearly every fire company in North Hudson took part." The water company built a public promenade around the reservoir that soon became a popular destination (Figure 16). Although the tower was functional for only a couple of decades, it became the company's icon. In 1936 *The Hudson Dispatch* noted, "The tower will probably remain for many years to come, as officials of the water company think too much of it as a landmark in the rise of the utility company to consider tearing it down."[24]

Figure 16: "The Hackensack Water Company." Scientific American, April 2, 1892. The Weehawken water tower and reservoir with its popular promenade, upper left; the reservoir intake pipes, lower left; and a steam-powered Worthington duplex pumping engine in the tower's engine room. Water Works Conservancy

Chapter 2

A Promising Field

The directors of the reorganized Hackensack Water Company had successfully transformed it from a small gravity service in the 1870s to an advanced operation delivering high and low service to two counties in the early 1880s. The basic system they put in place formed the foundation for expanding water service tenfold in the next century. But almost immediately the cleanliness of the water became an issue. In the 1880s and 1890s, water purity became a major health concern in America that public and private suppliers struggled to address. As population growth dramatically increased the pollution of water, engineers and scientists struggled to understand the causes and what they could do about it.

The summer following the opening of the Weehawken water tower was exceptionally hot and the water in the adjacent reservoir began to acquire "a very unpleasant vegetable odor and taste."[25] The source of the problem was the high level of vegetable and animal matter in the Hackensack River, which drained an area largely devoted to farming and therefore prone to runoffs. Holding the water in the reservoir exacerbated the problem. Standing water had long been known to be more susceptible to organic growths

Figure 17: Albert Ripley Leeds, a professor of chemistry at Stevens Institute of Technology in Hoboken, systematically analyzed the Hackensack Water Company's water from 1887 to 1900. Stevens Indicator, *April 1902*

than running water, but little was known about controlling these growths as they multiplied rapidly in warm weather. The water company turned to an obvious local source for help.

Albert Ripley Leeds was the prominent professor of chemistry at the Stevens Institute of Technology in Hoboken who had earlier identified the Hackensack River's potential as a major source of municipal water. He had graduated from Harvard and earned his Ph.D. in Germany, where much of the early work in microbiology was done and where young scientists in this field went to get their training. Leeds was one of several professional scientists and engineers who joined the quest for pure water in the 1880s to conquer the increasing number of typhoid epidemics and deaths caused by polluted water (Figure 17). The American Water Works Association was formed in 1881 and the New England Water Works Association in 1882. In proceedings published by these associations and by engineering, chemical, and bacteriological societies, a group of emerging "sanitary engineers" openly shared their efforts to purify water and to treat sewage. They wrote illustrated reports, aimed at water works superintendents and engineers, that were often accompanied by peer "discussions." These reports and professional meetings helped promote innovations in water purification around the country. In 1903 sanitary engineer George Whipple wrote, "At the present time there is no more promising field for a young graduate engineer than that of superintending the operation of filter plants."[26]

Albert Leeds was an early proponent of artificial aeration, a process that replicates the natural aeration of water when it flows over pebbles or rocks. In the eighteenth century some inventors and physicians experimented with blowing bubbles into distilled water and rainwater stored in cisterns to replenish the oxygen. A shipwright developed "an ingenious contrivance . . . to sweeten stinking water" in the well of ships by blowing air into it through a pipe. Early nineteenth-century efforts at purifying standing water included shooting it into the air and tumbling it down cascades.[27]

Professor Leeds was also a consulting chemist to the Philadelphia Water Department, which drew its water from the Schuylkill River. When ice covered the river above the Fairmount Dam in the winter of 1883, the water developed a noxious smell and taste. Leeds conducted experiments that showed that aeration decreased the organic content and increased oxygen in water samples from the Schuylkill. In September 1883, he applied for patents for an aeration process and an apparatus for restoring oxygen levels in standing water by pumping compressed air into pressurized distribution pipes, thus "destroying any deleterious substances." He recommended this treatment for Philadelphia, but the water department wasn't sure it would work. Leeds soon got the chance to test his treatment closer to home.[28]

With its Hoboken connections, the water company turned to Leeds in the summer of 1884 to address algae problems in the Weehawken Reservoir. Leeds later wrote that the unusually warm weather had accelerated the normal growth of organisms in the water, and that "in less than twenty-four hours, the previously clear water became covered in a thick coat of bluish-green algae." Leeds suggested that compressed air, at approximately 100 pounds per square inch, be pumped into the water main at New Milford so that it could work under pressure on the water as it flowed to Weehawken. "With the least possible delay," Leeds noted, "Mr. Charles Brush, the Chief Engineer, began the aeration. The growth of algae ceased immediately and the water was restored to its usual palatable condition."[29]

"it looks like springs and creates a favorable impression"

The aeration may have made the water in Hoboken palatable, but the water in Hackensack remained dirty at certain times of the year and local newspapers began to agitate about it. In February 1885, the *Hackensack Republican* reported "the water has an ancient fish-like smell that is very offensive—one gentleman likens it unto the liquid that is used for freshening salt mackerel." One account described Hackensack water as "the hue of milk" and another noted a "sudden occurrence of quantities of eels" in Hoboken water.[30]

While the directors wondered what to do about the quality of their water, they continued investing in the supply system. An essential characteristic of water supply is the ability to continue service despite breakdowns. By 1886 demand for water had sufficiently grown in Hudson and Bergen counties to warrant expansion of the Hackensack system to provide new service as well as backup for the original service. The directors authorized the construction of a second, slightly larger force main from the water works to the Weehawken Reservoir. They ran this 24-inch line on an eastward path to bring water service to "the bright and growing village of Englewood." To supply this line Brush built additions to the engine and boiler houses at New Milford, with designs that replicated the details of the original buildings (Figures 18, 19, and 20). He installed a 10-MGD Worthington duplex vertical engine in the 1886 engine house to pump water at high-service pressure through the new force main to Englewood and the Weehawken Reservoir, and three new boilers in the 1886 section of the boiler house.[31]

An 1888 report on the pumping station's efficiency highlighted its duplicate capacity: "The pumping station is supplied with two systems of pumps

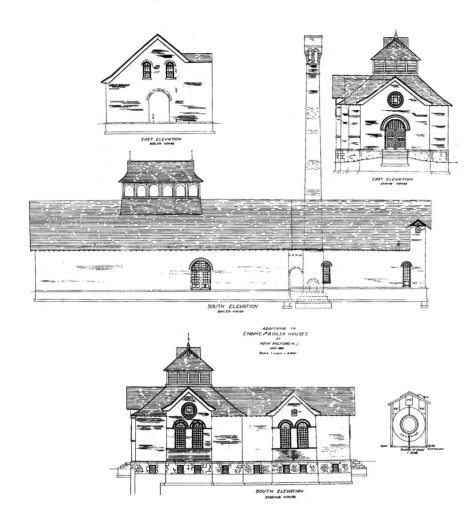

EAST ELEVATION
BOILER HOUSE

EAST ELEVATION
ENGINE HOUSE

SOUTH ELEVATION
BOILER HOUSE

ADDITIONS TO
ENGINE & BOILER HOUSES
AT
NEW MILFORD N.J.
NOV 1886
SCALE 1 INCH = 8 FEET

SOUTH ELEVATION
ENGINE HOUSE

*Figure 18: "Additions to Engine and Boiler Houses at New Milford NJ Nov 1886."
Charles Brush replicated the design details of his 1882 buildings on these first additions. United Water Resources*

Figure 19: 1886 additions to the boiler house and coal shed, left, and the engine house, right, c. 1890. The steam pipe passed over New Milford Avenue in this view looking west. Van Buskirk's Mill is visible in the distance behind the tree in the center. Frank Vierling

RIVER ROAD BRIDGE,
NEW MILFORD, N.J.

A.10630.

Figure 20: "River Road Bridge, New Milford, N.J.," c. 1900. The 1886 boiler house addition is on the left. The company's housing for pumping station employees is visible on the right. William Berdan and Alice Berdan

and two distinct batteries of boilers, so in case of the disabling of one, the other may be started and thus a regular water supply be maintained." The backup pumps were "kept in readiness to meet any such emergency as fire, the disabling of the boiler feed pumps, etc." The report noted that steam was conveyed from the boiler house to the engine house "through a pipe supported by a narrow bridge which also carries the boiler feed pipe;

17

an underwater steam pipe also connects the two buildings, and the 'headers' from each nest of boilers being connected we have a 'steam circuit.' So unless both steam supply pipes become disabled together, the pumps need not be stopped." The report also noted that "a small amount of steam was used to heat the house of the resident engineer, and as it became necessary, steam was furnished to a donkey-engine used in hauling coal from the railroad nearby to the coal room in the boiler house." Maintaining backup capacity was a key part of operating the plant throughout its service period.[32]

"the water supply limits increase in population"

While many municipalities were focused on developing water supplies, there was also a growing concern with water quality around the country. Some cities advised residents to let their yellowish-brown tap water stand for a few minutes before using it so particles could settle. Foul odors from organic matter in the water also exasperated residents, and newspapers were quick to report their comments:

> *The odor was so bad that it would be almost impossible to take it as far as the mouth to taste it. Horses refused it at the street watering-troughs and dogs fled from it.*
> *Strong, fishy odor and taste, also odor of smartweed. Popular complaint was dead fish in water mains. Very rank.*
> *The odor was so strong that we had to discontinue sprinkling the streets and lawns.*
> *The water is so bad that we have had to shut off the supply from June to December.*[33]

The worst problems were undetectable to the senses, and microscopic analysis was still in its infancy. Bacteria from untreated sewage dumped into rivers caused diarrhea, dysentery, typhoid, and gastroenteritis. Typhoid was rampant in cities that drew their water from sewage-fouled rivers, such as Lawrence, Massachusetts, and Albany, New York. In 1885 Albany hired Albert Leeds to study its water supply and to recommend solutions to conditions that were "detrimental to the health of the citizens." A committee studying the problem noted, "A very large portion of the citizens are anxious to be relieved from the necessity of using water contaminated with sewage." Leeds reported that the Albany residents were "drinking a residual portion of the sewage of Troy and a part of their own sewage," and recommended legislative action to force cities "to reclaim their sewage before emptying the purified effluent into a flowing stream." Noting that there was no guarantee of the safety of water "unless it can be thoroughly purified immediately before use (which) can be done artificially and naturally," he recommended a combination of aeration and filtration for Albany.[34]

Besides threatening lives, the lack of safe water threatened urban growth. As one observer noted, "No city can grow beyond the possibilities of its water supply, as the water supply limits increase in population." In response to the poor quality of water in Lawrence, the Massachusetts Board of Health established the Lawrence Experiment Station in 1887 to study raw Merrimack River water and the effectiveness of filtration and sewage treatment. The station initially focused on sewage treatment, but its subsequent work on water purification would soon have a national impact and ultimately affect purification developments on the Hackensack water supply.[35]

"as to analysis of samples of water"

Albert Leeds apparently began analyzing water samples for the Hackensack Water Company when the first algae bloom appeared in the Weehawken Reservoir in 1884, and he continued testing samples up to 1900, just two years before his death in 1902. A ledger of his tests from 1887 to 1900, titled *Water Analysis*, noted each one under the "Certificate

Hoboken, N. J., 16th July 1890

CERTIFICATE OF DR. ALBERT R. LEEDS,

Professor of Chemistry at the Stevens Institute of Technology, as to Analysis of Samples of Water, submitted by the Hackensack Water Co., Reorganized.

Nº 1408

When received, 8th July '90   Title of Label, temp. 72° F.

Source of Sample, Inlet Pipe, Weehawken Reservoir 14.30 o'clock

COLOR, 0°.7 clear   TASTE, earthy   SMELL very earthy

DATA OBTAINED BY ANALYSIS:

	Parts in 100,000.	Grains per Gallon.
I. FREE AMMONIA,	0.0038	0.0022
II. ALBUMINOID AMMONIA,	0.0192	0.0112
III. OXYGEN REQUIRED TO OXIDIZE ORGANIC MATTER,	0.627	0.365
IV. NITRITES,	0.002	0.0011
V. NITRATES,	0.1306	0.0763
VI. CHLORINE.	0.13	0.076
VII. TOTAL HARDNESS,	5.15	3.00
VIII. PERMANENT HARDNESS,	0.75	0.44
IX. TEMPORARY HARDNESS,	4.40	2.56
X. TOTAL SOLIDS,	8.60	5.01
XI. MINERAL MATTER,	6.20	3.61
XII. ORGANIC AND VOLATILE MATTER,	2.40	1.40

XIII. OTHER DATA, when required for judgment,

Carbonic Acid dissolved in 1 liter = 1.88 c.c.
Oxygen   "   "   "   " = 5.39 "
Nitrogen   "   "   "   " = 12.40 "
Total Gases   "   "   "   " = 19.67 "

INTERPRETATION OF RESULTS:

Moreover I think that prudence would involve anticipating the gradual increase of soluble organic matters through August, and that the installation of a filter plant which would certainly remove them, and this, analyses and repeated trial has demonstrated upon the Hackensack water should not be delayed

Signed. Albert R. Leeds

Professor of Chemistry, Stevens Institute of Technology.

*NOTE.—The U. S. Gallon is taken at 58,334.95 grains.

Figure 21: "Certificate of Dr. Albert R. Leeds . . . as to Analysis of Samples of Water, submitted by the Hackensack Water Co., Reorganized." Leeds' Water Analysis ledger documents some 1,100 water samples for the water company from January 14, 1887 to July 7, 1900. The entry dated July 16, 1890 notes, "the installation of a filter plant . . . should not be delayed." United Water Resources

of Albert Leeds . . . as to Analysis of Samples of Water, submitted by the Hackensack Water Co., Reorganized" (Figure 21). Leeds' firsthand account of early scientific efforts to document water quality illustrates the conditions that led the water company to purification.

Leeds' *Water Analysis* ledger notes the source of Hackensack water samples, primarily "New Milford" (the water works), "20 inch main at Little Ferry," "Inlet pipe at Reservoir" and "Top of Reservoir" (in Weehawken), and "Faucet at Chem. Labr'y., Stevens Institute." The ledger includes subjective information that provides an interesting lexicon of nineteenth-century water analysis. "COLOR" notations include values from .25 to 2, and descriptions such as "slight," "slightly opalescent," "yellow," "brownish," and "greenish." "TASTE" descriptions include "pleasant," "flat," "earthy," "peaty," "strawy," "wet hay," "ferruginous," "brassy," "dusty," "dry," "pondy," "muddy," "moldy," "musty," "marshy," "damp hay," "vegetal," "rank vegetable," "sour," and "tarry." "SMELL" descriptions include "slight," "peaty," "like vinegar," "sour," "strong grassy," "woody," "musty," "tarry," "marshy," and "sewagy." Water quality scientists eventually turned initial descriptions like these into "tastes and odors" standards for the water supply industry.[36]

Under "DATA OBTAINED BY ANALYSIS," Leeds recorded parts per 100,000 and grains per gallon for free ammonia, albuminoid ammonia, oxygen required to oxidize organic matter, nitrates, chlorine, total hardness, permanent hardness, temporary hardness, total solids, mineral matter, and organic and volatile matter. In a category titled "OTHER DATA, when required for judgement," he recorded oxygen, carbonic acid, nitrogen, and total gases in cubic centimeters per liter. He noted the final and often most interesting analysis under "INTERPRETATION OF RESULTS." The first entry on January 15, 1887 notes, "As compared with the month of December 1886, the quality of the water at the beginning of the present year shows a decided improvement."[37]

Leeds recorded that his analysis of samples in early 1887 was generally "satisfactory." When the water quality began to deteriorate in the spring, Leeds noted his concern and for the first time recommended "proper filtration" of the water:

> These samples are of such a character as to point to the probability of trouble arising in case steps are not taken soon to combat the evil. There is a large amount of large vegetable mould or humus. This gives rise to a corresponding excess of albuminoid ammonia and requires a large amount of oxygen to decompose it. . . . On standing, vegetable matter separates out and makes the water unsightly.
>
> During the past month constant observation reveals the fact that this deposit is taking place in all the samples drawn from the faucet day by day. At the same time there is exhaustion in part of the Oxygen and an increase in carbonic acid—symptoms which if not heeded will very soon trouble. I would strongly recommend that no time be lost in thoroughly aerating the water, and that proper filtration under pressure likewise be resorted to as being the only certain method of rendering the water of satisfactory quality.[38]

In June Leeds wrote, "the condition of the water was precarious" and "near the danger line." He noted that most of the oxygen being introduced by aeration was being used up in the pipes, and he recommended that "the amount of air used at present should be increased as much as it is safe." Brush nearly doubled the amount of air forced into the main at New Milford. On July 28 Leeds wrote:

> Receiving notice from the Chf. Engineer that an examination of the Reservoir was imperative, I went there with Mr. Wiggins July 22nd and found patches of algae in the corners, and a greenish cloud distributed through much of the reservoir. As the water boiled out of the (inlet) pipe (from the water works), it had no smell, a sparkling delightful taste and an almost crystal pellucidness. The analysis itself also showed a remarkable degree of purity. The greenish water of the reservoir itself tasted and smelt strong grassy. Its analysis, made upon the water after completely filtering off the green scum, shows an enormous amount of Ammonia. The chemical analysis not being sufficient I made a microscopic one upon all the suspended matters filtered from 24 gallons of the water. I found abundant diatomaceae, nostochaciae, paramaecia, desmids, and numerous spores of microphytes (bacteria).
>
> The great heat has stimulated the growth and development of spores in the [reservoir] water. The large volume of air pumped into the main [at the water works], delivers it sweet and sparkling with no evidence of growths visible to the eye. But on exposure to the great heat and direct sun, the small volume of water in the reservoir parts with its oxygen and semi-stagnation sets in.
>
> Direct aeration in the reservoir also, will preserve the water sweet and sparkling. No time should be lost.[39]

Leeds' comparison of the July 22 samples clearly showed the problem. The raw river water at the pumping station at New Milford had a "faint tinge," a "vegetable" taste, and a "faint" smell. The water treated by aeration in the main, sampled at the inlet to the reservoir, was "nearly colorless" and had a "pleasant" taste with no smell. The reservoir water, sampled near the top, had a "greenish, turbid" color, a "rank vegetable" taste, and a "strong grassy" smell. The extended heat wave had stimulated algae growth in the corners of the reservoir, and Leeds recommended blowing air though pipes to "rose-jets" placed below the surface of the water around the reservoir.[40]

Brush installed the aeration pipes and "rose-jets" and by October Leeds noted, "The water is in excellent condition for this season." Leeds later reported, "The air boils up at any or all of these points [above the jets] through the water, and the breaking up and disappearance of algae takes place forthwith. [Monthly analyses] show the beneficial effect of this system and the entire avoidance of the trouble, which it was introduced to remedy." Brush noted in an optimistic presentation that "We forced air into our pipes in 1884 and up to this time we have had no repetition of trouble. We are now aerating the water in the reservoirs as well as in the pipes. The public sees the air bubbling up in the reservoir. It looks like springs and creates a favorable impression[41] (see Figure 16)."

"the only certain method of rendering the water of satisfactory quality"

Leeds' analysis of Hackensack River water from different points in the water company's system in the late 1880s noted "Total Solids" that typically consisted of about three quarters "Mineral Matter" and about one quarter "Organic and Volatile Matter," mostly from plants and animals. The slight turbidity during the fall and winter apparently did not present much of a problem to customers. With heavy spring rains the total solids could more than double and the organic portion could increase to almost half the solids. While the resulting turbidity and unpleasant tastes and odors were troubling, the rapid growth of algae at Weehawken during warm weather indicated a bigger problem. The river water had too much organic content to be stored in small reservoirs where high water temperatures and lack of movement promoted the growth of algae. Aerating the pipes and the reservoir from April 15 to November 15 each year improved the oxygen content of the water and limited the growth of algae, and Leeds occasionally noted a "satisfactory" water condition in his ledger during 1888 and early 1889. However, aeration couldn't consistently reduce organic content or satisfactorily address the water's turbidity, especially as concerns and standards for water quality kept increasing.

While Leeds recognized as early as May of 1887 that filtration was "the only certain method of rendering the water of satisfactory quality," it was a process that scientists, engineers, and water providers all over the country were still trying to understand and perfect in order to make it feasible on a large scale. While the filtering of small quantities of water through sand and other media to remove particles had been practiced for ages, by the seventeenth and eighteenth centuries inventors were developing designs for filters that could handle larger quantities of water. In 1804 Scottish industrialist John Gibbs built the earliest known filter for purifying the water supply of an entire town in Paisley, Scotland. In the first half of the nineteenth century several other European cities experimented with filtering public water through sand and gravel. In America, however, there were only a few sporadic efforts to filter public water prior to the Civil War. A German engineer named Albert Stein designed a filter for Richmond in 1832 "to furnish an abundant supply of sweet and clear water," but it failed in its mission and there were no other American attempts to build a sizeable filter until the 1870s.[42]

"to remove suspended matter . . . and minute organisms"

Water purification in America effectively began in 1866 when the city of St. Louis sent J. P. Kirkwood, a civil engineer, to Europe to study the "English" system of slow sand filtration. Kirkwood reported on filters in nineteen European cities that were designed "to remove suspended matter . . . earthy materials . . . fine vegetable fibers . . . and minute organisms." Water in these filters descended through layers of sand and gravel that trapped many but not all particles. The filters for a sizable city required a lot of land, since about 2 MGD per acre of filter was about the maximum flow possible, as experiments in Germany had demonstrated. Kirkwood noted that successful filtration usually included a settling reservoir, which he thought would be adequate to clarify the "clayey discoloration" of many American rivers.[43]

Kirkwood designed a filtration system for St. Louis based on European models, but the city failed to act on his proposal. "English" slow sand filters took up a lot of land, they were expensive to build and operate since they required manual cleaning and replacement of sand, and their effectiveness on "muddy" water from rivers like the Mississippi was unproven. In fact, none of the European filters could have cleaned the water from muddy American rivers. In 1872 Kirkwood designed the first successful slow sand filtration system in the United Sates at Poughkeepsie, New York, where the Hudson River water came from a rocky watershed that resembled the sources of many European rivers. While other Hudson River cities and the town of St. Johnsbury, Vermont, built smaller but similar filters that also succeeded, filters based on the Poughkeepsie design failed in Lowell, Massachusetts, Toledo and Columbus, Ohio, and other cities where the river "water carried more suspended matter [that] affected the process to such an extent that the general method was not applicable." Small particles in rivers like the Ohio River usually slipped through the sand, leaving the water a yellowish-brown color.[44]

The ultimate solution to the turbidity problem lay in the development of "mechanical filters." European and American inventors patented various devices in the late eighteenth and nineteenth centuries that forced water under pressure through sand and then periodically reversed the flow of water through the sand to remove the accumulated dirt. The enclosed filter tanks were built of wood or metal, and typically contained revolving mechanisms to stir up the sand while "backwashing" it with water injected up through the filter drains. These mechanical filter tanks had a limited capacity but they filtered water up to forty times faster than slow sand filters, and they were easier and cheaper to clean. In many cases, however, they were less effective in purifying water than slow sand filters. Nevertheless, in the second half of the nineteenth century a number of inventors and entrepreneurs started companies to build mechanical filter tanks for factories and small towns.

In 1880 New Jersey inventor Patrick Clark patented a mechanical filter tank with vertical water jets for backwashing in Rahway, New Jersey. That year Clark incorporated the Newark Filtering Company with another inventor named John Hyatt, who subsequently patented an improvement to Clark's design. In 1881 a Clark-Hyatt filter tank was installed in Frankfurt, Germany, and in 1882 the company installed filters for municipal water in Somerville, New Jersey, and Newport, Rhode Island. While working as a sales agent for the company, Isaac Hyatt, John's brother, learned that Col. L. H. Gardner, the superintendent for the New Orleans Water Company, had tried clarifying muddy Mississippi River water using a positively-charged chemical agent to coagulate negatively-charged particles suspended in the water. The resulting coagulation, or curdling, produced a jellylike substance called flocc, which was easier to filter than individual particles.

Isaac Hyatt developed a process for simultaneous coagulation and filtration, and the patent he obtained for it in 1884 dominated mechanical filtration until it expired in 1901. The Newark Filtering Company installed the first pressurized Hyatt filter tanks with a "coagulating apparatus" for the Somerville Water Company in Somerville, New Jersey, in 1885, and followed up on its success with similar installations elsewhere. Because of their speed and the fact that much of their development occurred in this country, the use of mechanical filter tanks soon became known as "rapid sand filtration" or the "American" system of mechanical filtration. These early mechanical filter tanks were often unreliable and expensive to maintain, and Hyatt's patent discouraged their use by requiring licensing fees.

In 1886, William Deutsch, a former sales agent for the Newark Filtering Company, obtained the first of several patents for mechanical filter devices and incorporated the National Water Purifying Company in New York to manufacture them. Albert Leeds transferred his aeration patent to the new firm and became an advisor as well as a major investor in it. Unfortunately, the Newark Filtering Company filed a lawsuit against the National Water Purifying Company alleging infringement of its patents, and prolonged legal wrangling hobbled both firms.

In the meantime, Leeds' continued analysis of Hackensack water reinforced his conclusion that filtration was inevitable. On March 25, 1889, he noted the taste and smell of a water sample taken at New Milford as "earthy," and interpreted the test results as "Not Satisfactory. The water was turbid and brown from a variety of suspended matters which could be removed by filtering and filtering only." In October Leeds noted, "After the month of July the dissolved vegetable matters increased rapidly and arrived at a maximum amount during the month of September." The decrease in vegetable matters and the corresponding "falling off of the strength of yellow color which has characterized the water" continued in November. Heavy rains that December temporarily gave the water "an unsightly and objectionable appearance due to suspended mud . . . but owing probably to the dilution of the water draining off from fields which in the month of December should retain but little organic matter, the latter substances are diminished in amount."[45]

While his note that January water samples were "of *excellent* quality" signaled the start of another annual cycle, 1890 proved to be a critical year in Leeds' thinking about Hackensack River water. When the water samples became more turbid in the late winter, Leeds noted, "The Turbidity is due to suspended earthy matter, removable by filtration, a perfectly clear water resulting." In May Leeds conducted filtering tests to illustrate this. He first filtered a water sample "through $2\frac{1}{2}$ feet depth of sand," and this decreased some ammonia and organic matter by about 25 percent. However, he noted that "The coloring matter was not diminished—it was due entirely to vegetable substances in a state of solution." Prior to filtering the next sample through sand, he added alumina sulphate to coagulate suspended particles and reported the results:[46]

On adding Alumina Sulphate in the amount of $\frac{1}{2}$ grain per gallon this coloring matter was precipitated and combined with the alumina in the state of a lake or insoluble alumina compound. Not only the coloring matter but the alumina was thrown out of combination and separated as insoluble yellowish floccs. [Aluminum and organic matter were reduced more than half.] The coloring was entirely removed and the filtrate was perfectly white and clear.[47]

As the weather turned warmer Leeds noted a "very earthy" smell and an "earthy and unpleasant" taste. In July he expressed concern about the increasing levels of organic matter and concluded:

The analyses show a very sharp rise, which if it continues may involve serious consequences.

Moreover I think that prudence would involve anticipating the gradual increase of soluble organic matters through August and that the installation of a filter plant which should certainly remove them, and this analysis and repeated trial has demonstrated upon the Hackensack water should not be delayed.[48]

When the water problems persisted into the fall, instead of improving as they usually did, Leeds reiterated his recommendation for filtration:

For this season of the year the amount of oxidizable [sic] organic matter is unusually large and is accompanied by a dark color and an earthy taste and smell. This organic matter can be removed by means recommended previously and the water delivered entirely white and colorless and without taste and smell.[49]

In early March 1891 Leeds noted that the "organic matter still remains very high." He sent water samples to chemists at Princeton College and the Columbia College School of Mines, who reported conflicting results. H. B. Cornwall of Princeton reported a "slightly brownish" color and a "slightly woody" taste from "an organic constituent of peaty origin" and commented that "the analysis does not contain any dangerous contamination." C. F. Chandler, Ph.D., of Columbia, reported that the sample was "colorless-clear" with no taste or odor, and he commented, "The results are entirely satisfactory. The water is of excellent quality."[50]

While Leeds was clear that Hackensack River needed to be filtered for domestic use, Superintendent Charles Brush and the directors probably believed that none of the filtering options available at the time, including the pressure filter tanks produced by the National Water Purifying Company in which Leeds had invested, were certain to purify the water. They could have cited the benign analyses of the Princeton and Columbia chemists as justification to put off filtration until a process was developed that would definitely work. They could also justify their postponement of filtration because Hackensack water didn't have the clearly dangerous bacteria levels of other sources like the Passaic and the Merrimack.

Brush and the directors were also keeping an eye on two important filtration efforts then under construction. Lawrence, Massachusetts, was building a slow sand filtration plant based on experiments conducted by Allen Hazen, the chief chemist at the Lawrence Experiment Station (Figure 22). Hazen had tested various sand and gravel types and configurations, and gradually produced a satisfactory reduction of bacteria by nitrifying organic matter to reduce it as a food source. New Orleans had contracted with the National Water Purifying Company to build the largest mechanical filtration plant yet attempted to purify muddy Mississippi water. Leeds had recommended against this installation, arguing that the pressurized filters weren't up to the job, but the managers of the National Water Purifying Company had proceeded anyway. Sanitary engineers, water works operators, and public health officials in many parts of the country were awaiting the results of these two projects. As the Hackensack directors

Figure 22: Allen Hazen, chief of the Lawrence Experiment Station and one of the first "sanitary engineers." M. N. Baker, "The Quest for Pure Water"

waited for filtration improvements, Brush installed floating devices on the small settling pond at New Milford to skim off algae and debris, and continued seasonal aeration of the Weehawken Reservoir and the force mains at the water works to discourage algae growth.

"the back-breaking labor of hundreds of men"

The increasing demand from new customers preoccupied the water company while it considered filtration. When the second Hoboken main was completed through Englewood in 1887, the water company extended service to the towns of Dumont, Bergenfield, Tenafly, and Leonia. At the same time it extended service along the first main to River Edge, Ridgefield Park, Ridgefield, Fairview, and West New York, and later to Teaneck, Oradell, Closter, Westwood, and Rutherford. All these extensions required considerable capital, principally supplied by de Forest and the Kean and Stevens families, and considerable labor, often supplied by immigrants. Adrian Leiby noted that in an age of modern equipment:

It is hard to remember that each shovelful of dirt in each foot of main was lifted from trenches six feet or more deep by workmen with long-handled shovels, who often stood knee-deep in water to do the digging, that each length of pipe was let down into the trenches on ropes by hand and that each trench was backfilled with the same shovels that dug them. Much of the water that the people of Bergen and Hudson Counties drink today is the product of the back-breaking labor of hundreds of men now dead, many of them Italian, who came to America so that their children and their children's children would have a better life than their fathers had. Many of these men never

24

worked anywhere else, and were in the employ of the Water Company
until the day they retired, a day, fortunately, when they drove
machines instead of driving themselves.[51]

Problems associated with expanding water service often preoccupied the water company. In extending lines into Englewood and the adjacent towns on the western slope of the Palisades during the late 1880s, Charles Brush had apparently underestimated the impact of the rising elevation on the water pressure in the mains. Some uphill Englewood customers complained about little or no pressure in the lines, but the inadequacy of the system became obvious in September 1890 when firefighters had to watch a large house burn down because they didn't have enough water pressure to fight it. To the embarrassment of the water company, a local newspaper reported, "The hydrants are ornamental, and make excellent tie posts for horses, but for practical fire purposes are of no account." Building a reservoir on top of the Palisades above Englewood would have been costly, as the land was being developed for expensive homes and private estates.[52]

Miles Tierney, a company director with considerable construction experience, helped Brush solve this problem. Unlike de Forest, the Keans, and the Stevens family, Tierney was the son of immigrants and "his schooling consisted of a few years in a log school in the back country of Pennsylvania." Tierney got his start as a builder in Jersey City, developed ties with the Stevens family in Hoboken, and eventually became president of the Hudson Trust Company and vice president of the Hackensack Water Company. A local newspaper noted that he was "one of the most competent engineers in this line of work in the United States." His work as an outside contractor for the water company earned him the nickname "Ten Per Cent Tierney" but it enabled de Forest, the Keans, and the Stevens to maintain control over how their money was being spent. Brush and Tierney built a booster station in Englewood to increase the water pressure there.[53]

To supply the booster station and other new demands, Brush erected a second addition to the engine house at New Milford in 1891 (Figure 23).

To ensure visual continuity, he used the basic design and construction details of the 1882–1886 sections for the new 32-foot by 58-foot one-story addition on the north side of the 1882 section, but he set the front of the addition back from the 1882 façade to allow the original building to remain dominant (Figures 24 and 25). In the addition Brush installed the station's No. 3 pump—its largest to date—a 10-MGD Worthington high-service pumping engine to supply water at the higher pressure needed for Englewood and the adjacent towns along the Palisades. He also installed steam-driven DC generators to power the station's first electric lights.

"an important step in the development of the water-shed"

With the increasing rate of development in Bergen and Hudson counties, Brush and the directors knew that the water company would eventually have to increase its water supply, and they quietly began acquiring land along the Hackensack River north of Van Buskirk Island. In September 1891 the *Hackensack Republican* reported, "Miles Tierney, of Jersey City, has invested in 92 acres of land, much of which fronts on the Hackensack River. It is rumored that the purchase was made for the Water Company. The water at this point is very low in the river, and it is understood that the Water Company contemplates erecting an immense reservoir for water storage in the vicinity of Oradell. This would be a great benefit to the Water Company and will insure against any shortage that might occur."[54]

To help assess the potential for a reservoir, Brush and the directors hired Cornelius C. Vermeule, a civil engineer based in New York, to examine the watershed for its storage capacity, and in June 1892 he reported:

The water-shed of the Hackensack above New Milford embraces
an area of 114.8 square miles, 50.7 in New Jersey and 64.1 in New
York. About 50 percent of the area is forested, the remainder being
under cultivation. The underlying rock is red sand stone, but the

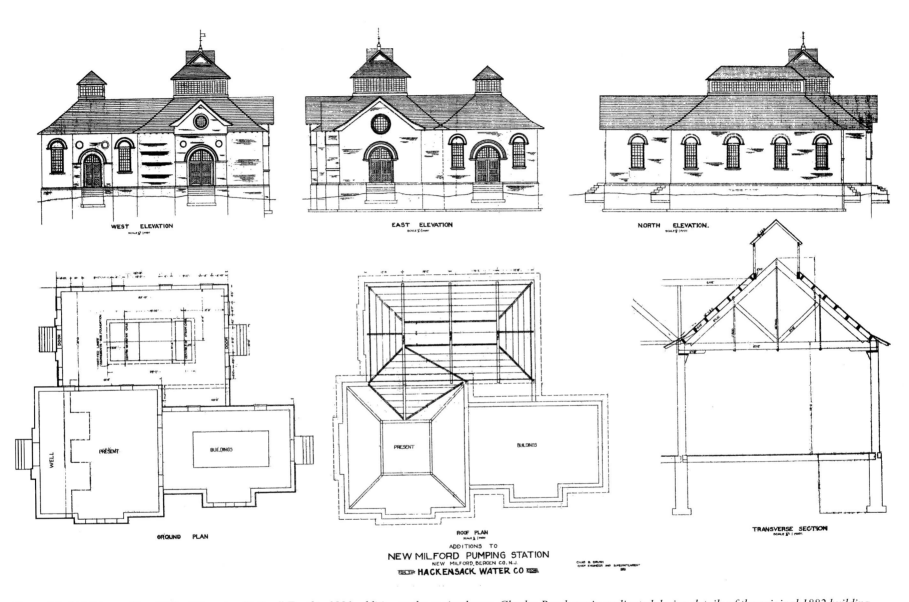

WEST ELEVATION

EAST ELEVATION

NORTH ELEVATION.

GROUND PLAN

ROOF PLAN

TRANSVERSE SECTION

ADDITIONS TO
NEW MILFORD PUMPING STATION
NEW MILFORD, BERGEN CO. N.J.
FOR THE HACKENSACK WATER CO

CHAS B. BRUSH
CHIEF ENGINEER AND SUPERINTENDENT

Figure 23: "Addition to New Milford Pumping Station." For this 1891 addition to the engine house, Charles Brush again replicated design details of the original 1882 building, but set the front back from the 1882 façade to allow the earlier building to dominate. United Water Resources

26

Figure 24: New Milford pumping station, c. 1892. 1891 and 1882 sections of the engine house, left; 1886 and 1882 sections of the boiler house, right, separated by New Milford Avenue. The original settling basin is in the front, with intake gates, left, and overflow conduit, right. Frank Vierling

Figure 25: New Milford pumping station, c. 1895. Storage building, left; 1891 and 1882 sections of the engine house, center; 1886 and 1882 sections of the boiler house, right; waste gate for overflow of the intake pond, front. The landscaping in front of the engine house and the woman pushing the baby carriage in front of the storage building contribute to the appearance of the site as a public park. The open doors welcomed passersby and local children to take a look at the fascinating steam pumps inside. United Water Resources

whole is quite heavily covered with glacial drift, sand and gravel; the drift covering is especially heavy in the flatter portions of the valley, near the streams. There are millponds, some quite large, and also quite an area of swamp bordering the streams. These act to regulate the flow somewhat and carry a considerable flow from wet periods into subsequent months.[55]

From the records of rainfall and river flow over several years, Vermeule figured that without any storage the amount of water that could be collected daily from the river for distribution would range from a minimum of around 11 million gallons during a particularly dry period to a maximum of 29 million gallons. With storage of around 2.25 billion gallons, Vermeule predicted that the yield would be around 77 million gallons. Regarding "surfaces reservoirs for storage," he reported that "the best site for such, on the lower water-shed, is above Veldran's dam," about a half mile north of the pumping station, where a new dam built:

to a height of 25 feet above mean tide and drawn down ten feet would afford a storage of about 1.4 billion gallons . . . enough to ensure a supply of 35 million gallons daily. The site is in all respects good, the banks being steep . . . and the reservoir would be valuable as a settling basin as well as for storage. Any project having in view the full utilization of the water-shed would require such a reservoir ultimately and it could be secured now much better than later on.[56]

To prepare for the eventual construction of a reservoir and "to obviate the difficulty which may arise from the holding of water at [Veldran's] dam during a dry period," Vermeule recommended "the control of Veldran's Mill property," stating, "I am convinced that that is an important step in the development of the water-shed"[57] (Figure 26).

Figure 26: "Triple Dam Showing the Feed Mill on the Hackensack River, Oradell, N.J.," c. 1905. Veldran's mill was purchased by the Hackensack Water Company in 1901 for the construction of the Oradell Reservoir. Frank Vierling

Figure 27: Elm Street Bridge, Oradell, New Jersey, c. 1905. Marked with the sign, "Erected by T. W. Stagg 1892," it is a "Phoenix" bridge with large beams and a 73-foot span. Rebuilt in 1965, the historic bridge remains in service today. Frank Vierling

In 1892 Bergen County erected a new truss bridge over the Hackensack River for Elm Street at the north end of Van Buskirk Island. The *Bergen County Democrat* noted, "The new bridge to give Peetzburgh (present day New Milford) more direct connection with New Milford depot is to be an iron truss of 80 feet span, and it will be completed in two months. The contract was awarded to J. W. Stagg, the plans having been first examined and approved by Chief Engineer Brush, of the Hackensack Water Co."[58] (Figure 27).

In the spring of 1892 *Scientific American* featured an article on the Hackensack Water Company, noting that "it now supplies a population of over 100,000 people" (see Figure 16). The article described the water system in detail, including the main pumping station, the intake, and the watershed:

The New Milford pumping station includes two batteries of steel boilers, supplying Worthington pumps. One six-million gallon per day high duty and two three million gallon per day low duty

pumps have been at work there for some time, and at present there has just been completed a ten million gallon high duty pumping engine . . . [an example of the] highly efficient, direct-acting pumping engine, which by its performances, has fairly established an era in the history of pumping machinery. In daily operation the back pressure at New Milford is never less than equivalent to 200 and sometimes to 250 feet above tide water. . . . The total pumping capacity is 22,000,000 gallons per day and the two force mains can pass 12,000,000 gallons per day.

[At the New Milford intake] the river is crossed by a dam which shuts out all salt water. A branch or race leading from above the dam conducts the water into a settling tank and thence into a pump well. As there is a very large surplus of water, there is a constant overflow from the race.

*One hundred and fourteen square miles of drainage area,
including Rockland Lake and the southern portion of the highlands
in Rockland County, N.Y., are tributary to this supply. In different
years the average daily flow of the river varies from 100 to 200 millions of gallons. With proper storage 50 to 60 millions may be
obtained. The smallest daily flow on record is 14 millions of gallons. As the present consumption is about six millions of gallons, it
will be seen that less than 5 per cent of the average flow is utilized.
The drainage area is free from all pollution, and it is believed it will
never attract factory interests or other sources of pollution.*[59]

"liable to be contaminated"

When *Scientific American* stated that the Hackensack River drainage
area was "free from all pollution," it was referring to obvious sources of
raw sewage and industrial contamination. Referring to the Weehawken
Reservoir, the article noted, "It was found some years ago that the water was
liable to be contaminated by organic matter and a growth of algae. Analyses
indicated a deficiency of oxygen in the water. The whole difficulty was due
to vegetable matter, as there is no sewage pollution in the drainage area. To
cope with this trouble aeration under pressure was adopted. . . . The difficulty was at once disposed of, and the water is now of a high degree of
purity." For his comment on the "purity" of the water, the reporter may
have been relying on the favorable analyses a year earlier by the Princeton
and Columbia scientists, who had characterized the water as "safe" and of
"excellent quality." Leeds' regular analyses, of course, indicated that the
water was generally satisfactory during the winter but often unsatisfactory
during the summer.[60]

Leeds recorded his growing concern about bacterial pollution in his
ledger. He first began documenting colonies of bacteria in October 1891.
Leeds compared Hackensack River water with New York City's Croton

water supply from the Catskill Mountains in upstate New York. Leeds, or
perhaps an assistant, apparently took the ferry from Hoboken to New York,
as the source of the Croton sample was recorded as "Faucet in Courtland St.
Ferry House." It contained thirty-two colonies of bacteria per cubic centimeter. The Hackensack water sample was taken from the "Faucet in Ferry
House, Newark St., Hoboken," and it contained 222 colonies. Leeds wrote,
"As compared with the Croton, [the Hackensack water] has more color,
developed on keeping [standing] a musty odor, and contained 7 times more
bacterial organisms."[61]

In February 1892, Leeds compared Hackensack River water to samples
from the Passaic River, the adjacent watershed to the west. He recorded the
oxidizable organic matter in the Hackensack water at 0.45 parts per one
hundred thousand, noting that it was "more satisfactory this month than
during the preceding, though it is still inexplicably high for this season of
the year:"

*It may be compared with that of the neighboring watershed—the
Passaic—the water of which taken about the same time at the
Jersey City intake, contains .38 parts per hundred thousand, and
at the Newark intake .414. In the latter case, a considerable part of
the organic matter was unquestionably derived from sewage, since
it contained the enormous number of 12,555 colonies of bacteria
per cubic centimeter. The New Milford sample contains 512
colonies, of which four species were evident, and of (these)
16 were fludifying colonies. This is also a large number.*[62]

Although the Hackensack River water had some bacteria, the level was
mild compared to that of the Passaic. When the bacteria count in the Hackensack water declined to 320 colonies in the following month, Leeds wrote,
"It is interesting to compare this with the [Passaic] river water unquestionably polluted with *sewage* in large quantities." The bacteria count in the four
Passaic samples was actually alarming, ranging from 23,400 to 43,300
colonies per cubic centimeter.[63]

Leeds' tests of Hackensack Water Company samples showed that bacteria remained relatively low during the next couple of years, but there were periodic signs of trouble in the watershed. In October 1892 he recorded "the enormous number of 7245 colonies per cubic centimeter" from a creek sample, noting, "The chemical and bacteriological analyses show that this water is very impure & the source of pollution injurious to the wholesomeness and safety of the water when used for drinking and domestic use." When a Hackensack Water Company sample in November showed 1,130 colonies, Leeds wrote, "This sample has much too large an amount of oxidizable organic matter, and too great a number of bacteria." Leeds was echoing a growing concern about bacteria linked to typhoid, as many cities posted reports of increasing numbers of citizens becoming sick and often dying from waterborne diseases.[64]

In 1893 Lawrence, Massachusetts, one of the worst cities for typhoid, opened its slow sand filtration plant based on Allen Hazen's studies at the Lawrence Experiment Station. When the number of new typhoid cases in Lawrence fell dramatically, many people began to believe for the first time that sand filtration could remove sufficient bacteria from American river water to make it safe for domestic use. But the Merrimack River in Lawrence didn't have the high levels of suspended particles that created the turbidity in many other rivers, including the Ohio and Mississippi. In 1893 the National Water Purifying Company's new plant with its mechanical filter tanks in New Orleans failed in its attempt to purify Mississippi River water. The city refused to pay for it, and National Water Purifying soon collapsed. This water purification calamity in New Orleans set back the development of the pressurized mechanical filters that many had viewed as the possible solution for turbidity.

"getting to the danger line"

While the results of the Lawrence filter were encouraging, they still didn't offer Robert de Forest and Charles Brush a solution to the problem of purifying Hackensack River water. The bacteria level in Hackensack water was relatively low compared with that of the Merrimack, Schuylkill, and Passaic Rivers, but it was nonetheless troublesome and it was increasing. Likewise, the turbidity level of Hackensack water was significantly lower than that of Midwest rivers like the Ohio and Mississippi, but it was high enough to generate persistent problems with the water's color, taste, and smell. The water company continued to rely on aeration as its primary water treatment. In July 1893, when Leeds noted that the levels of organic matter in Hackensack samples "are increasing and getting to the danger line," he suggested that "the aeration should be well looked after." Leeds credited his aeration treatment with keeping the problems with the Hackensack water under control, in comparison to "the Croton water which at present is much complained of, yet has not so much vegetable matter . . . which is allowed to develop algae." The water company continued aerating its water until 1905, making it "the longest-lived installation of the Leeds system of aeration."[65]

1893 was also a year of economic distress as a financial panic gripped the country. Because of its steady income and the growing population of Bergen and Hudson counties, the Hackensack Water Company was less affected than other businesses. Robert de Forest, according to Adrian Leiby, saw the panic as an opportunity for the water company to help relieve the situation with the second reservoir that it was building in Weehawken. Leiby noted that the directors resolved "that this company, instead of stopping work on its new reservoir during the winter months, as has heretofore been its intention, direct the contractor to continue to employ a full force of men . . . in the belief that the best remedy for the threatened distress among the laboring classes is for private employers to give out work whenever possible." In the era of civic capitalism, when most businesses were locally or regionally owned, such paternal actions were common.[66]

The failure of its New Orleans filters and the general economic malaise forced the National Water Purifying Company into a merger with its archrival, the Newark Filtering Company. These financial troubles must have weighed heavily on Albert Leeds, who had invested most of his savings in the former company. While he continued analyzing Hackensack water until 1900, his analyses after 1893 are less detailed than those in the previous years. His occasional interpretations after 1893 confirm his continuing emphasis on aeration. Noting a seasonal increase in organic matter in July 1895, he wrote, "But thus far the aeration has been successful in preventing any notable taste or smell arising there from." Leeds offered no new ideas about improving Hackensack water, and his role in the national development of water purification was on the wane.[67]

"first treatise on the art and science of filtration"

In the mid 1890s, Allen Hazen and George Warren Fuller were emerging as the national leaders in the development of water purification and both would soon consult with the Hackensack Water Company, albeit with different solutions to its water problems. After completing his experiments in Lawrence, Massachusetts, Hazen continued his research on slow sand filters in Europe, and in 1895 he published *The Filtration of Public Water Supplies*, called the "first treatise on the art and science of filtration." Hazen's book paid scant attention to mechanical filtration, which was still considered novel and unproven. The Lawrence experiments, the success of the Lawrence slow sand filters, and Hazen's book all helped to convince Americans that filtration could purify water, just "when water borne diseases, endemic and epidemic, [were] taking a heavy toll." These improvements tipped the balance and "American cities and water companies were at last willing to pay the cost of efficient purification."[68]

Albany represented this transition. Albert Leeds had recommended aeration and filtration a dozen years earlier, but the city had dickered around for years by looking for water sources other than the polluted Hudson River. With filtration now looking like a realistic solution to its typhoid problem,

the city hired Hazen to develop a plan to filter its Hudson River water supply. In his 1897 report Hazen recommended that the city build a slow sand filtration plant, citing the success of this type of filtration in Poughkeepsie and Lawrence, which had similar water conditions. While his estimates indicated that rapid mechanical filters would be cheaper to build and operate, Hazen noted that "no city has yet used rapid filtration for water so highly polluted as the Hudson," and that slow sand filtration was "the only system which has been demonstrated to be capable of purifying such a source of supply."[69]

"the evidence is very decisive"

George Warren Fuller had worked under Allen Hazen at the Lawrence Experiment Station. He was a chemist and bacteriologist trained at MIT, and he had also worked at the Berlin Water Works in Germany. In 1895 Charles Long, the president of the Louisville Water Company in Louisville, Kentucky, hired Fuller to conduct experiments on the effectiveness of filtering its supply of muddy Ohio River water through mechanical filters (Figure 28). Long had experimented with slow sand filters like the ones in Lawrence, but had found that the clay in Ohio water soon clogged the sand layers, which then had to be cleaned too frequently for practical operation. The mechanical filter tanks used in small cities were impractical for a city the size of Louisville, which their failure in New Orleans had demonstrated. But Long was determined to find a filtration method that worked.

Fuller believed that mechanical filtration could more efficiently remove the suspended matter in water from rivers like the Ohio that drained non-glacial land areas with comparatively little surface rock. Fuller tested mechanical filter tanks installed by three companies, and while they all clogged too quickly, he figured out why and theorized a solution. He recognized that the Hyatt process, the 1884 patent on coagulation immediately prior to filtering that all the filters used, was faulty. In his 1887 report Fuller

Figure 28: *The Louisville Experiment Station. George Warren Fuller, in the first row, third from right, is considered "the father of sanitary engineering" in the United States. M. N. Baker,* The Quest for Pure Water

wrote, "The evidence is very decisive that so far as practicable the suspended matter should be removed before reaching the sand layer, and that, at that point, the water should be thoroughly coagulated." In other words, following the coagulation, the flocculant needed time to settle. The treated or settled water could then be filtered efficiently through layers of sand.[70]

Fuller also noted another problem with the mechanical filter tanks then in use: "The several filters represent the prevailing size in practice (sand surfaces 9.5–12.5 feet in diameter), but for economy of operation, the individual filters should be much larger, the limit to be determined by the successful operation of mechanical appliances to stir the sand effectively while it is being washed by a reverse flow of water." Purification of turbid water from sources like the Ohio required a new type of mechanical filtration on an unprecedented scale. "There is no room for doubt," Fuller wrote,

"that satisfactory provisions as outlined herein . . . would not only aid in furnishing a filtered water of better quality, but would also give the water consumers a better service in other regards." Described as "classic" by water purification historians, Fuller's 1897 report on the Louisville experiments "brought mechanical filtration to a point where it was able to deal in an efficient and practical manner with many of the most difficult American waters." However, it took a decade for Louisville to complete a mechanical filtration plant as Fuller had recommended. Based on his success in Louisville, Cincinnati hired Fuller in December 1897 to conduct a series of detailed experiments on various filtration alternatives for its Ohio River water supply, which was especially turbid during much of the year.[71]

While the Hackensack River had its problems, it would not have been classified in 1897 as one of America's most difficult. There was no large-scale industrial or sewage dumping, as there was in the Hudson and Merrimack rivers, and the turbidity was less than that of the Ohio and Mississippi rivers. By 1896 Leeds was noting "diatoms," algae, and "infusoria," and he began noting specific microorganisms. Although his analyses periodically indicated some higher than normal levels of bacteria, he noted, "All the bacteria belong to harmless species, naturally present in surface water, and are purifying agents. They are not detrimental to health." He also recorded some remarkably good conditions that spring: "The tap sample [taken in his laboratory] is of very satisfactory nature—clear, of little color, and pleasant taste." Within a few years, however, the quality of the Hackensack River water supply would take a serious turn for the worse as development in the watershed led to increased pollution.[72]

"much appreciated by his clients and associates"

In 1897 Charles Brush died at the age of 55. In his fifteen years as chief engineer and superintendent, he guided the company's transition from a

32

local source to a regional supplier of customers in two counties through a complex pumping and distribution system. His work established a standard of quality engineering and design that provided a firm foundation for the company's phenomenal growth in the next century. In a memorial tribute, fellow engineer Louis Tribus wrote, "Personal friendship was his dominant characteristic—clients became friends, students became admirers, employees respected and served him loyally . . . and, his ability to assemble and present ideas in intelligent and convincing form was much appreciated by his clients and associates." Adrian Leiby called him "a great pioneer in the field of water engineering."[73]

In 1895 Charles Brush had made his senior assistant, W. F. Whittemore, a partner and their Hoboken firm was thenceforth known as Chas. Brush and Co., Civil Engineers. When Brush died in June 1897, he was most likely working on a major expansion of the New Milford pumping station to meet another burst of demand. In the mid 1890s trolley transportation took off as electric motors replaced horses as the source of power. Traction companies expanded their lines to connect Hackensack and Hoboken with towns all around Bergen and Hudson, stimulating another boom in development. As populations grew along the trolley lines, residents incorporated new boroughs within the earlier townships. In 1894 the villages of New Milford and Oradell were incorporated as the new Borough of Delford, a combination of the last syllables of each name. Delford included the water company's main pumping station on Van Buskirk Island that was formerly considered part of the village of New Milford along the west side of the Hackensack River in Midland Township. In 1897 Westwood was incorporated just northwest of Delford and in 1903 Emerson was incorporated north of Delford. (In 1920 Delford changed its name to Oradell. In 1922 the adjacent village of Peetz-burgh, east of the Hackensack River in Palisades Township, changed its name to the present-day New Milford.) Besides additional water customers, the increasing density within the towns along the trolley lines brought more demand for fire hydrants, which could draw great quantities of water.

To meet the current and projected demand and to prepare for the eventual construction of a filtration plant, the directors concluded that the pumping station had to be doubled in size. On January 6, 1898, F. W. Whittemore signed a drawing by "Chas. Brush and Co., Civil Engineers" for a new boiler house, the first step in this expansion (Figure 29). To complement the engine house, Whittemore noted, "Height of (Boiler House) Truss to be determined from measurements from Present Buildings to make eave lines of same height." The exterior design combined Charles Brush's traditional ornamentation with the site's first use of steel trusses for the roof. During construction, some of the ornamentation was eliminated, including molded brick arches and chevron door panels. These changes may reflect the company's appointment of D. W. French, a long-time employee, as its new superintendent. The son of a New England shoemaker, French was a self-educated man who rose up through the ranks and served the water company for nearly forty years.

The four boilers were laid out in banks of two, which allowed one set to operate while the other was idle or being worked on (Figure 30). The boilers were rated at 250 hp each, for a total capacity of 1,000 hp. Workers brought the coal from the coal house to the boiler house via hopper cars that ran on tracks across New Milford Avenue. The firemen who operated the boilers shoveled the coal into them from handcarts. The water company erected a square chimney 110 feet high to vent the boilers.

While completing the new boiler house, French was also planning a two-story addition to the engine house for the site's first vertical triple-expansion (VTE) pumping engines. The elevation and section drawing notes "D. W. French, Sup't." and was signed "W.H.L., 9/3/98" (Figure 31). "W.H.L." was most likely an employee of the water company, as he signed other company drawings over the next fourteen years, but whether he was a draftsman or an engineer remains unknown. To accommodate the height of the VTEs and

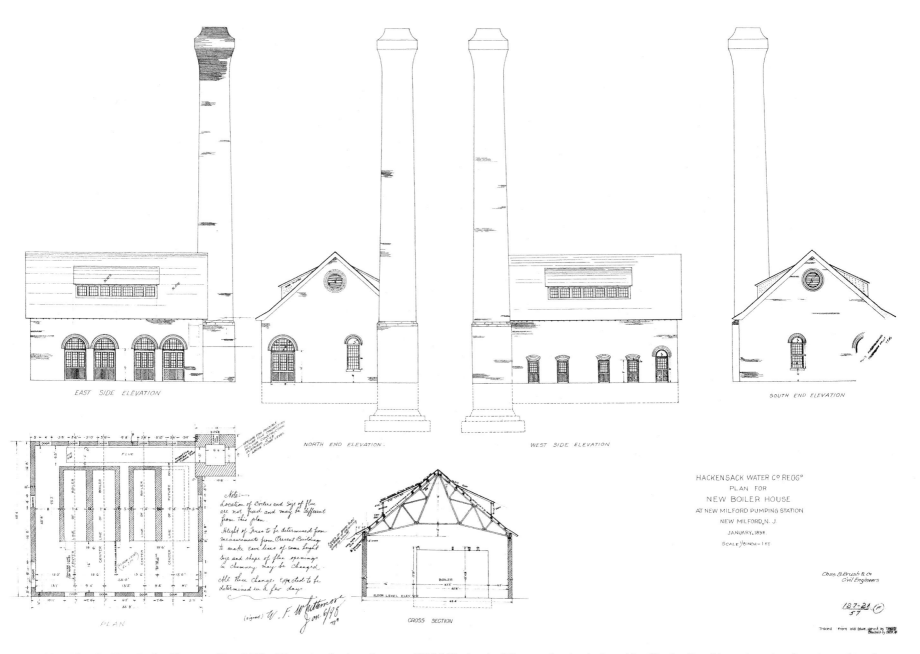

EAST SIDE ELEVATION

NORTH END ELEVATION.

WEST SIDE ELEVATION

SOUTH END ELEVATION

PLAN

CROSS SECTION

HACKENSACK WATER CO REOG°
PLAN FOR
NEW BOILER HOUSE
AT NEW MILFORD PUMPING STATION
NEW MILFORD, N. J.
JANUARY, 1898.
SCALE 1/8 INCH = 1 FT

Chas B Brush B Co
Civil Engineers

Figure 29: *"Plan for New Boiler House at New Milford Pumping Station, January 1898." The last building on the site designed by Charles Brush's engineering firm, it combined traditional details with innovative steel roof trusses. In the actual construction, some of the exterior ornamentation was simplified. United Water Resources*

Figure 30: 1898 boiler house, c. 1912. The boiler firemen shoveled the coal into the burners from a small coal hopper on rails. They raked the ash from below the burners and dumped it into the hoppers to haul it away. Each boiler had the words "Hackensack Water Co. Reorganized" cast into the front plates at eye level. United Water Resources

The VTE pumping engines represented the height of steam engineering technology. They had three cylinders of increasing sizes, which were successively powered by steam that declined in pressure as it passed from the first chamber to the last (Figure 32).

> *The highest distinction in steam engineering . . . was reserved for that small group of engine designers and builders who, in the closing decades of the century, carried the development of the multiple-expansion pumping engine to a remarkable level of performance . . . to an unusual degree this achievement was associated with one engineer, a single engineering works, and a specific type of engine: Edwin Reynolds, the E.P. Allis Company [which later became the Allis-Chalmers Manufacturing Company], and the vertical triple-expansion pumping engine. It was this engine, in origin associated with advances in British marine engineering from the 1850s, that set the pattern for the largest class of waterworks pumping engines in the United States for a generation to come. . . . Economies on this scale quickly made themselves felt, and the rule of the vertical triple engine developed by Reynolds and Allis continued as the favored equipment of the largest class of pumping stations until the eventual takeover by the steam turbine many years later.[75]*

The machinery plan for the 1898 section, signed "W.H.L., 7/21/98," shows the 30-inch piping through which each engine drew water from the suction well on the west end of the building (Figure 33). The piping connections to the three cylinders of each engine are labeled "L.P.," "I.P.," and "H.P." for the low-, intermediate-, and high-pressure cylinders. The Edward P. Allis Company of Milwaukee manufactured the No. 5 and No. 6 VTE pumping engines, one rated at 12 MGD and the other at 18 MGD (Figure 34). One original drawing of the No. 6 VTE pumping engine has surfaced,

complement the earlier sections of the engine house, the designer drew upon several of Charles Brush's traditional details—Romanesque arches, date medallions, and hipped roofs—and added new details like leaded stained-glass window transoms and second-story windows. To further integrate the new with the old, the water company upgraded the window transoms on the earlier sections to leaded stained glass and replaced the old chevron doors with glass and panel doors like those on the new section. On the interior, the builders erected steel columns within the brick masonry to support steel roof trusses and a traveling crane for installing and servicing the VTEs. Miles Tierney supervised all the construction for his customary fee of 10 percent.[74]

Figure 31: *"Additions to New Milford Pumping Station, West Elevation & North Elevation, W.H.L., 9/3/98." For the first two-story building on the site, the designer copied several of Charles Brush's traditional details from the earlier sections, including Romanesque arches, date medallions, and hipped roofs, but added second story windows and stained glass in the first floor window transoms. The interior included steel columns supporting steel roof trusses and a traveling overhead crane that was used to install and maintain the pumping engines, right. United Water Resources*

although others may exist (see Figure 185). When the water company put the 1898 section into service in 1901, it more than doubled the total capacity of its Hackensack Water Works from 22 MGD to 54 MGD (Figure 35).

"the typhoid record . . . mounts higher and higher"

In 1899, reflecting the country's increasing concerns about harmful bacteria, Albert Leeds began noting test results in his ledger "as to the presence of Coli Communis." Communis is a species of coliform bacteria that is used as a standard indicator of potentially harmful pathogens in water. As water supply had initially developed, "the earliest standards for pure water had been physical—color, turbidity, temperature, odor, color and taste—and could be observed by the layperson." As the nineteenth century ended, scientists and water suppliers were struggling to identify bacteriological standards for potable water. Leeds, however, was nearing the end of his career and his ability to use his considerable knowledge to protect public health was waning. He stopped analyzing Hackensack water in 1900 and died two years later. His gradual departure from sanitary engineering coincided with a marked increase in the public awareness of water-borne diseases.[76]

Figure 32: *"Reynolds Triple Expansion Pumping Engine, Chicago." The vertical triple-expansion engines (VTEs) used one blast of steam three times at decreasing pressure in three cylinders of increasing size. The VTE technology derived from British marine engineering in the 1850s. Archive of Industry*

REYNOLDS' TRIPLE EXPANSION PUMPING-ENGINE, CHICAGO.

Capacity, 18,000,000 gallons daily.

BUILT BY THE EDW. P. ALLIS CO., MILWAUKEE, WIS.

The incidence of typhoid was reaching epidemic proportions in many cities, and officials struggled with their limited options to protect public health. In March 1899 *Engineering News* reported:

> *THE TYPHOID RECORD in Philadelphia mounts higher and higher, notwithstanding which the Select Council again voted down the filtration loan last Thursday, this time on reconsideration. A total of about 4,500 cases and 450 deaths since Jan. 1 has now been reached. Nearly one hundred cases were reported on a single day last week. An appropriation of $37,000 for filters in the public schools has been recommended by the Council's Finance Committee. In Newark about 300 cases of typhoid and 25 deaths have been reported thus far in March alone. Camden has also joined the list of fever-stricken cities, with 50 cases from Feb. 15 to March 15 and 61 cases during the subsequent 12 days. The city recently abandoned the Delaware River for a new artesian well plant, but the latter proving deficient some 20 to 25% of the supply has been taken from the river of late.*[77]

In early 1899 George Fuller completed his filtration experiments on Ohio River water for the Cincinnati Water Commission and in May he submitted his *Report on the Investigations into the Purification of the Ohio River Water for the Improved Water Supply of the City of Cincinnati.* Fuller described the appearance of the river water as "almost always unsatisfactory and uninviting, and for about half the time so turbid that it is repulsive when considered for domestic use." His tests on experimental "English" and "American" filters in Cincinnati confirmed his Louisville findings: "The experience and data indicate clearly that the American system would be less difficult to operate, would be somewhat cheaper, would give the same satisfactory quality of filtered water, and could be much more readily enlarged for future requirement." With his reputation firmly established by his work and his reports, Fuller opened a consulting office in New York in 1899, setting the stage for his involvement first with the East Jersey Water

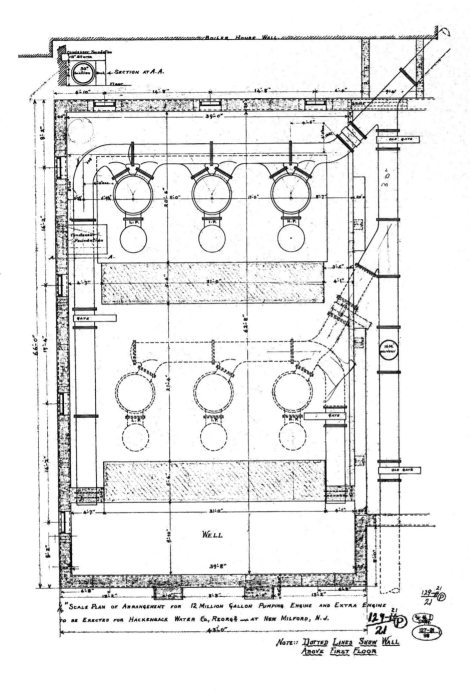

Figure 33: *"Plan of Arrangement for 12 Million Gallon Pumping Engine and Extra Engine to be Erected for Hackensack Water Company Reorgd. at New Milford, N.J."* Signed *"W.H.L., 7/21/98."* The basement included a suction well along the west side and 30 in. piping for the low-, intermediate-, and high-pressure cylinders on each engine. *United Water Resources*

Company in Little Falls, New Jersey, and then with the Hackensack Water Company.[78]

"what results could be accomplished by the different methods of filtration"

In the summer of 1899 Albany completed its slow sand filtration plant, designed by Allen Hazen. Its eight filters, made of unreinforced concrete and covering 5.6 acres, could purify water at the rate of almost 17 MGD. An adjacent 5-acre sedimentation basin with a capacity of 14 million gallons allowed particles to settle from the water, which was subsequently aerated, but there was no pretreatment with a coagulating chemical. Hazen's design included a chemical and bacteriological laboratory for regular testing of the raw and purified water.

Robert de Forest and the other officers of the Hackensack Water Company were no doubt monitoring the progress of Hazen's slow sand filtration plant in Albany. In October 1899, just a few months after the plant opened and had demonstrated the success of its design, they hired Hazen to study the Hackensack water supply to see "what results could be accomplished by the different methods of filtration." In November they instructed Hazen to report on "whether or not it is necessary or desirable to filter the water of the Hackensack River, the best method of filtration to be used, the cost of installing and operating such a system."[79]

For the January 1900 issue of the *Transactions of the American Society of Civil Engineers*, Hazen wrote a detailed report on the Albany filtration plant. He noted that while the concrete of the filters had developed some

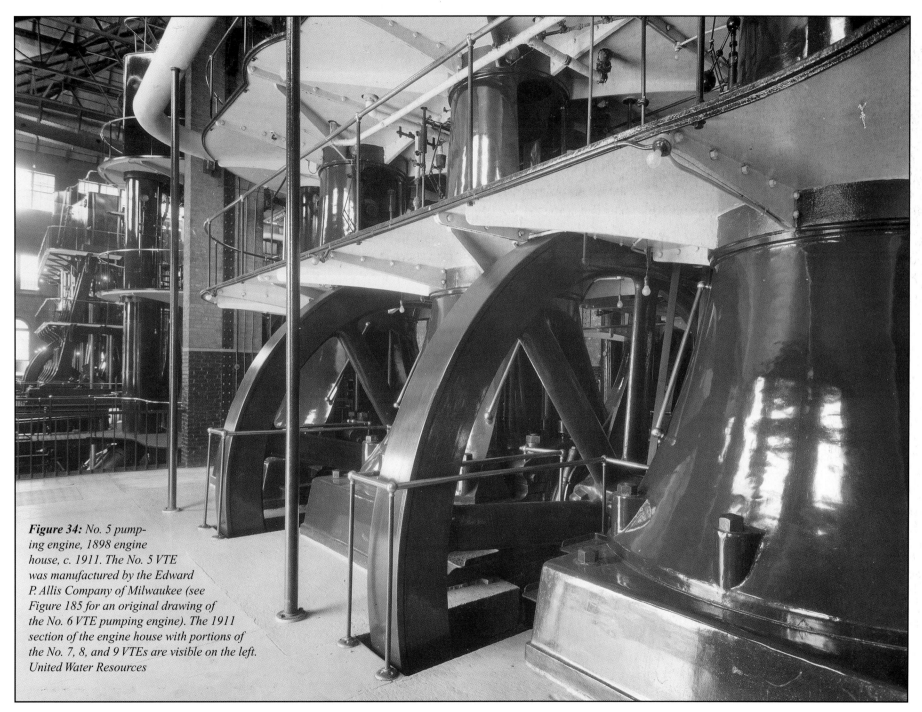

Figure 34: *No. 5 pumping engine, 1898 engine house, c. 1911. The No. 5 VTE was manufactured by the Edward P. Allis Company of Milwaukee (see Figure 185 for an original drawing of the No. 6 VTE pumping engine). The 1911 section of the engine house with portions of the No. 7, 8, and 9 VTEs are visible on the left. United Water Resources*

Figure 35: New Milford pumping station, 1907 postmark. The two-story 1898 addition (left) complemented the 1891 and 1882 sections of the engine house, and doubled the capacity of the pumping station. Local residents enjoyed the country setting canoeing on the intake basin in the foreground. William Berdan and Alice Berdan

cracks, they nonetheless "reached a bacterial efficiency of over 99 percent, and it is expected that their use will result in a great reduction in the death rate from water borne diseases in the city. They also remove a part of the color and all of the suspended matters and turbidity, so that the water is satisfactory in its physical appearance." In one of five peer reviews that accompanied Hazen's report, George Fuller noted that "the Hudson flows through glacial drift formation and not through a clay-bearing region" and that slow sand filtration can "remove only about one-third of the color of the applied water." Regarding the construction of the Albany filters, Fuller noted, "For the first time in this country the vaulting for the filter covers has been made entirely of concrete."[80]

In another peer review, George Whipple commented, "Experiments have shown that simple sand filtration is not capable of removing more than about one-half of the coloring matter from water, under favorable conditions, and that ordinarily the amount of reduction is not more than one-third or one-fourth," and while experts understand this, "the ordinary consumer does not understand why the filtered water should not be colorless." Whipple also noted, "At Albany sand filtration is not always effective in removing certain odors from the applied water." Another reviewer, William B. Fuller (no relation to George Fuller), was particularly interested in the design and construction of the sedimentation basin and filters, and he would soon have an opportunity to use his extensive knowledge of concrete at the New Milford Plant.[81]

"a source of real danger"

On January 25, 1900, Hazen reported his findings on the Hackensack water supply to Robert de Forest. Noting that he had examined "the analyses by Professor Leeds extending from January 1887 to the present time [Leeds' *Water Analysis* ledger] . . . the water-shed of the Hackensack River . . . and the mortality statistics of the larger cities supplied by this water," Hazen reported that "deaths from typhoid per 100,000 living" in Hoboken in 1899 were 21, about half of its average rate a decade earlier. Hazen wrote:

> *I find that the water-shed of the Hackensack River is . . . comparatively densely populated and the population is increasing rapidly, but there are no large towns or cities upon it, . . . no sewers are tributary to the river above your intake, and very complete measures have been taken to prevent the entrance of minor pollution. The water supply is thus unusually well protected for one draining a water-shed with so dense a population.*
>
> *The chemical analyses do not indicate that it is bad in quality or that it is materially deteriorating . . .*

The mortality statistics show that . . . the death rate from typhoid fever compares favorably with other communities in the neighborhood of New York . . .

The indications are thus that the water as supplied during recent years has been of fair quality, and there is no apparent evidence that it has been unwholesome.

On the other hand, the large and growing population on the water-shed constitutes a source of real danger to the purity of the supply and the health of those who drink it; and in my opinion, it will be necessary to filter the water at no remote date, in order to make it conform to the requirements of good engineering practice, and to avoid epidemics in the cities using it, which experience in other cases shows will be likely to occur, sooner or later, as a result of the increasing population upon the water-shed, under the existing conditions. [82]

While noting that it was unnecessary for him to describe the differences between sand filtration and mechanical filtration, "and of the advantages of each, as these matters have been treated in various public reports accessible to you," Hazen wrote:

Mechanical filtration has two distinct advantages in connection with the Hackensack River. First, it can be installed in smaller space [than sand filtration] and the ground which you own is sufficient for a much greater extension of the system than would be possible with sand filtration; . . . and second, with the use of a coagulant [sulphate of alumina] the color would be removed from the water in greater measure that it is possible to remove it without chemicals. To secure water free from color is always desirable; but in your case the color of the Hackensack water is not very great, and the people are accustomed to it; and so far as I have heard do not particularly object to it. [83]

Hazen discounted these advantages in comparison to the superior health benefits derived from sand filtration: "As a protection against actual or possible water borne diseases sand filtration is decidedly to be preferred, and as this is, I believe, the chief reason for filtration, I think that, all things considered, you will find sand filtration more suitable to your conditions and more satisfactory." [84]

To estimate the cost of filtration, Hazen wrote that "I have made preliminary plans for a system of sand filtration in connection with your pumping station at New Milford." The plan included "low lift pumps to lift the water from the river to the filters" and 6 acres of open or uncovered filters (in contrast to the covered Albany filters) spread over all the available land on Van Buskirk Island. The filters could typically supply 15 MGD, slightly above the 10 million to 12 million that the pumping station then averaged, and could be pushed "for short intervals, in case of necessity, [to] 20 million gallons per day." For future expansion, Hazen projected that "by filling the old channel leading to the lower waste weir an additional area of land, extending nearly to the railroad, will be made available, and a very considerable addition to the filtering area can be built upon it when required." Hazen also included a 2-million-gallon "pure water reservoir . . . to have some storage for filtered water. Hazen estimated that the capital cost would be $275,000, and the operating cost $12,000 per annum for an average of 12 MGD, or $10 per million gallons annually. He acknowledged that a "mechanical filter plant would probably be a little cheaper in first cost . . . [but] in operation it would be more expensive, owing to the considerable cost of the sulphate of alumina." [85]

"the adequacy of supply is . . . even more pressing"

In developing his proposal for the sand filters, Hazen concluded that "this preliminary examination indicates that the question of the adequacy of supply is an even more pressing one for you than the question of filtration." Noting that "The population of the district is growing rapidly, and is likely to continue to grow in the future," Hazen wrote, "Under these conditions it will not be surprising if the quantity of water actually required will double in the next 15 years . . . the average consumption will reach twenty million in 1915, while twenty-five to thirty million gallons will be required at certain times during dry weather. Works now constructed should certainly contemplate extension to this capacity."[86]

In analyzing Hackensack River flow records compiled by Charles Brush, Hazen noted that the average flow of 12 MGD over a 15-day period in the dry years of 1894 and 1895 was almost equal to the current rate of consumption. He predicted that with a similar dry spell "your distributing reservoirs would be drawn down before the stream flow could be depended upon to replenish them. . . . If the year 1900 should be as dry as the years 1894 and 1895 you would be embarrassed for water. Every year that the matter remains in its present condition, with increasing population and consumption, the danger of shortage, and the seriousness of it when it occurs, will be increased."[87]

Hazen computed that a daily consumption of 20 million gallons would require a storage reservoir of 225 million gallons, while a 50-million gallon consumption would require 3,400 million gallons of storage. "To meet with safety the requirements of the immediate future," he recommended, "I am of the opinion that at least one billion gallons of storage is necessary, and that a larger quantity is desirable." Recognizing that the Hackensack watershed was "extremely flat," Hazen remarked that:

> any reservoir which can be constructed will have a very large area
> of shallow flowage, a condition favorable to the growth of innumer-
> able plants, and unfavorable to securing water of the greatest
> purity. The water, however, can be aerated as it is drawn from the
> reservoir, and as it will be allowed to flow through the natural
> channels to New Milford, opportunities will be given to throw off

> by evaporation that part of the tastes and odors which is due to dis-
> solved gases, and filtration at New Milford will further improve it.[88]

Based on his analysis of topographical maps, Hazen identified three promising sites for one or more large reservoirs. He concluded that "The only available site on the main stream is just above Old Hook . . . [where] it would apparently be possible to build a reservoir flooding 1,300 acres to an average depth of $6\frac{1}{2}$ feet and holding 2,800 million gallons." The second site was on "Pascack Creek (Pascack Brook) directly above Westwood," where a reservoir flooding 460 acres to an average depth of 11 feet could hold 1,700 million gallons. The third site was "on a small tributary of Pascack Creek, namely Musquapsink Creek, where a reservoir covering 1,000 acres could be made with an average depth of 10 feet, holding a little over 3,000,000,000 gallons." Hazen concluded his report by stating that "it would seem to me highly important that this matter [of water storage] should be decided upon before the matter of filtration is taken up, as it may be that the conditions in this respect will have an important bearing upon the construction of filters."[89]

The Hackensack Water Company hired him to further investigate reservoir storage, and in his subsequent report, submitted in June 1900, Hazen noted, "One of the most serious difficulties in storing water upon the Hackensack River . . . is to get reservoirs of sufficient depth." While a reservoir could be created from the marshes along the river, "weeds would grow in the shallow water and innumerable organisms would develop . . . with the result that the water would become highly colored or very objectionable in taste and odor particularly during the warmer months of the year. Even though the water is purified by flowing to New Milford through the natural channels which afford it opportunities for aeration and afterwards filtration, some of the objectionable properties would remain."[90]

Hazen identified other potential reservoir sites, including a 1,040-acre site on the Hackensack River above West Nyack that could store 6 billion gallons, and smaller sites on the Pascack Creek above Hillsdale and

Rivervale, and near the New York State border. Because of the shallow flowage in a reservoir on any of the lower sites, including Old Hook, Hazen believed "that the water would become offensive in such a reservoir during hot weather" and the opportunities for aeration during the flow to New Milford "would be less than with the more distant reservoirs, while the need for purification would be much greater." Hazen concluded "that the best site for the construction of a comparatively small reservoir . . . is on Pascack Creek near the state line, and the best site for the construction of a much larger reservoir is upon the Hackensack River above West Nyack. In either case the stored water when required would be allowed to flow through the natural channels to the [pumping station] intake, a distance of some 13 or 15 miles, and this flow would afford opportunities for the removal of tastes and odors which might come from the growth of organisms in the reservoirs."[91]

French and the directors were not convinced by Hazen's recommendations to build a sand filtration plant at the pumping station in Oradell and one or more reservoirs near or above the state line. While sand filtration was effective in removing harmful bacteria, sanitary engineers had noted its inability to clarify turbid water, like the Hackensack River supply. With the projected rise in population, the potential for expanding a sand filtration plant on Van Buskirk Island seemed too difficult and limited. In addition, the water company was committed to building a reservoir on the Hackensack above Veldran's mill. Cornelius Vermeule's 1892 report had confirmed the feasibility of this location and the water company had been quietly purchasing land along the river for nearly a decade. Hazen had recommended remote reservoir sites because he thought that slow sand filters could not handle the problems with water stored closer to the intake at the New Milford Plant. Years of algae problems at the Weehawken Reservoir had taught people at the water company a lot about storing small quantities of water, and they wanted to minimize any potential problems with water that would be stored in the much larger Oradell Reservoir by maximizing the effectiveness of filtration.

By the middle of 1900 French and the directors were closely following filtration developments on the Passaic River, the adjacent water shed in northeast New Jersey that was more similar to the Hackensack River than the Hudson at Albany. The East Jersey Water Company was proceeding with an innovative mechanical filtration plant on the Passaic at Little Falls. In the meantime, French and the directors followed up on two of Hazen's suggestions. In the fall of 1900 the water company bought the Spring Valley Water Works and Supply Company in Rockland to develop a "supplementary source of supply" and, as de Forest noted, to protect "the watersheds from which both companies draw their source of supply from pollution." The directors also decided to build a reservoir before building a filtration plant.[92]

"hydraulic engineers and sanitary experts"

After George Fuller completed his filtration experiments in Cincinnati in 1899 and opened his office in New York, the East Jersey Water Company had hired him to study filtering options for its Passaic River water supply at its new 50-MGD pumping station in Little Falls, about 4 miles southwest of Paterson and 12 miles southwest of Oradell. In May 1900 Fuller recommended that East Jersey build a mechanical filtration plant, and in September East Jersey hired him to supervise its design and construction by the New York Continental Jewell Filtration Company of New York. While consulting on the Little Falls plant in 1901, Fuller entered into a partnership with Rudolph Hering, a fellow sanitary engineer who had gained prominence through his work on sewage treatment. Located at 170 Broadway in New York, the firm of Hering & Fuller described itself as "Hydraulic Engineers and Sanitary Experts."

After the plant opened, Fuller described his rationale for mechanical filtration at Little Falls in a detailed report he wrote for the *ASCE Transactions*: "There are no towns or cities discharging sewage into the Passaic River within 20 miles of the intake at Little Falls . . . [but there] are a number of towns and small cites [farther upriver] where some sewage may reach the stream indirectly, especially following heavy rains." Reflecting the public health standards of the time, Fuller cited the unremarkable annual death rate from typhoid fever of about 20 per 100,000 people served by East Jersey to support his observation that "in its sanitary character the water of the Passaic River at Little Falls is ordinarily very satisfactory." This rate was quite similar to the rate in Hoboken, where people used Hackensack water. With suspended matter of 2.5 to 10 parts per 100,000, Fuller noted that the water was "not muddy, comparatively speaking," but that:

> at times the water is very noticeably colored, due to dissolved vegetable matter coming from several large swamps situated on the upper portions of the drainage area. . . . Frequently, the water contains quite large amounts of amorphous matter, consisting principally of finely divided organic material . . . [which] together with the color which appears in the water, gives it at times what might be called a dirty appearance, and causes it to be less desirable for domestic use than the analyses indicate. . . .
>
> With the view of making the water thoroughly satisfactory in appearance, and to guard against the accidental pollution which may be possible occasionally, the Water Company investigated the feasibility of filtration. . . .
>
> It was recommended that the filtration works be of the American, or mechanical, type, partly on the account of the great desirability of removing the high amount of color, which the river possesses at times, and especially on grounds of economy. It was possible to construct a mechanical filter plant on the small area of ground below the pumping station. . . . If a sand filter had been installed it would have involved the expense of an additional pumping station to lift the river water to a suitable site upon the cliff above.[93]

George Fuller's analysis of water conditions and filtration possibilities at Little Falls was remarkably applicable to Hackensack River water and the Hackensack Water Works. Hackensack water and Passaic water both contained relatively mild amounts of harmful bacteria, although levels in the Passaic water could spike dangerously higher at certain times of the year. The water supplies had similar levels of suspended matter, and both suffered periodically from discoloration and unpleasant tastes and odors from high levels of organic matter. The Little Falls site and Van Buskirk Island both had limited space for a slow sand filtration plant and building one at a remote site would require an additional pumping station.

Given these similarities, the officers of the Hackensack Water Company decided to wait for the results of the Little Falls Filtration Plant, which East Jersey began building in April 1901, before deciding how to filter their own water supply. French stated publicly that the water company was planning to build a filtration plant, and while he and the other officers, as Leiby noted, had "no reason to suppose that the water company could not move with reasonable prudence and still be far ahead of other water companies. They were soon to be disabused."[94]

"a flood of complaints"

While waiting for East Jersey, French and de Forest decided to proceed with the reservoir in Oradell. The reservoir "would store water against periods of drought . . . [and] by giving the water time to settle, it would eliminate much of the sediment which the stream picked up in its course through low wooded land which ran for miles north of Oradell." They hoped that the sedimentation of suspended matter in the reservoir would take some of the pressure off of the future filtration plant. What they didn't realize was how much the reservoir construction would lower the quality of the water just at the time when "water purity, which had pretty much been taken for granted in the Hackensack valley, which had been (relatively) free of typhoid while other areas of the east suffered devastating epidemics, . . . had recently come very much to the public mind."[95]

By December 1901 the water company had purchased Veldran's Mill (see Figure 26) and $1 million of farmland and woodlots along the river above Oradell for a 250-million-gallon "impounding reservoir" that would contain the river for over a mile. Clearing and excavating the land along the river, described by the *Bergen Evening Record* as "a dense growth of timber and brush, a veritable wilderness," was a huge undertaking that required steam shovels and dozens of laborers (Figure 36). A flood in the spring of 1902 disrupted the work and submerged much of Van Buskirk Island (Figure 37). The mud stirred up by the flood and the reservoir construction produced "discolored water that started a flood of complaints about the water supply and its purity." In prior years, complaints about discoloration and unpleasant tastes and odors were usually chalked up to summer algae growth and largely ignored. But with the wide reports linking typhoid epidemics to polluted water, residents and public officials were increasingly worried about the safety of domestic water.[96]

Responding to complaints of "fishy" tap water, health officials found dead animals and a coating of algae in a company tank in Rutherford. This discovery and the general discoloration of the water from the construction prompted the local newspapers to question the safety of the entire water supply. When health officials and physicians inspected the watershed, they found chicken yards, pig farms, dairy farms, and outhouses along the river's banks, as well as stagnant ponds covered with algae. Though pollution from these sources was minor when compared to the raw sewage that was regularly dumped into rivers like the Hudson, Merrimack, Ohio, and Mississippi, this distinction was lost on the public.

Citing a bacteriologist's report, the county medical association declared the company's water unsafe for drinking and recommended boiling it before use.[97]

D. W. French countered that the company's own analyses, done by Dr. Albert Leeds from 1884 to 1900, and currently being done by the highly regarded Dr. Ernest Lederle, a former New York City Health Commissioner and founder of Lederle Laboratories in Rockland County, showed that the water was safe. Unimpressed by the credentials of these bacteriologists and by French's pleas for time to finish the reservoir and to plan the filtration

Figure 36: *Oradell Reservoir construction, c. 1902. The water company used steam shovels on platforms to excavate the "wilderness" along the Hackensack River for the reservoir. It removed soil with a high amount of organic matter to prevent the growth of vegetation along the shallow edges of the reservoir. United Water Resources*

Figure 37: *1902 flood. Superintendent's house, left; engine house, right. United Water Resources*

Figure 38: *"The Little Falls Filters of the East Jersey Water Company," c. 1903. East Jersey built the first large-scale mechanical filtration plant on the Passaic River next to its 1898 pumping station. George Fuller supervised its design, construction, and initial operation. Allen Hazen,* Clean Water and How to Get It

plant, the newspapers demanded action. French could have argued that filtration was still experimental and offered no guarantee of success, but this too would have been lost on the public.

On September 4, 1902, the East Jersey Water Company placed its 32-MGD mechanical filtration plant in service and hired George Fuller to supervise the first year of its operation (Figure 38). His record of the first two months of the plant's operation, which he was still refining, showed that the filtered water had a 70 to 80 percent reduction in turbidity, a 65 to 85 percent reduction in color, a 75 percent reduction in amorphous matter, and a 98 percent reduction in bacteria. These results were apparently good enough for French, de Forest, and the other officers of the Hackensack Water Company, given the pressure they were under from the newspapers. In November 1902, "when the filtration affair was at its height, the water company . . . switched from the Hazen engineering firm, the leading proponents of slow sand filters, to the George W. Fuller firm." Hering & Fuller

began working almost immediately; the earliest of their drawings for the filtration plant at the Hackensack Water Works is dated January 1903.[98]

"the best means of accomplishing it"

In February 1903 Rudolph Hering submitted a preliminary report to the water company on additional reservoir sites, including temporary sites for "the coming season should a low rainfall cause the stream flow . . . to become very low" and on the "feasibility of filtration . . . the best means of accomplishing it and the probable cost of construction and operation." For a large storage capacity, Hering & Fuller recommended a "Reservoir on the Hackensack River Above Rivervale." A 15-foot dam at this location, "about one mile above Rivervale and one-half mile below the New York

State line," would flood about 573 acres, hold 1 billion gallons and yield 17 MGD, while a 20-foot dam would flood about 866 acres, hold about 2 billion gallons, and yield 26 MGD. Noting the swampy conditions in Rivervale, Hering cautioned that "the quality of Hackensack River water obtained from a reservoir built upon swampy ground depends largely upon the thoroughness with which the organic matter is removed from the bottom of the basin." Hering noted that "It is wise to strip the bottom and sides [of the basin] until the soil holds no more than 2 per cent of organic matter."[99]

For smaller reservoirs Hering & Fuller recommended an "Upper Reservoir on Pascack Creek West of Pearl River" in New York and a "Lower Reservoir on Pascack Creek above Hillsdale." At the Pearl River site a 45-foot dam would flood 85 acres, hold 200 million gallons, and yield about 3 million gallons. The steeper grades in this area would have "little shallow flowage," and, as the site was not swampy, it did not need to be stripped. At the Hillsdale site, a 35-foot dam would flood 215 acres, hold 900 million gallons, and yield 9 million gallons "in the four driest months of the driest year of which we have records." While only portions of this site required stripping, Hering noted that "at the Hillsdale reservoir the number of residents in the immediate locality is not a desirable feature, but danger from pollution can be obviated by efficient patrol of the watershed in the neighborhood."[100]

Under "Quality of Stored Water," Hering wrote, "With the reservoir bottoms cleaned . . . and with the sides excavated to improve shallow flowage, . . . a satisfactory quality of stored water can be obtained from each of the reservoirs considered. As they continue in service there would be slight accumulations of organic matter in the sediment deposited from the water . . . [but] these accumulations would be too slight to facilitate objectionable growths." Of the three sites, Hering concluded that the "upper Pascack project would be cheapest" but would yield the least amount of water. "For a material increase in the daily supply," he reported that the "lower Pascack site . . . is at present more economical than the Rivervale site." He also

noted, however, that "If the quantity of water to be supplied increases in the future as it has increased in the past, it will be necessary eventually to resort to the use of both the lower Pascack and Rivervale sites. The comparison between them shows that if the former is built first there will be a savings in cost for about fifteen years. . . . From these facts we recommend for a material increase of your supply the lower Pascack reservoir be built first." The water company would proceed with the lower Pascack site in Woodcliff within a few years.[101]

"both types of filtration are capable of doing good work"

Under the heading "Filtration Works," Hering recommended building a plant at Oradell with a nominal capacity of 24 MGD, since by the time it was completed "your daily pumpage will average about 18 million gallons, and the works should be of such size to make it unnecessary to add to them during the next eight or ten years." Noting that "any plant of proper design should be capable of being operated, at least for limited periods, at rates considerably in excess of the nominal rates," he projected that with a 24-MGD plant "it should be feasible for short periods to obtain 35 million gallons daily, and week after week to obtain 30 million gallons."[102]

In comparing slow sand filtration and rapid mechanical filtration, Hering, who was one of the top sanitary engineers in the country, summarized the state of filtration in 1903:

> Both types of filtration are capable of doing good work under favorable conditions, and as a general rule there is not a very great difference in the total cost, including both operating and capital charges. Sand filters are held by some to be . . . preferable for the treatment of sewage polluted waters, whereas mechanical filters are clearly the best for the treatment of waters which are muddy or highly colored by a vegetable stain. Mechanical filters

produce a colorless water, while sand filters remove only about one-quarter to one-third of the color. During the past few years mechanical filters have been thoroughly studied, and . . . when properly built and operated . . . are quite as efficient in removing sewage pollution and such disease germs . . . as may find their way into the water. . . . During the cold seasons of the year they are slightly more effective and during the warm seasons the reverse may be true.

Mechanical filters, operating at a velocity at least forty times greater than sand filters, require that the water first be treated with a coagulant, which masses together the various impurities contained in the water, including the bacteria, and forms them into flakes of such size that they can be removed by passing through sand at the higher velocity. Such coagulation can be produced by sulphate of alumina, which is the chemical ordinarily employed at this time. In some quarters there has been a tendency to raise objections to the use of sulphate of alumina, sometimes called alum, on the ground that it "medicated" the water and appeared in the filtered water. In order that this coagulant may become effective, it is necessary for it to become decomposed by the lime contained in the river water, and with careful management it is hardly possible for any undecomposed sulphate of alumina to reach the consumer. In fact, in studying the history of mechanical filters in this country, the objections which may be raised to the process are confined almost wholly to insufficient use of this chemical, rather than to excessive use and its appearance in the filtered water.[103]

Hering's discussion of Hackensack water clearly tied Hering & Fuller's recommendations to their experience at Little Falls:

The character of the Hackensack River water with reference to the selection of a method of filtration has been studied from the records of analyses which were made for many years by the late Professor Leeds, and particularly from comparisons made of the results of analyses of the past two years with those of other waters with which we are more familiar, such as the Passaic River waters at Little Falls. In general we find that the water of the Hackensack River and the Upper Passaic are quite similar in character. Each becomes somewhat turbid or muddy following heavy rains, each contains a vegetable stain due to dissolved coloring matter coming from swamps upon the drainage area, each at times possesses quite an appreciable taste and odor, but both are free from gross pollution shown by the comparatively slight amount of sewage entering the streams and by the typhoid fever records year after year in the communities using these waters. . . . We may safely conclude that the Hackensack River at New Milford requires substantially the same treatment as is the case with the Passaic River at Little Falls, and that purification works should be capable . . . of turning out a water of good appearance both as to freedom from all turbidity and vegetable stain such as are noticed by the ordinary water consumer . . . that the treatment should be sufficiently thorough to eliminate the effect of any accidental pollution such as might occasionally occur, and it should also remove, so far as practicable, those properties which occasionally give rise to disagreeable tastes and odors.[104]

Hering stated that a 24-MGD sand filter plant at Oradell would "consist of eight (filter) beds, averaging one acre in area each, with necessary piping, connections, regulators, sand washers, etc., and a small compensating basin holding about one million gallons of filtered water which would act also as a suction well for the pumps." The filter beds should be covered because "the care of open filters in this climate at a point, distant from large towns, when it is difficult to procure extra labor, is quite an expense, and according to experience elsewhere on an average fully reaches the capital charges on the cost of a filter cover." Hering noted that "The gross area required for a sand filter plant of this size is more than eleven acres. The grounds at and near your pumping station are not well adapted to the construction of such a plant, owing to the character of the soil, the limited area of available land and manner in which it is cut up by roads and water courses, thus requiring beds of irregular shape and increased cost." To build a sand filter plant, "it would probably be necessary to fill in the (west creek) and the headrace canal and extend the plant to the railroad property line." Regarding future expansions, Hering wrote: "To build sand filters here to increase the nominal daily rate beyond 24 million gallons does not seem feasible."[105]

Hering wrote, "We conclude from our studies that it would cost from $550,000 to $600,000 to construct a sand filter plant of the stated size, including low lift pumping machinery, filtered water basin and connecting piping." He estimated the cost of operating the plant at a rate of 18 MGD to be $6.93 per million gallons annually, and at 24 MGD to be $5.75 per million gallons.[106]

"hygienically as pure . . . and superior in appearance"

Hering reported that "For a mechanical filter plant at New Milford, it is clearly necessary to pump the water with centrifugal or other low lift pumps from the river to the filter plant." His preliminary description of the filter plant provides a glimpse of Hering & Fuller's thinking early in the design process:

First, a coagulating basin of about three million gallons capacity, in which coagulant is added to the river water and some of the impurities allowed to settle before the water reaches the filters proper; second, the filters, consisting of 8,646 square feet of filtering surface, together with all the necessary connections, piping,

wash water pumps, devices for stirring the sand, etc., and third, a small clear water basin, placed beneath the filter tanks and holding about one million gallons of filtered water, to serve as an equalizing basin when either the pumps or the filters are started or stopped. A house should be built over a portion of the coagulating basin, in which to place the necessary operating machinery and to provide storage for the chemicals. A narrow building is also required over a portion of the filters. The remainder of the filters should also be under cover.

Such a layout for a mechanical plant would occupy an area of about one acre, and could be conveniently located at the rear of the present pumping station, allowing the space of say 100 feet for extensions of the latter. The river water would then be taken through the present conduits to the low lift pumps, thence to the purification works and back to the suction of the high lift pumps . . .

In the sketches we have prepared for the purpose of making approximate estimates of cost . . . the coagulating basin would carry its full depth of 20 feet of water and the filter tanks would have a depth of less than one half of this amount. Beneath the filter tanks is the clear water basin, in which about 10 feet in depth of filtered water could be stored. This arrangement resembles that of the recently constructed filter plant at Little Falls, N.J.

It is possible to construct a mechanical filter plant, excepting of course the machinery, piping and connections, almost entirely of concrete. For a large portion of the plant this is doubtless the best construction. Concrete filter tanks, if well built, are also superior to tanks constructed of wood or iron. The Little Falls plant with the filter tanks and superstructure built of concrete according to the Ransome method seems thus far to be very satisfactory *under the conditions encountered at that site. It is perfectly practicable, however, to construct a plant without the Ransome method, using groined arches in place of the flat construction. In our estimates of the cost of a mechanical plant at New Milford we have assumed that the basins and filters would be built without metal reinforcement, and that the buildings would be of brick.*[107]

Hering wrote, "We estimate the cost of the completed plant, including the low lift machinery placed in the present station and all the connections to and from the filters to be $300,000. This is based on unit prices . . . corresponding to Little Falls prices, and with 10 per cent added for contingencies. It is feasible to build such a plant without interference with patents, but the design would require thorough detailed study. It requires about one full season to build such a plant." Hering & Fuller estimated the cost of operating a mechanical filtration plant at a rate of 18 MGD to be $5.55 per million gallons, and at 24 MGD to be $4.70 per million gallons. In summary, Hering wrote:

Comparing the cost of the two projects, it is seen that a mechanical filter plant requires only about one-half as large an investment for construction as a sand filter plant; and in total annual cost it causes a saving of about $9,000. Besides being less expensive, a mechanical filtration plant is capable of being extended readily in the future as occasion requires, which is not the case with sand filters, on account of lack of room. With the grade of supervision and quantity of coagulant provided in our estimates for mechanical filters, they would produce filtered water hygienically as pure as obtained by sand filters and superior in appearance, due to the practically complete removal of the vegetable stain. In view of these facts we recommend that you adopt mechanical filtration.[108]

D. W. French and the water company directors had hired the two top sanitary engineering consultants in the country, Allen Hazen and Hering & Fuller, to advise them on the best way to filter Hackensack River water.

Hazen had recommended slow sand filters because he thought they were more effective in removing harmful bacteria, which he believed was the "chief reason for filtration." Hering & Fuller had recommended mechanical filtration because they believed that it would be less expensive, equally effective in removing bacteria and better in removing turbidity, and more easily expanded. The Little Falls Filtration Plant provided compelling support for Hering & Fuller's proposal.

"the first adequate demonstration of the principles of mechanical filtration applied on a large scale"

When George Fuller presented a detailed report on "The Filtration Works of the East Jersey Water Company" in Little Falls to the annual meeting of the American Society of Civil Engineers in New York on April 1, 1903, D. W. French or another representative of the Hackensack Water Company was surely in attendance. In his report, published in the April 1903 *ASCE Transactions*, Fuller noted that "the design of this plant was the result of numerous conferences and discussions between the representatives of the [East Jersey] Water Company and the [New York Continental Jewell] Filtration Company." He wrote, "It is gratifying to report that the Water Company instructed the writer not to spare expense in making the plant capable of giving thoroughly efficient service." This had been Fuller's first opportunity to put his ideas into practice on a large scale, and for it he had developed a number of innovations that enabled many cities to purify their water supplies.[109]

In Louisville Fuller had recognized that chemicals used in treatment prior to filtering had to be precisely applied to the water and then allowed sufficient time to coagulate and settle particles. To accomplish this in Little Falls, he designed a system of mixing tanks with semiautomatic controls for introducing the chemicals, and a 1.75-million-gallon coagulation basin to allow them to work. To efficiently clean the filters, Fuller and the filtration company developed a new design of hydraulically-controlled air and water jets that efficiently backwashed the sand and gravel through the underdrains of the filters. They designed monolithic concrete filter boxes for extra durability and to keep the water as clean as possible. The engineers designed a filter gallery between the rows of filters that provided a view of one end of each filter (Figure 39). They designed operating tables where the filter operators could control the filtering and backwashing processes while visually monitoring the conditions in the filter (Figure 40).

Eleven sanitary engineers, all ASCE members, provided peer reviews for Fuller's East Jersey report. Citing the Louisville experimental filters as a prototype for the Little Falls filters, Allen Hazen wrote, "In this plant a decided step has been taken in securing devices to insure the continuous application of the coagulant." He noted the "excellent manner in which concrete has been used in all parts of the design," and that the increased capacity of the coagulation basin was "most advantageous, and it may be questioned whether still further increase would not be desirable." Another engineer, R. S. Weston, noted that "the Little Falls construction represents many new departures" and that "certainly, the experience which will undoubtedly be gained from the operation of this plant will establish the system of rapid filtration upon a firm, rational, and scientific basis."[110]

Figure 40: "An Operating Table, Little Falls Filtration Plant," 1903. Filter operators controlled the filtering and backwashing process from the operating tables in the filter gallery while visually monitoring the conditions in each filter. George Warren Fuller, "Filtration Works of the East Jersey Water Company," ASCE Transactions, 50, 1903

Figure 39: "Interior of Filter House, Little Falls Filters of the East Jersey Water Company," 1903. The filter gallery provided a view of the ends of the four filters that were arrayed on each side. Large windows brought considerable daylight to the interior. Allen Hazen, Clean Water & How to Get It

George S. Whipple wrote that the Little Falls plant "is the first adequate demonstration of the principles of mechanical filtration applied on a large scale, and its many unique features distinguish it sharply from the conventional type of mechanical filters used heretofore." Noting that "the bacterial efficiency of mechanical filters depends absolutely and entirely . . . upon the continuous application of the coagulant in the proportion which the raw water calls for," L. J. Le Conte wrote, "The new devices invented and applied for controlling the feed of the coagulant in this plant seem to be a great improvement over former designs, and [George Fuller] certainly deserves much credit for them and their good work."[111]

Two ASCE reviewers of Little Falls would later work on the design of the filtration plant at the Hackensack Water Works: William B. Fuller, who also served as the resident engineer in charge of the East Jersey construction, and John H. Gregory. William Fuller wrote, "As has been well said, the completion of this plant stands as a milestone marking distinct progress . . . in the art of mechanical filtration. In a lesser though still distinctive way, it stands as a milestone...in that it has been constructed throughout almost entirely of concrete. This has been done with an idea of making the entire structure as durable and permanent as possible." He noted that the filters were made watertight "by building each tank as a monolith, the bottom, the sides, and the top as one continuous operation. They thus became for all intents and purposes like a nest of boxes, each box being free to move by itself under varying conditions."[112]

Regarding George Fuller's report on the plant, J. H. Gregory wrote that he knew of "no place where so much valuable information requisite for designing a mechanical filter plant properly is available as is given in condensed form in this paper." Noting that he visited the plant frequently during its construction and early operation, Gregory stated, "The type of construction adopted at Little Falls is radically different from that used heretofore for mechanical filter plants, and . . . a great improvement over that used for certain other plants built recently. The design of mechanical filter plants in the future will, it is to be hoped, . . . be modeled . . . closely after the Little Falls work."[113]

Chapter 3

A Perfect Model in Every Sense

The filtration plant at the Hackensack Water Works was the first of several designed by Hering & Fuller. The firm had begun working on a preliminary design of the plant just a few months after the opening of the Little Falls Filtration Plant, where George Fuller had served as consulting engineer. A detailed memorandum of discussions in Hering & Fuller's office in late April 1903 indicates that representatives of the Hackensack Water Company were actively involved in developing the design for its plant. The memo noted that "In considering the position of the filter plant, conversations with Mr. Tierney during the visit to New Milford last December showed that he considered it advisable to leave a vacant space north of the new pumping station buildings, about 100 feet wide." While the water company had built its third addition to the engine house in 1898, Tierney was already contemplating a fourth addition.[114]

The April memo includes references to the Little Falls Filtration Plant that illustrate its influence on the design of the filtration plant at the Hackensack Water Works: "It was considered that the clear water basin might be placed beneath the filters in a manner somewhat similar to the arrangement at Little Falls." The memo also shows how the design evolved over time. Reflecting changes since the preliminary report in February, which had specified a machinery and storage house over a portion of the coagulation basin, the memo noted, "It would now seem desirable to consider the feasibility of having a building . . . placed at the south end of the filters to serve for the machinery, coagulating department, laboratory and offices." While

Hering had suggested a 3-million-gallon coagulation basin for New Milford, the memo showed that the designers and the water company were considering more than doubling the size of the basin: "It would be advisable to make it of such a size that it would last for a much longer period in the future . . . than would the filter plant proper as now considered . . . It is suggested that sketches and approximate estimates of cost be made for a coagulating basin with earth embankments, with a capacity of three, five and eight million gallons." The water company and their consultants subsequently pushed this recommendation even further, and Hering & Fuller ultimately designed a 12-million-gallon basin, quadruple the size in their original proposal.[115]

In June 1903 the Hackensack Water Company directors "approved the construction of a new filter plant using the Fuller system." Hering & Fuller produced over seventy-five drawings for the plant. The earliest, dated January 1903, probably reflects a note in the April memorandum referring to "the sketches made in the early winter, on which we based the estimates for the preliminary report." The last drawing is dated November 1904, indicating that Hering & Fuller continued designing portions of the plant after construction was underway. While most of the drawings were signed "Hering & Fuller," a few were signed "Rudolph Hering." Both Fuller and Hering were members of the ASCE; Hering was an engineer, while Fuller was a chemist and bacteriologist.[116]

In the summer of 1903 the directors approved construction of a second impounding reservoir along the Pascack Creek in Woodcliff, about 5 miles north of New Milford. Hering and Fuller had recommended this site for a small reservoir in their preliminary report in February. A severe drought early that year had convinced the water company to increase its storage capacity as soon as possible, and 200 men were soon at work on the new reservoir, while others began excavations for the filtration plant. Torrential rains in October flooded both construction projects, washed out completed portions of the Woodcliff Lake dam, and swept away several area bridges, including a new bridge over the Hackensack River at Oradell Avenue. The flood halted operations at the pumping station for a couple of days and carried away stacks of lumber and other materials for the new filtration plant. Workers quickly pumped out the excavations and were soon back at work on both building sites.

"the quality of the water has not promised to be wholly satisfactory at all times"

While construction on the filtration plant was underway, *Engineering Record* ran two articles in November 1904 on "The Mechanical Filters of the Hackensack Water Company," noting in the first that "the quality of the water has not promised to be wholly satisfactory at all times and about two years ago the water company took up the problem of improving it with Messrs. Hering & Fuller. Experience on the Little Falls purification plant led them to use reinforced concrete very largely, to prepare new designs for the strainers, controllers and washing system, to employ larger filter units, and to depart in some other respects from the Little Falls designs." The second article noted, "Messrs. Hering & Fuller are the consulting and supervising engineers for the plant, which was designed under their direction, by Messrs. William B. Fuller and John H. Gregory." William Fuller had been the resident engineer at Little Falls, and John Gregory had visited the construction there frequently.[117]

The Hering & Fuller engineers used their experience at Little Falls, which had been the first large-scale mechanical filtration plant in the country, to develop numerous innovations for the Hackensack Water Company filtration plant. Some of these improvements were immediately apparent,

like the larger filters and separate coagulation basin, while others were less obvious, including concrete collection blocks in the bottom of the filters and refinements in the filter backwashing devices. These improvements made the plant the most advanced mechanical filtration facility in the country until it was superceded by improvements elsewhere.

Hering & Fuller's plan for New Milford required reworking the pumping station to pump "raw water" to the new filtration plant and "filtered water" primarily to the distribution system but partially to the filtration plant to power equipment and to clean filters. The filtration plant included four new components (Figure 41): an above-grade coagulation or settling basin covering about 3.3 acres east of the pumping station; a 400-square-foot gate house west of the coagulation basin to control the flow of water and treatment chemicals; a filtration house covering about four tenths of an acre, beginning about 120 feet north of the existing pumping station; and a 40-foot-diameter wash-water tank between the filtration house and the coagulation basin.

The *Engineering Record* acknowledged the contribution of the company's in-house engineering and construction expertise: "The Hackensack Water Company is doing the work by day labor, Mr. Miles Tierney, vice president, acting as construction manager, and Mr. John Tierney (his son), as resident superintendent." The company's twenty years of construction experience in building the pumping station, the Weehawken water tower, the distribution network, and four reservoirs was invaluable in this new, complex construction. In contrast, the East Jersey Water Company had hired outside contractors to build the Little Falls Filtration Plant.[118]

"it was believed to be more economical"

The original design of the filtration plant at the Hackensack Water Works illustrated the efficient use of gravity and pressurized water to minimize capital and operating costs. The plant utilized gravity to direct the flow of

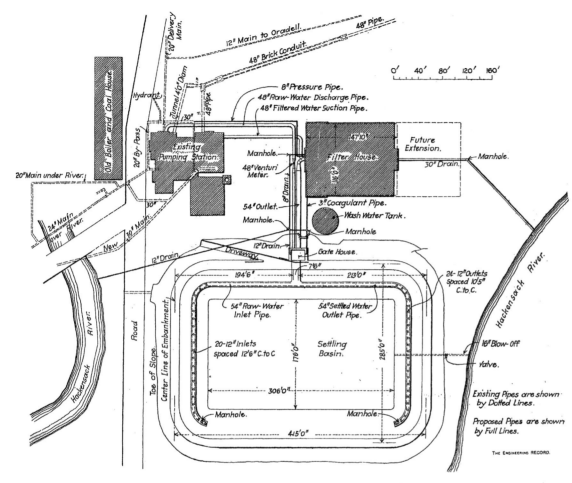

General Plan of the Purification Works of the Hackensack Water Co.

Figure 41: *"General Plan of the Purification Works of the Hackensack Water Co."* Hering & Fuller located the "Filter House" 100 feet north of the existing pumping station to allow for the latter's expansion. They located the coagulation or "Settling Basin" to the east, with the "Gate House" and "Wash Water Tank" in between the basin and the "Filter House." "The Mechanical Filters of the Hackensack Water Company," Engineering Record, *November 12, 1904*

Not only did the filtration plant increase the demand on the pumping station, the water company also had to contend with increased demand by Hoboken and the adjacent towns that the water company supplied. Expanding the pumping station and building an additional 48-inch supply line to Hoboken would be expensive and time-consuming, so "D. W. French conceived the idea that a relay pumping station situated at precisely the right point on the line would double its capacity quickly and avoid the need for a new line." He supervised the design of the relay station and built it in the New Durham section of North Bergen Township in Hudson County at the western end of the Palisades ridge (Figure 42). Once it no longer had to pump water up to Weehawken, the New Milford pumping station could supply twice the volume of water in the existing lines. French's brilliant plan had an additional benefit as well. When he completed the New Durham pumping station in 1904 (Figure 43), the additional pumping capacity close to Hoboken enabled him to take the high-maintenance Weehawken water tower out of service.[120]

With the Hudson County supply problem solved, de Forest and Hering & Fuller only had to alter the New Milford pumping station for the new filtration plant instead of having to expand it as well. To accommodate the filtration plant, they had to separate the pumping capacity into the raw water

water and chemical treatment solutions in as many areas as possible. It used hydraulic power "from a 10 in. pressure main from the pumping station [that] is carried through the pipe gallery and supplies filtered water under pressure for the hydraulic cylinders [the valves for operating the filters], for power for air compressors and wash water pumps, mixing chemicals, and for the miscellaneous uses in the building," including operating an elevator.[119]

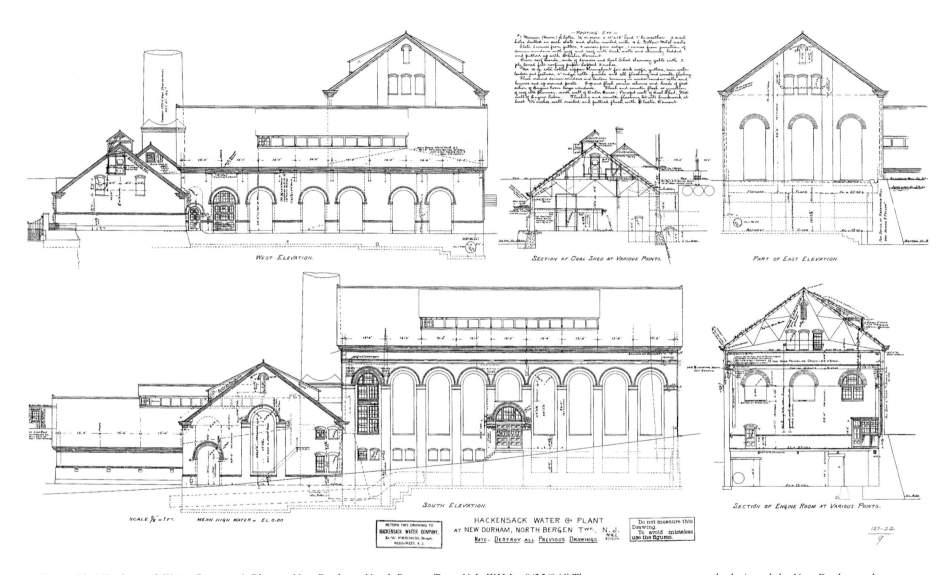

WEST ELEVATION.

SECTION OF COAL SHED AT VARIOUS POINTS.

PART OF EAST ELEVATION.

SOUTH ELEVATION.

SECTION OF ENGINE ROOM AT VARIOUS POINTS.

SCALE ⅛" = 1 FT.   MEAN HIGH WATER = EL. 0.00

RETURN THIS DRAWING TO
HACKENSACK WATER COMPANY,
D. W. FRENCH, Supt.
WEEHAWKEN, N. J.

HACKENSACK WATER Cᵒˢ PLANT
AT NEW DURHAM, NORTH BERGEN TWP., N. J.
NOTE.. DESTROY ALL PREVIOUS DRAWINGS.

Do not measure this
Drawing.
To avoid mistakes
use the figures.

127-22
9

Figure 42: *"Hackensack Water Company's Plant at New Durham, North Bergen Twp., N.J., W.H.L., 8/25/04." The water company apparently designed the New Durham relay pumping station in-house, as the drawings have the same appearance and were done by the same draftsman who drew the plans for the 1898 addition to the engine house (see Figure 31). United Water Resources*

Figure 43: New Durham Pumping Station, Hudson County, c. 1920. D. W. French built this booster station to increase the flow of water from the water works in Oradell up to the Weehawken Reservoir on the Palisades. The view is north along Tonnelle Avenue in North Bergen. United Water Resources

"each with a nominal capacity of 24,000,000 gal. per day, equal to the nominal capacity of the filters . . . to force water into a [coagulation] basin about 100 feet from the pumping station through a 48 in. cast-iron pipe about 200 ft. long with a total lift including friction, of approximately 27 feet." This cast-iron "discharge pipe" exited the 1882 engine house on its west side, headed about 200 feet north, and then turned east in front of the filtration plant where it extended another 200 feet toward the coagulation basin (see Figure 41).[121]

"in a manner which will make its own record"

The raw water entered the coagulation basin through the gate house located in the center of its west embankment. Hering & Fuller designed the gate house to "control the flow of raw and settled water and provide a means for bypassing the basin," when it was being cleaned. The building consisted of a concrete gate chamber measuring 17 feet in width by 23 feet in length by 22 feet in height, "divided into raw water, settled water, and overflow chambers, the two former being partially subdivided by low walls into two compartments which can be wholly isolated by stop planks" (Figure 44). For the portion of the gate house above the chamber, Hering & Fuller designed a one-story brick superstructure with a hipped roof and double-hung windows to complement the style of the pumping station (Figures 45 and 46). Water flowed through the 48-inch pipe from the engine house into the raw water chamber, where the coagulant solution was added, and the resulting treated water flowed through an inlet pipe to the coagulation basin, or to an outlet pipe to the

required for treatment and filtering, and the filtered water for distribution and processing. *Engineering Record* noted that "The pumping station contained two Worthington engines of the old type (in the 1882–1886 Engine House sections), two new Allis vertical triple expansion engines of 18,000,000 and 12,000,000 gal. per day (in the 1898 engine house), and a high-duty Worthington engine of 10,000,000 gal. (in the 1891 engine house)" While the raw water flowed by gravity to a suction well in the 1882 engine house, it would have to be pumped up to the above-grade coagulation basin. To accomplish this, the engineers replaced the 6-MGD Worthington in the original 1882 engine house with two 24-MGD centrifugal pumps, manufactured by the Edward P. Allis Company of Milwaukee,

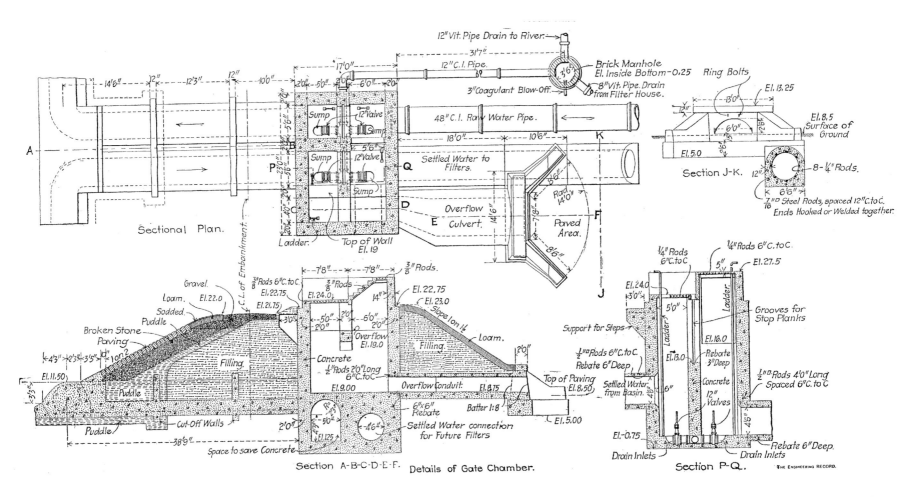

Figure 44: *Hering & Fuller: "Arrangement of Gatehouse at Junction of Twin Conduits." The engineers placed the gate house in the center of the west embankment of the coagulation basin to control the flow of raw water from the engine house to the basin, and "settled water" from the basin to the filtration plant. When the maintenance crew cleaned the basin, plant operators adjusted the valves in the gate house to send raw water directly to the filter house. "The Mechanical Filters of the Hackensack Water Company,"* Engineering Record, *November 12, 1904*

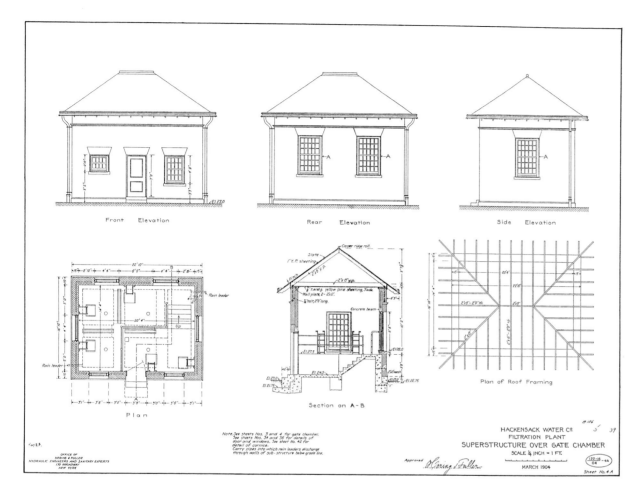

Front Elevation

Rear Elevation

Side Elevation

Section on A–B

Plan of Roof Framing

Plan

HACKENSACK WATER CO
FILTRATION PLANT
SUPERSTRUCTURE OVER GATE CHAMBER
SCALE ¼ INCH = 1 FT.

MARCH 1904

Figure 45: Hering & Fuller: "Superstructure over Gate Chamber, March 1904." The engineers designed the one-story building on top of the gate chamber with a hipped roof and window details to complement the other buildings on the site. United Water Resources

Figure 46: "Gate-House, Coagulation Basin, New Milford, 4/21/34." Built into the west embankment of the coagulation basin, the gate house consists of a one-story brick superstructure over a concrete foundation with mixing chambers, where treatment chemicals were applied to the raw water. United Water Resources

filter house if the basin was being cleaned. In case the water flow got too high:

> *The overflow arrangement is extremely simple. From the chamber a concrete culvert extends through the [coagulation basin] embankment and debouches upon the road leading past the filter house toward the pumping station. There is no gate or other obstruction in the culvert except a light trap door at its outer end to prevent animals entering and [to] exclude drafts of wind. The engineer who allows the water to rise in the basin above El. 19 will soon be aware of the fact in a manner which will make its own record.*[122]

"a greater settling time would improve filter performance"

The freestanding coagulation basin was one of Hering & Fuller's major innovations at the Hackensack Water Works (see Figure 41). Allen Hazen had suggested in his review of the Little Falls Filtration Plan that a "further increase" in the size of the settling basin would be desirable, and Fuller had acknowledged that a larger basin would require less frequent cleaning, which was a big maintenance expense, and that "a greater settling time would improve filter performance." In response, Hering & Fuller designed the coagulation basin with a capacity of 12 million gallons, nearly seven times larger than the 1.75-million-gallon basin in the basement of the filtration house at Little Falls, even though the capacity of New Milford after its anticipated expansion to 48 MGD would be only 1.5 times larger than the 32 MGD at Little Falls. Besides holding considerably more water, the open-air coagulation basin at the water works in Oradell was much easier to clean than the enclosed basin at Little Falls, which was "not easily accessible," according to an engineer at that plant.[123]

"embankments made in this way are extremely solid"

Hering & Fuller designed the coagulation basin to take advantage of the natural fill that created Van Buskirk Island, placing it about 60 percent above the existing grade and 40 percent below (Figure 47). *Engineering Record* described the construction in considerable detail: "It is formed in excavation and embankment, 285 × 415 ft. on center lines of embankments and 20.5 deep at high water level. The embankments are of fine sand taken from the excavation from the basin and filters, deposited in layers, but not rolled or compacted except by teaming over it. . . . The elevation of the bottom of the basin was made as low as possible to permit emptying [into the river] several times a year at extreme low tides."[124]

The water company built the slopes with particular care to ensure that they were stable and watertight. The job was labor intensive and backbreaking:

The outer slopes are $1\frac{1}{2}$ to 1, and with the top are loamed and grassed. On the inner side the slope is 2 to 1, and the sand is pro-tected by concrete, rip-rap [loosely-laid stones] and dry stone paving, the dependence for water tightness being placed in a layer of carefully made puddle. This consists of 1 part clay and 2 parts sand and gravel containing no stones larger than $\frac{3}{4}$ in. It was mixed in an American Clay-Working Machinery Co.'s pug mill to the consistency of wet concrete, and deposited in this condition on the embankment, where it was spread in a layer about 6 in. thick. After being spread it was allowed to dry until it was stiff and began to crack, when it was thoroughly rammed with 20 lb. hammers. After drying it was sprinkled by a hose connected with a pipe laid around the bottom of the embankment, and again rammed, particular attention being paid to the pieces where cracks occurred. This process was repeated until the puddle was very dry, some parts having been sprinkled and rammed six to eight times. A second and third layer of the same thickness were then placed and treated in the same way, making the total thickness of the finished puddle 12 in. above, and 15 in. below a berm in the embankment.

The bottom of the basin and the slopes below the berm are covered with concrete 6 in. thick, and the slopes above are protected by 30 in. of coarse to fine graded and broken stone and hand-placed paving of roughly square stones 12 in. thick. The bottom of the basin is on sand overlying good clay at an average depth of 9 or 10 ft.[125]

In describing a similar construction for the embankments of the sedimentation basin at the Albany filtration plant in 1899, Allen Hazen wrote, "The embankments made in this way are extremely solid, stand up to vertical sections when cut, are not readily washed [away], and no leakage through them has appeared at any point." The granite paving along the upper portion of the inside of the embankment protected it from damage from expanding and contracting ice that could form on top of the water in the winter.[126]

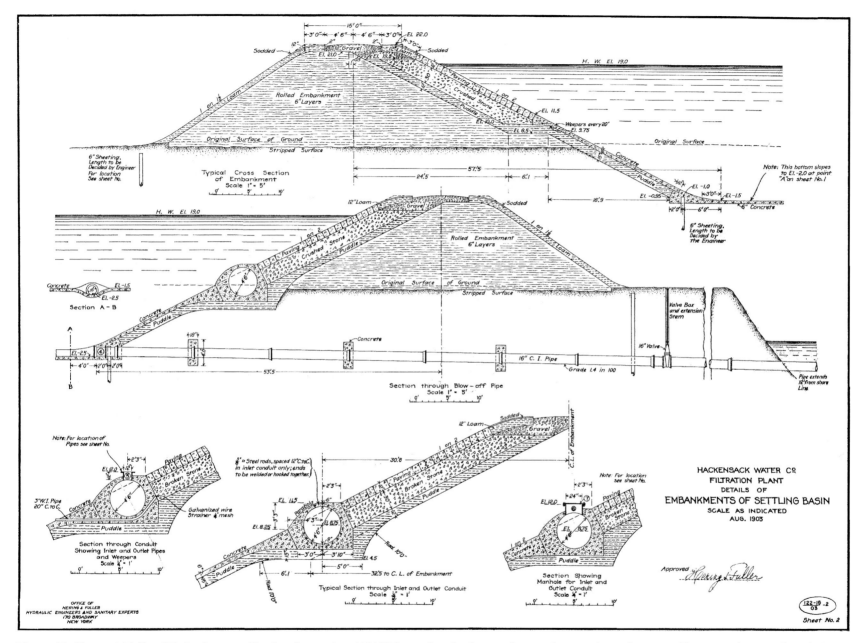

Figure 47: Hering & Fuller: "Embankments of Settling Basin, Aug. 1903." The earth embankments forming the coagulation basin are 60 percent above grade and 40 percent below grade. The interior slopes are lined with granite "Paving" above the intake and outlet conduits and concrete below them. The bottom of the basin is also concrete (see Figures 100, 101, and 118–122). Below the granite and concrete, a "Puddle" layer of compacted clay, sand, and gravel made the basin watertight. The 16-inch "Blow-off Pipe" allowed the residue that accumulated in the bottom of the basin to be washed out to the river. United Water Resources

61

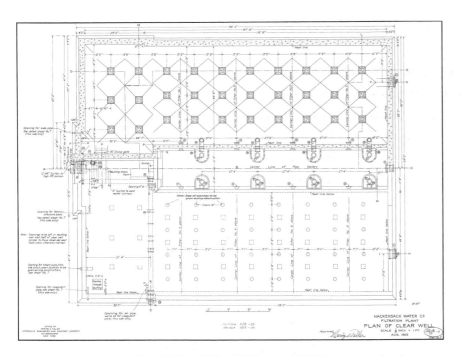

Figure 48: Hering & Fuller: "Plan of Clear Well, Aug. 1903." Built entirely of reinforced concrete, the basement story of the filtration house has a narrow pipe gallery between clear wells for filtered water. The drawing shows the west clear well, top, with the pattern formed by square columns and the inverted groined-arch floor, and the east clear well, bottom, with only the mid-points of the square columns. United Water Resources

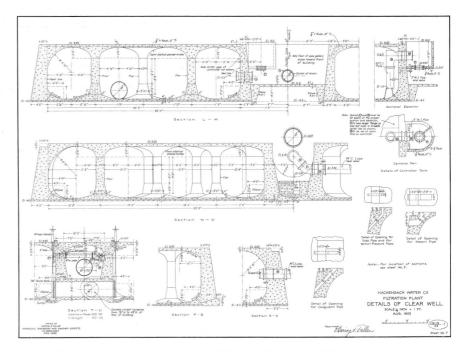

Figure 49: Hering & Fuller: "Details of Clear Well, Aug. 1903." The engineers' innovative design of the reinforced concrete construction of the clear wells consisted of "Semi-elliptical groined arches" on the ceiling and inverted groined arches on the floor, noted with "Ellipse" and "Parabola," to prevent the accumulation of debris. United Water Resources

Hering & Fuller placed a 54-inch concrete conduit about halfway up the interior slope of the embankment at just about the original ground level. The inlet conduit extended around the southern half of the basin, and the outlet conduit around the northern half, and this "arrangement obliges the water to pass the full length of the basin." The treated water from the gate house flowed into the inlet conduit and exited into the basin through twenty 12-inch inlets spaced along the top of the conduit. As the treatment chemical alum worked on the water, suspended particles coagulated into floccs, which settled to the bottom of the basin. The "settled" water gradually flowed northward across the basin and into the outlet conduit through

twenty-four 12-inch outlets. The outlet conduit directed the flow back to the gate house into the settled water chamber. *Engineering Record* noted, "From the Gatehouse the water is conveyed to the Filter House Pipe Gallery through a reinforced circular concrete conduit. Just outside the Gallery, the conduit is reduced to a 48 in. cast-iron pipe" (see Figure 41).[127]

"all the appurtenances of the filters"

The filtration house was the most complex part of Hering & Fuller's filtration plant design because it served multiple functions, including filtered water storage, chemical mixing and storage, water testing, and filtering. The southern portion of the building consists of a "coagulant house," also known as the head house or chemical house, with two- and four-story sections that contain storage, laboratories, offices, and machinery. The northern portion is a "filter house" with eight one-story filters separated by a two-story central "operating gallery" (Figure 48).

Hering & Fuller specified brick on the exterior of the filtration house to match the pumping station, but they designed the interior structure entirely of reinforced concrete, as they had recommended in their preliminary report (Figure 49). Although the Little Falls Filtration Plant was built of reinforced concrete, it was still a relatively new structural material, and Hering &

Fuller expanded its use at the Hackensack Water Works. *Engineering Record* summarized their innovative design:

> *The filter house is about 130 feet from the pumping station, and the filters have a nominal daily capacity of 24,000,000 gal., or about three-fourths that of the Little Falls plant. The filters and the filtered water reservoir are contained in an 118 × 148-ft. building with a concrete substructure and a brick superstructure, that latter being four stories high in its central portion and two stories in each wing, in the head house, and one story high in the rear extension over the filters proper. This structure also contains all the appurtenances of the filters except the wash-water and air tanks and the settling basin.*[128]

Figure 50: "Placing the Floor of a Filter," Albany, N.Y., 1899. The Hackensack Water Company used similar construction methods in building the clear well at the New Milford filtration plant, including the tramway and wire rope used to carry the concrete in a hopper to each wooden form that provided the shape for the floor and ceiling. Allen Hazen, "The Albany Water Filtration Plant"

Figure 51: "General View of Vaulting, Under Construction," Albany, N.Y., 1899. The Hackensack Water Company also used temporary wooden vaulting to form the concrete groined arches in its filtration plant at the Hackensack Water Works. Allen Hazen, "The Albany Water Filtration Plant"

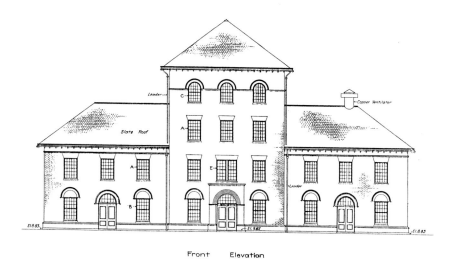

Front Elevation

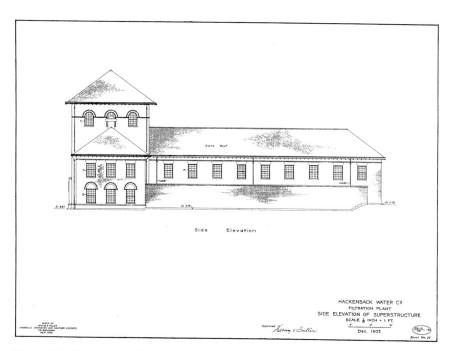

Side Elevation

HACKENSACK WATER C?
FILTRATION PLANT
SIDE ELEVATION OF SUPERSTRUCTURE
SCALE ⅛ INCH = 1 FT.
Dec. 1903

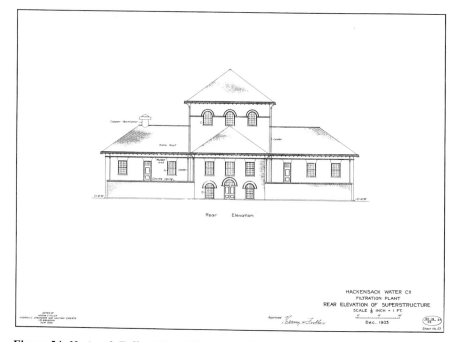

Rear Elevation

HACKENSACK WATER C?
FILTRATION PLANT
REAR ELEVATION OF SUPERSTRUCTURE
SCALE ⅛ INCH = 1 FT.
Dec. 1903

The basement of the filtration house consists of two 52 × 154-foot clear wells or filtered water reservoirs along the east and west sides, with a narrow pipe gallery in the middle (see Figure 48). At Little Falls, the clear wells were built of reinforced concrete with posts spanned by beams and simple arches, and flat floors. In their preliminary report for the filtered water reservoirs at the water works, Hering & Fuller had recommended a more elaborate construction, as *Engineering Record* described:

> *It is of groined arch concrete construction, about 12 ft. deep, and has a capacity of about 1,200,000 gal. [see Figure 49]. The two compartments are connected at the front of the building by a 36" reinforced concrete pipe with a circular sluice gate at each end.*

The columns [supporting the ceiling of the reservoir] are of concrete 2 ft. square with the lower $2\frac{1}{2}$ ft. battered out to 3 feet square at the base; they are spaced 11 ft. 8 in. by 13 ft. 8 in. on centers under the filters, and slightly different under the head house to accommodate the structural arrangement of the building.[129]

The design included semi-elliptical groined arches on the ceiling and inverted groined arches of ellipses and parabolas on the floor. Some slow sand filters had employed this complex geometry to support roof structures and to eliminate corners on the floor where debris could collect. The Albany slow sand filters, designed by Allen Hazen and completed in 1899, had a similar design (Figures 50 and 51, p. 63), but the piers were brick and there

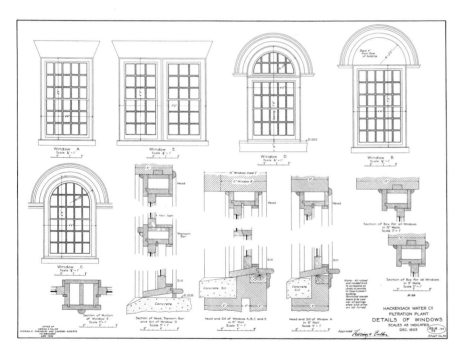

Figure 55: *Hering & Fuller: "Details of Windows, Dec. 1903." For the filtration house, the engineers replicated several traditional details of the 1882–1889 engine house, including semicircular arches over the windows. They also included innovations like concrete window sills tinted to look like the brownstone sills on the earlier buildings. United Water Resources*

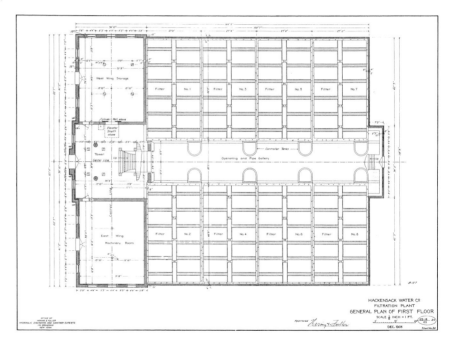

Figure 56: *Hering & Fuller: "General Plan of First Floor, Dec. 1903." The coagulant house, left, has a machinery room in the east wing, storage in the west wing, and an entrance hall in the center tower. The filter house, right, has four filters on each side of the operating and pipe gallery. United Water Resources*

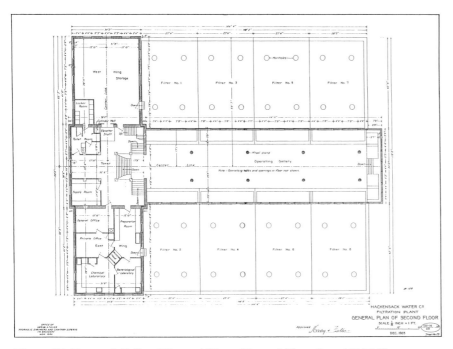

Figure 57: Hering & Fuller: "General Plan of Second Floor, Dec. 1903." The coagulant house, left, had the chemical and biological laboratories and offices in the east wing, storage in the west wing, and toilet and supply rooms in the stairwell in the tower. In the filter house, right, the eight filters extend into the operating gallery for visual monitoring of filtering and backwashing. United Water Resources

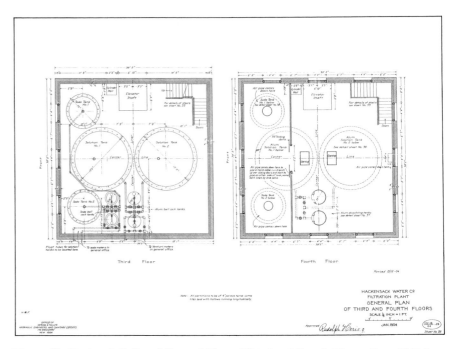

Figure 58: Hering & Fuller: "General Plan of Third and Fourth Floors, Dec. 1903." The third floor had duplicate pairs of concrete tanks for mixing the alum and soda solutions, so that the chemical applications would not be disrupted by maintenance or repairs. Operators inserted the raw chemicals into the tanks through holes on the fourth floor. United Water Resources

was nothing above the roof of the filters. At New Milford, the clear wells had to support the superstructure of the building and the filters above, and were therefore more substantial.[130]

Above the clear wells, Hering & Fuller designed the exterior of the filtration house with a brick veneer and hipped roofs to complement Charles Brush's pumping station. On the south end, facing the pumping station, they designed a coagulant house with a four-story square tower in the center and two-story wings (Figure 52, p. 64). The coagulant house provided space for storing and mixing the chemicals used to treat the water prior to filtering; for a laboratory for testing raw, treated, and filtered water; and for machinery used in backwashing. For the filter portion of the filtration house they

designed a filter house with a two-story central gallery and one-story filters on each side (Figures 53 and 54, p. 64). Hering & Fuller replicated many details of the earlier buildings, including the entrance porticos, the window patterns, and the semicircular arches over the first-story openings (Figure 55, p. 65). They continued these patterns and details on the sides of the coagulant house and on the filter house gallery, particularly on its north end, where the design complemented the south tower.

Hering & Fuller's design of the coagulant house with a four-story tower was a considerable departure from the design at Little Falls, where the coagulation basin was in the basement of the filtration house. At New Milford, the tower elevated the chemical mixing operation so that the chemical

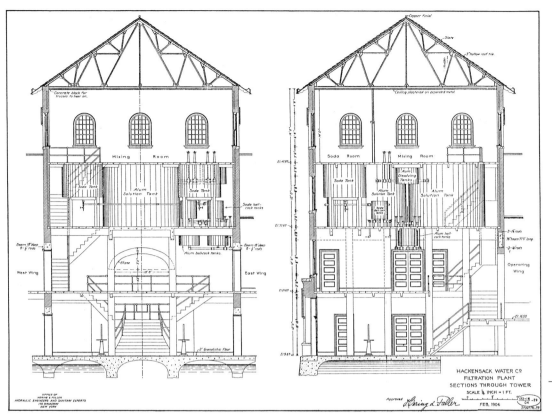

Figure 59: Hering & Fuller: *"Sections Through Tower, Feb. 1904."* An Otis elevator lifted the dry chemicals to the fourth floor mixing room, where operators deposited them into the concrete tanks on the third floor; from there the chemical solutions flowed into the settling basin by gravity. *United Water Resources*

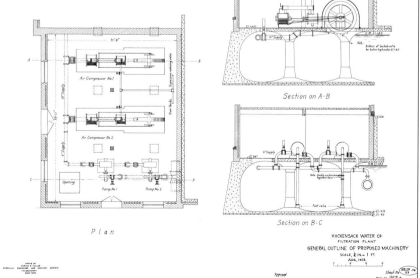

Figure 60: Hering & Fuller: *"General Outline of Proposed Machinery, Aug. 1903."* The engineers designed an efficient system to power machinery in the filtration plant with Pelton water wheels that operated air compressors and wash water pumps for backwashing the filters. Pressurized water from the pumping station shot through nozzles in the east clear well to turn the 8-foot-diameter undershot wheels. *United Water Resources*

solutions could flow to the gate house for mixing with raw water as it flowed into the coagulation basin. *Engineering Record* described the layout and functions of the coagulant house:

> *The west wing is devoted to the storage of chemicals or other supplies. The first two stories of the four-story tower are occupied principally by the stairways and halls [Figure 56, p. 65], but on its second floor are a 12 × 14-ft. room for laboratory and office supplies and a toilet room of the same dimensions containing baths and other conveniences [Figure 57, p. 66]; its third story contains the chemical solution tanks [Figure 58, p. 66], and the top story is the mixing room, where the dry chemicals are received by a 3,000-lb. Otis elevator from the storage rooms, weighed and fed into the tanks on the floor below. In the machinery room on the first floor of the east wing are the compressors, pumps, and other apparatus [for backwashing the filters]; on the second floor of this wing are the offices and the chemical and biological laboratories.*
>
> *From the mixing room in the top of the tower the chemicals move wholly by gravity to the points where they are applied to the water.*[131]

The engineers designed the first and second stories of the tower with a substantial structure of concrete to support the weight of the solution and soda tanks on the third story (Figure 59, p. 67). These concrete tanks support the fourth floor, and steel trusses support the roof. The fourth floor was originally divided into two rooms for separate mixing of alum, or sulphate of alumina, for coagulating, and bicarbonate of soda, used to lower the pH of the water. To carry the chemicals to the fourth floor, the Otis Elevator Company installed a hydraulic elevator powered by high-pressure water from the pumping station. For the north side of the entrance hall, the engineers designed a grand stairway to the operating gallery and the second floor.

In the machinery room on the first floor of the east wing, the engineers designed an efficient system that used centrifugal pumps to raise water to the wash water tanks, and air compressors to fill air tanks for backwashing the filters (Figure 60, p. 67). *Engineering Record* noted, "It was believed to be more economical to install comparatively small pumps and compressors and run them steadily to keep reservoirs full rather than to put in larger machinery and run it only spasmodically, when needed for the cleaning of a filter." The engineers designed these systems in duplicate to ensure continuous service. While the filtration machinery at Little Falls was driven by electric motors powered by generators in its engine house, the filtration machinery at the New Milford Plant was all hydraulic. Hering & Fuller specified water wheels manufactured by the Pelton Company to drive the pumps and compressors. *Engineering Record* noted that "Filtered water under pressure, taken from the 10-inch main from the pumping station, will be used to actuate the water wheels, and the discharge from the wheels will be turned down into the filtered water reservoir, so that it will not be wasted."[132]

In its first two decades of operation, the Hackensack Water Company had relied on offsite testing at irregular intervals by Dr. Albert Leeds, in his laboratory at Stevens Institute. By the turn of the century sanitary engineers and water works operators had come to realize that regular testing programs were necessary to monitor the contamination that caused epidemics of typhoid and other diseases, and to determine the effectiveness of treatment and filtration. In his design of the Albany slow sand filtration plant, which opened in 1899 as the first large-scale plant of its type in the United States, Allen Hazen had included a small laboratory building. In his January 1900 report on the Albany plant he wrote:

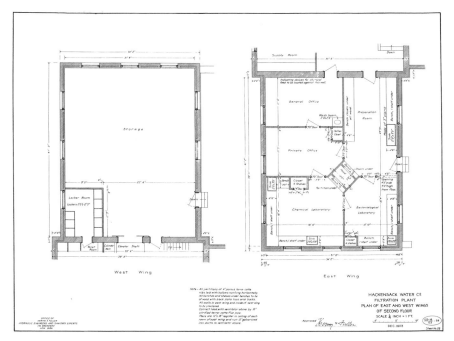

West Wing   East Wing

HACKENSACK WATER C°
FILTRATION PLANT
PLAN OF EAST AND WEST WINGS
OF SECOND FLOOR

Figure 61: Hering & Fuller: "Plan of East and West Wings of Second Floor, Dec. 1903." The design of the laboratories in the east wing of the coagulant house included a chemical laboratory and preparation room with sinks, workbenches, and a common vent hood, a bacteriological laboratory, a private office, and a general office. United Water Resources

> *The scientific control of filters is regarded as one of the essentials to the best results, and to provide for this there is a laboratory . . . supplied with the necessary equipment for full bacterial examinations, and also with facilities for observing the colors and turbidities of raw and filtered waters, and for making such chemical examinations as may be necessary.[133]*

As a chemist and bacteriologist, George Fuller had analyzed water extensively at the Lawrence, Louisville, and Cincinnati experiment stations, and he included laboratory space in the 1901 design of the Little Falls Filtration Plant. For New Milford, Fuller designed similar laboratory space, with a preparation room, a chemical laboratory, and a bacteriological laboratory,

but it was 50 percent larger than the space at Little Falls and included a private office (Figures 61 and 62).

"work was prosecuted continuously"

With the experience they gained at Little Falls, Hering & Fuller were able to develop a design for the New Milford filter house that was considerably more efficient to build and operate. Little Falls had thirty-two rectangular filters, each measuring 24 feet by 15 feet by 8 feet, or 360 square feet, with a total capacity of 32 MGD. These were arranged in two groups of eight

Figure 62: Chemical laboratory, 1906. This southeast view shows apparatus, storage, and work areas for analyzing samples of raw and filtered water. United Water Resources

filters in a row on each side of two operating galleries. For New Milford, the engineers designed eight filters that were each over three times larger than those at Little Falls, for a total capacity of 24 MGD. In the New Milford design, "The eight filter tanks are arranged in two banks of four on either side of the pipe gallery above the filtered water reservoir, which is divided into two compartments by the gallery" (Figure 63). The filter gallery or operating gallery is directly above the pipe gallery (Figure 64).

Building the large filter boxes out of concrete was challenging because of their size and the need to make the pour continuous to avoid seams that could crack and leak. *Engineering Record* noted:

Each filter tank is a concrete monolith 46 ft. 8 in. long, 25 ft. 10 in. wide, and $9\frac{1}{2}$ ft. inside, with walls 9 in. thick. . . . Walls of adjacent tanks are in contact. The floors are 6 in. thick . . . and rest directly on the cover of the filtered water reservoir. The exterior walls are protected from the weather by 4-in. brick walls and 3-in. air spaces. Except a few feet at one end included in the operating gallery, each filter tank is covered by a [4-in. thick] reinforced concrete roof, which is part of the monolithic construction. . . .

In forming the filter tanks and similar monoliths work was prosecuted continuously, day and night if necessary, the time required for placing the concrete in a filter tank being about 20 hours.[134]

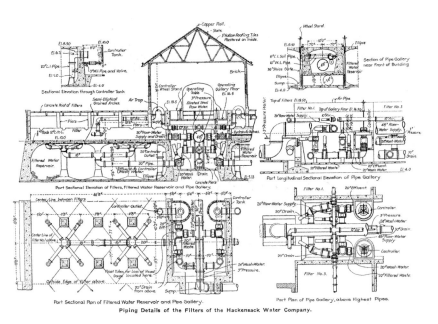

Figure 63: Hering & Fuller: "Piping Details of the Filter of the Hackensack Water Company." The filters sit on top of the filtered water reservoirs, or clear wells, on each side of the two-story pavilion that contains the operating gallery above the pipe gallery. The "48-inch raw water supply," center and right, fed water from the coagulation basin into the filters. "The Mechanical Filters of the Hackensack Water Company," Engineering Record, *November 19, 1904*

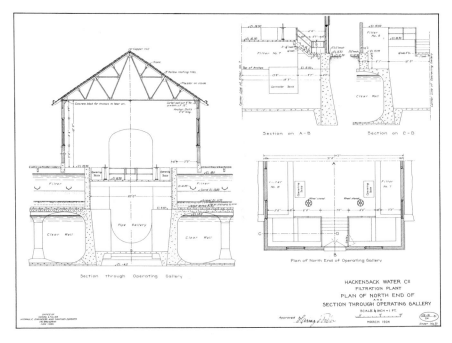

Figure 64: Hering & Fuller: "Section Through Operating Gallery." The filter operator regulated the various filter processes from the operating table and the controller wheel stand, while being able to look into the end of the filter that projected into the gallery. The filters sit directly on top of the clear wells on each side of the gallery. United Water Resources

Figure 65: Hering & Fuller designed innovative concrete block strainers, left, for the bottom of the filters and set them in a grid pattern, bottom right. They also designed a pipe grid for the air portion of the backwash system, top right. "The Mechanical Filters of the Hackensack Water Company," Engineering Record, *November 12, 1904*

Hering & Fuller designed the filters to facilitate the control of raw water, wash water, and air from the central gallery: "Each filter is divided longitudinally by a reinforced-concrete trough 30 in. wide overall, which is the inlet for raw water and the main outlet for wash water, and also contains the main air pipe" (Figure 65). The trough walls rise to about half the height of the filter walls, creating "two independent sand beds [on each side of the trough] with a combined area of 1,089 sq. ft.," about three times the size of each filter at Little Falls. Over the sand beds "from each side of the main trough at its top extend six lateral troughs or gutters." The top of the main trough and gutters have overflow lips about 1 foot above the sand level to collect the wash water from the sand beds.[135]

For the floor of each filter unit, Hering & Fuller developed several innovations for collecting the filtered water and for backwashing: "In designing the strainer, collector and air systems, considerable departures have been made from previous practice. The strainer and collector system in each filter is divided into eight units, four on either side of the central trough, with a main collector channel on the center line of each unit. . . . The shape of the upper surface of the collector and strainer system is designed to aid in preventing the undue disturbance of the gravel and securing a proper distribution of the wash water when a filter is being cleansed, and is an outgrowth of experience elsewhere."[136]

The water collector channels have four cover blocks, each measuring approximately 17 inches by 36 inches (see Figure 65). In between the channels there are sixteen collector blocks, each measuring approximately 9 inches by 5 feet. Together these blocks form a geometric pattern across the floor of each filter unit. "The tops of all blocks are so formed that when assembled the upper surface of the unit is a checker-work of

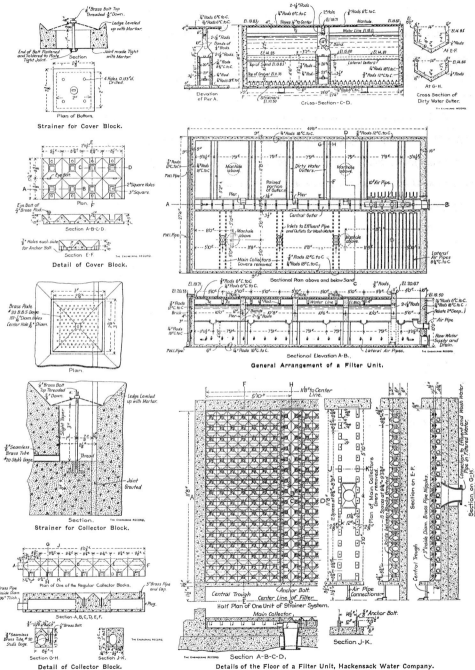

Details of the Floor of a Filter Unit, Hackensack Water Company.

hopper-shaped square depressions separated by sharp ridges intersecting at right angles." At the bottom of the depressions there are block pockets, 2 inches square in the cover blocks and 3 inches square in the collector blocks. The collector pockets are covered with strainers made of sheet brass plates with $137\frac{1}{16}$-inch holes and pressed into the shape of a flat, truncated pyramid, while the cover block strainers have only four holes. Overall, the eight filters contained 14,336 strainers, 256 cover blocks over the collector channels, and about 2,000 collector blocks over the other floor areas. All the blocks were "cast of fine concrete in cast-iron molds made by Mr. Joseph Sharpe of Paterson, N.J." The collector pockets are drained by $\frac{3}{8}$-inch brass tubes: "These small apertures . . . [are] intended to furnish the necessary resistance to the flow of water to insure a uniform and not too rapid motion through the filter at all times."[137]

Allen Hazen recognized Hering & Fuller's innovative design of the New Milford filter beds in his 1907 book, *Clean Water and How to Get It*: "The use of cement blocks for the bottoms of the filters, containing the necessary channels for the effluent and wash water, in place of the metal structures previously used, was introduced at the filters of the Hackensack Water Company, built in 1904." By contrast, the Little Falls Filtration Plant had used perforated brass manifold pipes both to collect the filtered water and to backwash the filters with air and water.[138]

For the air portion of the backwashing system at New Milford, Hering & Fuller developed a design with air piping that delivered air to all areas of each filter bed: "The air pipe system for supplying compressed air for scrubbing a filter consists in each case of a 10-in. cast-iron main and laterals of 1-in. brazed brass tubing connected in sets of three" (see Figure 65). Spaced 8 inches apart, the lateral air pipes have holes every 8 inches to ensure a uniform distribution of air in every square foot of the sand in the filter bed. A 10-inch air main connected each filter with compressed air tanks that Hering & Fuller placed below the wash water tank east of the coagulant house.[139]

George Fuller's description of the use of air at Little Falls applies to New Milford as well:

> *Compressed air, under a low pressure, is used in agitating the sand layer and facilitating the removal of the accumulated materials during washing, in place of the mechanical stirring devices with rake arm, such as has been used in the majority of filter plants now in service . . . From the main air line, running lengthwise of each pipe gallery, there is a branch to each filter. . . . The air is delivered . . . through the manifold piping system.*
>
> *In no instance is agitation with air used at the same time that the wash water is applied to the filters. The application of air forms the first step in the process of cleaning, and then, after the wash water has been applied to secure fairly thorough cleaning, the air has been again applied for about one minute to effect further cleaning. During the application of the air the water stands in the filters about 4 ins. above the top of the sand surface, or 8 ins. below the top of the overflow gutters. The applied air raises the sand layer about 3 ins., but it does not cause the entire mass to become floated as in the process of washing. Water is always used after the last application of air, and thus the sand layers are freed from any entrained air. The application of air in the manner described does not effect any appreciable grading of the sand grains.*[140]

"the filter sand was obtained from the seashore near Sea Girt"

Hering & Fuller's specification for the selection and placement of the filter medium was typically precise to ensure successful operation of the filter, as described by *Engineering Record*:

> *Over the strainers and air pipes there are graded gravel and filter sand. The tops of the strainers are 6 in. above the filter floor*

surface; the top of the gravel is 10 in. above the strainers; the sand is $2\frac{1}{2}$ ft. deep, and the usual depth of water will be 4 ft. 2 in. above the sand, or 8 ft. above the filter floor. The lips of the [dirty water] gutters are 1 ft. above the level of the sand surface, experience having shown that this is a suitable allowance for the disturbance of the sand during the operation of cleaning the filter.

The gravel will be graded from $\frac{1}{8}$ in. to $\frac{1}{2}$ in. in size. The filter sand is required to have a uniformity coefficient of 1 and an effective size between .42 and .5 millimeter; not more than $1\frac{1}{2}$ per cent of it may be smaller than .2 millimeter. The filter sand was obtained from the seashore near Sea Girt, N.J.[141]

Hering & Fuller designed the controllers (see Figures 48, 49, and 63), which regulate the flow of filtered water into the filtered water reservoir, to specifically handle the size of the New Milford facility: "The controllers are unusually large, because of the high capacity of the individual filters. They are of the float and balanced valve type, but have some novel features designed specially for this plant. They were made by the Builder's Iron Foundry, of Providence. . . . Each controller is set within a concrete-steel tank 6 ft. wide, 6 ft. long, and 5 ft. 10 in. deep, with its outer end rounded. The tank is in the pipe gallery built against the filter wall . . . with its top 2 feet above high water level in the filtered water reservoir." The

Figure 66: *"The Filter Gallery and Tables for Operating the Filters." The ends of the filters projected into the light-filled gallery, enabling the operators to see the conditions in the tank while they controlled its cleaning at the adjacent operating table.* The Hackensack Water Company Filtration Plant, New Milford, N.J., 1906. *United Water Resources*

valve consists of a float and open cylinder that are "attached to the lower end of a threaded stem extending up to a wheel stand on the floor of the operating gallery, beside the operating table." From the operating gallery, the filter operator turned the controller wheel to adjust the distance between the float and cylinder. "The controller having been set for a given rate of filtration, the (cylinder) rises and falls with the float so that its lip is kept a certain distance below the water level in the tank; if the inward flow through the valve is too great or too small, the rising or falling of the float changes the opening of the valve so as to correct the rate of flow."[142]

At New Milford, Hering & Fuller repeated the basic configuration of the Little Falls filter house and designed an operating table for each filter in the New Milford operating gallery (Figure 66 and see Figures 39 and 40). "The various devices for controlling each filter are mounted on an operating table, and the eight tables are placed symmetrically along the two sides of the operating gallery. . . . All the valves necessary for the operation of the filters [are] located in the pipe gallery, [and] are fitted with hydraulic lifting cylinders, so that they may be opened or closed from the operating gallery [Figures 67, 68, 69, and 70]. . . . The floor of this gallery is only 3 ft. below the tops of the filter walls, or $1\frac{1}{2}$ ft. below the water level in the filters, so that when standing on this floor a person can easily look into the filters."[143]

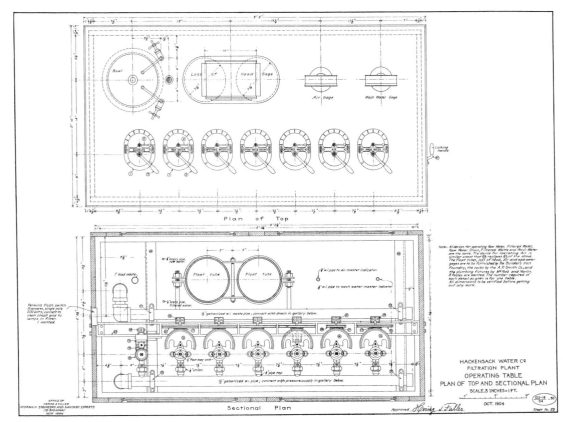

To hold the filtered water used for backwashing the filters, Hering & Fuller designed a wash water tank with a conical roof and located it between the coagulation basin and the coagulant house (see Figure 41). This tank sat on a high concrete platform so that the wash water could flow by gravity to the filters. *Engineering Record* described the backwashing process: "When a filter is to be washed, air under suitable pressure and water under the required head will be drawn from reservoirs of relatively large capacity. The wash water reservoir is a concrete-steel tank $10\frac{1}{2}$ ft. in depth and 43 ft. in diameter,

of 10,000 gal. capacity, set on concrete columns so that its high water surface is about 31 ft. above the surface of the filter sand" (Figure 71). To supply the air for backwashing the filters, Hering & Fuller designed eight large air tanks and placed them under the wash water tank to protect them from damage: "The eight compressed air tanks are 6 ft. in diameter, 22 ft. 6 in. high, with hemispherical tops and bottoms, and are made of $\frac{1}{2}$-in. steel. They are arranged in two rows of four each under the water tank . . . [and] are designed for a pressure of 150 lb. per square inch, but the air will be delivered to the

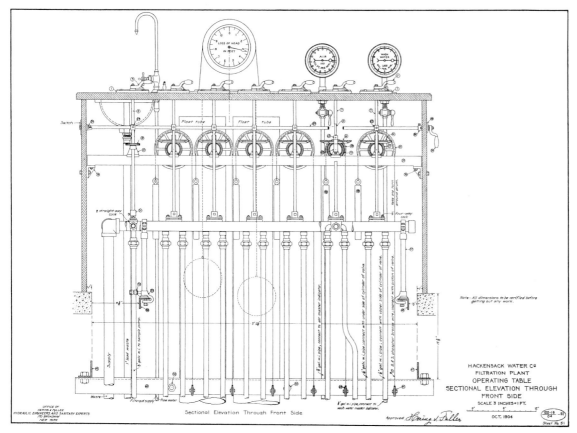

filter, when scrubbing, at a pressure of only 3 lb., through reducing valves" (Figure 72). The water-powered centrifugal pumps and air compressors that Hering & Fuller installed in the coagulant house machinery room kept the wash water and air tanks filled for backwashing (see Figure 60).[144]

The filtration process began with raw water from the coagulation basin, sometimes called "settled water," flowing by gravity through a $4\frac{1}{2}$-foot-diameter concrete conduit that extends underground from the gate house to the front of the filtration plant (see Figure 41). The raw water then entered a

4-foot-diameter pipe that extends the full length of the pipe gallery and fed the water through 20-inch pipes into each of the eight filters. In the filter gallery, the filter operator controlled the flow of water into and out of the filters through hydraulic valves at the operating table.

To clean a filter, the operator closed the valve in the 20-inch inlet pipe, and the water level decreased as the remaining water filtered through the sand and gravel into the clear wells. After closing the filter drain, the operator opened the air valves for about two minutes to disturb the sand with compressed air from the air pipes at the bottom of the filter. The operator then opened the wash water valve, and the filtered water used in backwashing flowed by gravity from the wash water tank into the filters until the water level rose above the gutters that drained the dirty water into the central trough. When the wash water became clear, the operator closed the wash water inlet and opened the "raw" water inlet to refill the filter with settled water from the coagulation basin. When the filter was full of settled water, the operator opened the filter drain to restart the filtering. The whole process could take about fifteen minutes, depending on the time of year and the condition of the raw water. Jim Flynn, who worked at the water company for 34 years, describes the process from an operator's perspective on page 155.

In January 1905 seventy-five engineers from the ASCE's annual convention in New York toured the construction of the filtration plant at the Hackensack Water Works. The water company completed the Woodcliff Lake Reservoir and dedicated it with a large celebration on April 1, 1905. To provide more steam capacity, the water company began constructing an extension on the north side of the boiler house, which more than doubled its size (Figures 73 and 74). The design replicated the brick masonry walls and steel truss roof construction of the 1898 boiler house. The water company

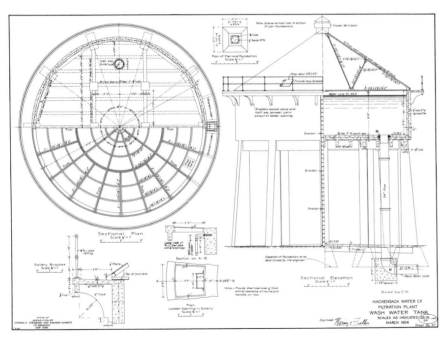

Figure 71: *Hering & Fuller: "Wash Water Tank, March 1904." Hering & Fuller placed the concrete tank on piers so that the wash water would flow by gravity to the filters. (For a later view of the tank, see Figure 112.) United Water Resources*

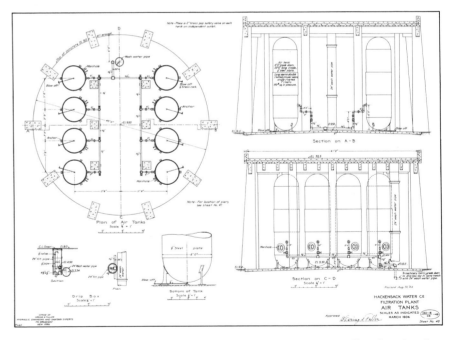

Figure 72: *Hering & Fuller: "Air Tanks, March 1904." Hering & Fuller placed eight steel air tanks between the piers of the wash water tank to hold compressed air for backwashing the eight filters. United Water Resources*

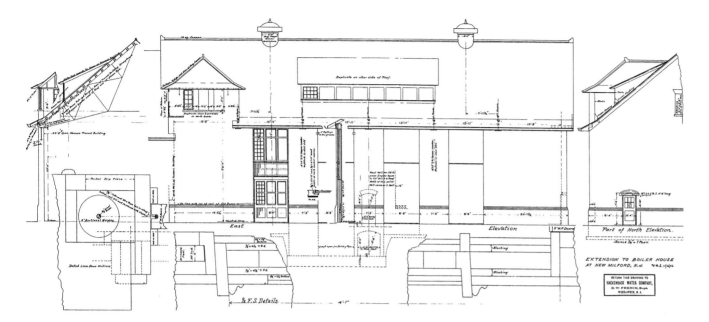

Figure 73: "Extension to Boiler House at New Milford, N.J., W.H.L., 11/16/05." The water company designer took pains to match details to the 1898 boiler house with notes like "Same Rake and Design as those of Present Building" and "On line with top of rail of Old Doors." The 8-foot, 8-inch by 10-foot doors were double hung with five sectional weights so they could be fully raised to provide an unobstructed opening. United Water Resources

began operating the filtration plant in late 1905 (Figure 75) and began recording laboratory analyses on December 15.

At the beginning of 1906 the plant purified 18 MGD, the average amount Hering & Fuller had anticipated. By the end of 1906 it was purifying an average of 21 MGD and had already reached half of the 6 MGD reserve capacity that Hering & Fuller had designed into it. Reaching these levels so quickly confirmed the water company's choice of mechanical filtration over sand filtration, as the latter would have required filters covering all of Van Buskirk Island to meet the demand for water. The water company formally opened the filtration plant in June 1906. Dr. Earnest J. Lederle, the eminent bacteriologist who had assumed the job of analyzing the company's water following the death of Albert Leeds in 1902, "highly praised the new plant." Lederle oversaw the establishment of the company's new testing laboratories on the second floor of the coagulant house. To help make the public aware of the efforts that the water company was making to provide clean and safe water to its customers, it produced a pamphlet that celebrated the new plant and extolled the virtues of filtration (see Color Plate 3).[145]

This little pamphlet has been designed to bring to our patrons some of the more important features of the system which we have installed for the purpose of purifying our water supply. In the hustle of every-day life few of us consider seriously the quality of the water which we drink: if it is clear and cold and tolerably free from unpleasant odors, we are satisfied and give it no further thought—but that is not sufficient. In the light of recent knowledge we find that the sources of our drinking water cannot be too carefully guarded: the germs of disease will find entrance unless we take great precautions, and it is in great part to effect their removal that we have instituted the modern methods of Filtration. Such methods are costly to install, requiring expensive appliances and expert management, but the sparkling purity of the product, combining delight to the eye and taste, as well as protection against infectious disease, gives it an

Figure 74: The Hackensack Water Works from New Milford Avenue near Elm Street, 1906. The newly completed filtration house is on the left, with the circular wash water tank and its conical roof just beyond. The 1898 section of the engine house is on the right, and the 1906 boiler house extension is under construction behind it. The Hackensack Water Company Filtration Plant, New Milford, N.J. 1906. *United Water Resources*

Figure 75: The Hackensack Water Works from the east side of the coagulation basin, c. 1908. The new filtration plant consisted of the coagulation basin, foreground; the circular wash water tank and the filtration house behind it, right; and the gate house on the west embankment of the coagulation basin. The 1906 boiler house extension is behind the gate house on the left. United Water Resources

added value to the customer. We take pleasure in presenting this booklet which will, we believe, evidence more generally the measures we have taken to ensure to our patrons at all times water of superior quality. The Hackensack Water Company Filtration Plant, New Milford, N.J., 1906[146]

The pamphlet contained some technical information but largely relied on the flowery language of the day to convey that the water was pure and safe. (See *What Does Filtration Accomplish?*)

Under the heading "Results of Operation," the water company described its "model" program and facilities for monitoring the purification process:

"The actual condition of the water, before and after filtering, is very carefully determined three times each day, at eight-hour intervals, model laboratories and a competent Chemist being provided for the purpose. In this way the process is constantly under supervision, with the result that water of the same uniform degree of excellence is delivered at all times."[148]

In this brochure, a summary table of water analyses over five days in January 1906 showed bacteria levels in the Hackensack River that were significantly higher than the average levels recorded by Leeds in the 1890s (Figure 76). This disparity could result from a difference in the testing methods,

The records of this plant and other similar institutions show that over ninety-eight per-cent of the bacteria present in the water as it comes to the filter beds are removed in the process. We get then, as the result of scientific treatment of the water, a product which is devoid of the unsightly color and turbidity so common to ordinary supplies—absolutely free from noxious odors and tastes, and above all, protective against the ever-besetting danger of bacterial infection.

JAN. 1906.

| DAY | PARTS PER MILLION | | | | | | BACTERIA PER C. C. | | | | |
| | TURBIDITY | | COLOR | | ALKALINITY | | HACK. RIVER UNFILT'D | HACK. RIVER WATER, FILTERED | | | |
	RIVER	EFF.	RIVER	EFF.	RIVER	EFF.		AVERAGE	WATCH 1	WATCH 2	WATCH 3
1	8	0	33	1	30	21	2283	48	35	33	75
2	7	0	31	1	32	23	1383	65	65	95	34
3	6	0	29	1	35	26	1040	33	33	30	34
4	22	0	33	1	34	23	4233	33	26	44	28
5	18	0	39	1	23	19	3633	18	27	15	13

Figure 76: Water analysis table. Test data of the filtration plant's early performance in January 1906 indicate that it removed all of the turbidity, 96 to 98 percent of the color, and 95 to 99 percent of the bacteria from the raw water from the Hackensack River. The data also show the high fluctuation of daily conditions in the river. The Hackensack Water Company Filtration Plant, New Milford, N.J. 1906. *United Water Resources*

deterioration in the water quality, or both. In any case, the increasing amount of bacteria was exactly what Allen Hazen had predicted in his consulting report to the water company in 1900. The wide range in turbidity and bacteria levels over the five days illustrates the daily fluctuations of water quality in the river. While the testing details are unknown, the initial results no doubt exceeded the expectations of the water company directors and the engineers, and indicate that the plant was performing very well from an early date. At its inception, the filtration plant at the Hackensack Water Works appears to have been more successful in removing turbidity and color from raw water than the Little Falls Filtration Plant had been in its early operation, although some of the difference may come from the variations in the raw water from the Hackensack and Passaic Rivers. The water works filtration plant, of course, included innovations based on the experience of operating Little Falls, the first year of which was overseen by George Fuller.

"water . . . as good and pure as any modern method of filtration can possibly make it"

The pamphlet also highlighted the company's efforts to prevent the pollution of its source of water and appealed to the public to help. Exactly when the water company started its "Department of Sanitary Inspection" is unknown, but this corporate example of watershed protection was a harbinger of public efforts that developed many decades later:

For a number of years past the Hackensack Water Company has maintained a department for the proper supervision of the watershed draining into the Hackensack River and its tributaries. The system of inspection of property adjacent to streams, examination of samples of waters from these streams, and constant effort to prevent and abate nuisances has had a marked effect upon the quality of the water and the work is being extended and continued. In this work our inspectors meet with many and varied conditions: nuisances which can be easily remedied by the parties concerned, but which are not attended to by them except under compulsion; others in which the offenders are public spirited and comply with the requirements of the law willingly and voluntarily. The work is of a nature which should appeal to every citizen, inasmuch as the man who allows a nuisance to be committed upon his premises is like the bird that fouls its own nest, with the added offense of polluting that of its neighbor. It is hoped that a suggestion in this article will reach many who have perhaps never considered fully the object of our watershed work and that they will cooperate with us in cleaning out nuisances ofttimes unwittingly committed.[149]

Dr. Albert Leeds had written in his *Water Analysis* record in 1890 that "the installation of a filter plant . . . should not be delayed." Although the water company waited for filtration technology to mature, its watershed protection efforts no doubt helped prevent further deterioration of Hackensack River water above New Milford during most of the 1890s. Leeds' continuing analyses had in fact shown little deterioration and occasionally some improvement in the quality of the water. By the end of the decade, when population growth in the watershed and public perceptions of water purity and health hazards required action, the water company hired the most prominent sanitary engineers in the country—first Allen Hazen and then Hering & Fuller—to examine the feasibility of filtration, and then it hired Hering & Fuller to design a filtration plant that reflected state-of-the-art practice while incorporating numerous innovations as well.

With its in-house experience and expertise, the water company had built a new boiler house with four boilers (1898), an addition to the engine house with two enormous steam pumps (1898), the first Oradell Reservoir (1902), the New Durham Pumping Station (1904), the Woodcliff Lake Reservoir (1905), the filtration plant (1905), and an addition to the boiler house with two large boilers and room for two more (1906). In recognition of all these accomplishments, the directors elected Superintendent D. W. French to the water company board in 1906.

While the filtration plant might not have been really "perfect" or "beyond criticism" as the water company stated in the 1906 pamphlet, it genuinely expressed the pride that the directors and employees took in their accomplishment:

While our Filtration Plant is a perfect model in every sense, and as complete as modern engineering and experience has been able to devise, yet it is no more of a model in many respects than the Pressure Pumping Station immediately adjacent, in which is installed the latest type of pumping machinery, boilers, economizers, and all of the equipment that goes to make up an efficient and economical plant. As the youngster felt proud of his new jack-knife, so we confess that we feel proud of our Filtering Plant, not so much because of the Plant itself, but . . . because of the satisfactory results that we are able to produce, and because we know that the quality of water now being supplied to a population varying between 250,000 and 300,000 people is absolutely beyond criticism, and is as good and pure as any modern method of filtration can possibly make it.[150]

Chapter 4

The Height of American Steam Engineering

"one of the men to whom millions of people owe a debt of gratitude"

With its new filtration plant, the Hackensack Water Company's New Milford facility was indeed a model water works. The water company filled in the old settling basin in front of the engine house and planted a broad lawn at the intersection of Elm Street and New Milford Avenue. The open lawn and shade trees along the roads and river created a parklike setting that was a popular destination for residents and visitors enjoying carriage and motorcar rides (see Color Plate 2). Van Buskirk Island and the pumping station were also highly visible from the Erie Railroad line along the west bank of the Hackensack River (Figure 77).

In keeping with its tradition of hiring exceptionally talented people, the water company hired George R. Spalding to supervise the operation of its new filtration plant. Spalding was a young chemist who had graduated from MIT, like George Warren Fuller. He worked for a time at Lederle Laboratories in Pearl River, where Dr. Lederle had taken over the testing of the Hackensack Water Company's water after Dr. Albert Leeds had stopped in 1900. Spalding was working at the East Jersey Water Company's laboratory at its filtration plant in Little Falls when Robert de Forest and D. W. French persuaded him "to come and take charge of the new chemical laboratory at the New Milford Plant. There he spent the rest of his business life, one of the men to whom millions of people owe a debt of gratitude of which they are completely oblivious." In his four decades with the company, Spalding earned considerable respect and instituted innovations that placed the water company in the forefront of water purification.[151]

Figure 77: Erie Railroad Station, New Milford, New Jersey, c. 1910. The New Milford Station sat on the east side of the railroad at its intersection with New Milford Avenue on the west bank of the Hackensack River (see Figure 88). The filtration house is visible in the background on the right. William Berdan and Alice Berdan

Under Spalding's guidance, the Hackensack Water Company was among the first water supply operations to adopt chlorination. In 1909 the water company began applying hypochlorite to its filtered water as a disinfectant to eliminate any bacteria that remained after filtration. In the 1880s Dr. Albert Leeds had foreseen the use of chlorination as a treatment for water that was heavily contaminated by bacteria. Leeds had received the first American patent on the chlorination of water in 1888, but the process remained experimental for many years. Chlorination of water supply on a regular basis began in 1908 at the Boonton Reservoir of the Jersey City

Water Works. The East Jersey Water Company had taken over the operation of the Boonton Reservoir water supply from a previous company that had operated it for Jersey City. The water was periodically contaminated by coliform bacteria from sewage systems along the watershed, and the city had subsequently sued East Jersey for failure to provide "pure and wholesome [water] free from pollution deleterious for drinking and domestic purposes." In a settlement, East Jersey hired Hering & Fuller to design a chlorination plant as a less expensive alternative to filtering the Boonton water supply, and the plant began operating in September 1908. The Hackensack Water Company and the city of Poughkeepsie both began chlorinating their water supplies in February 1909, only five months after regular chlorination at Boonton had demonstrated its effectiveness.[152]

During the 1890s and the 1900s the population of Bergen County quadrupled and the population of Hudson County doubled. The continuing growth increased water demand faster than the Hackensack Water Company or its consulting engineers had anticipated. By 1910 the filtering rate at the filtration plant had just about reached its nominal design capacity of 24 MGD, although it could be operated at higher rates for short periods, as Rudolph Hering had suggested. The water company began planning another construction campaign at New Milford "to increase the capacity of the system, both by enlarging the pumping station and filter plant and by increasing the storage capacity of the Oradell Reservoir"[153] (Figure 78).

As a drought plagued the region in 1910, the water company hired civil engineer Cornelius C. Vermeule, who had first consulted on the feasibility of building a large reservoir on the Hackensack River at Oradell back in 1892, to examine the possibility of expanding it. In his preliminary report of December 23, 1910, Vermeule noted, "The data you have placed at my disposal covering twenty-one years experience at New Milford . . . render it possible to reach far more exact conclusions than those of the report of 1892." Noting that the total water supply capacity was 25 million gallons, which the plant had almost reached, Vermeule wrote, "I find that the

Figure 78: Oradell Reservoir expansion, c. 1911. The larger of two steam-powered dredges that the water company built to expand the reservoir had a 20-inch suction pipe that removed mud from the bottom of the lake and along the banks of the river. Crews of twelve men operated the dredges day and night for four years. United Water Resources

proposed reservoir [expansion] at Oradell with a storage capacity of 1,400,000,000 gallons will increase your available supply to 35,000,000 gallons daily. . . . I strongly recommend construction of this reservoir as quickly as possible."[154]

While recognizing that the water company had "exercised great diligence in reducing the consumption and avoiding waste," Vermeule noted, "During the past twenty-five years the population has increased on the average about twenty-five per cent every five years." Vermeule predicted that "your future consumption will probably increase at the same rate as the increase in population." He projected a water demand of 49 MGD by 1925, and he figured it would require additional storage of 3.8 billion gallons. Vermeule concluded that the water company had to acquire additional storage capacity before it

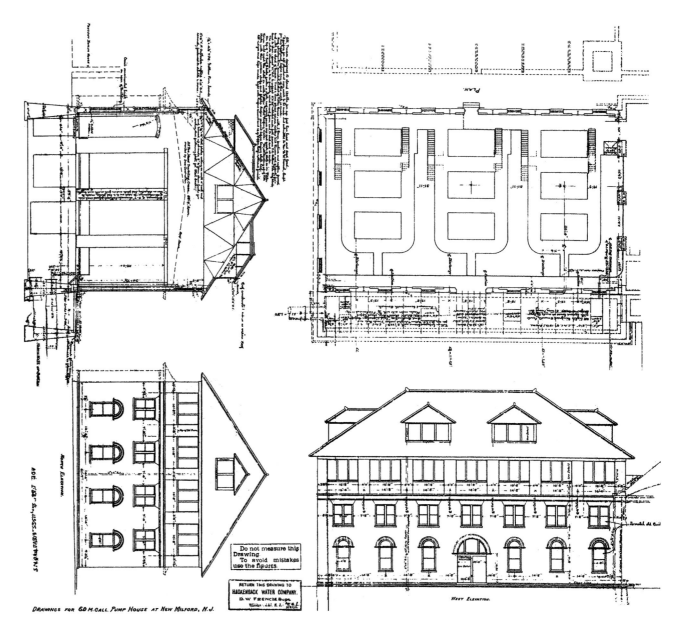

Figure 79: *"60 M. Gall. Pump House at New Milford, N.J." In designing the exterior of the 1911 engine house addition, company employees combined traditional and modern features: arch-topped windows based on Charles Brush's 1882 building for the first story and modern industrial steel-sash windows for the third story. United Water Resources*

was too late: "I believe that sites for this storage can be found at present, but the difficulty of securing such sites will steadily increase with the development of the suburban population on the watershed. It therefore appears to me that if you intend developing the watershed to its capacity, this matter of storage sites should be immediately investigated and steps taken to secure the necessary property."[155]

Figure 80: Foundation construction for the 1911 engine house, looking north toward the 1905 filtration plant. The suction well is on the lower left and the foundation for the west wall of the engine house is in the center. United Water Resources

Figure 81: Foundation construction for the 1911 engine house, looking south. The 1898 engine house is on the upper left, the 1882–1886 boiler house is visible in the distance, and the suction well and the foundation for the west wall of the new building are in the center at the bottom. United Water Resources

With Miles Tierney and his son John C. Tierney serving as general contractors, the water company began expanding the engine house (Figure 79) and the reservoir in Oradell in 1911. Expanding the reservoir required extensive dredging that continued for five years. As woodcutters cleared the lowland along the river above the original Oradell Reservoir, the Tierneys built a timber-crib dam to raise the water level enough to float barges. They built two barges with suction dredges on the riverbank, one with a 12-inch pipe and one with a 20-inch pipe, and they operated these steam-powered behemoths day and night (see Figure 78). The dredging "stirred up a good deal of mud in the river . . . which put a heavy burden on the filters, and even after filtration, left a cloudy residue in the water which had no effect on its wholesomeness but certainly did little to please customers." In a

replay of the first Oradell Reservoir construction in 1902, complaints about turbid water stirred up public concern and led to a hearing in 1913 at the Hackensack Board of Health, at which George Spalding had to defend the potability of the company's water. When the Tierneys completed the reservoir expansion, it extended up to Emerson.[156]

"to match old building"

The original drawing of the "60 M. Gall. Pump House at New Milford, N.J." suggests that company employees designed this final addition to the engine house. The addition dwarfed the earlier sections of the engine house, doubled the building's floor area and tripled its volume

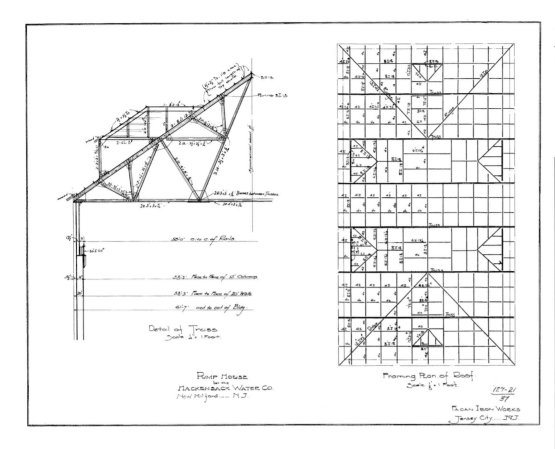

Figure 82: "Pump House for the Hackensack Water Company, New Milford, N.J.," 1911. Fagan Iron Works of Jersey City, New Jersey, fabricated the intricate steel roof frame for the 62-foot by 106-foot clear span of the 1911 engine house. United Water Resources

Figure 83: Erection of the steel frame for the 1911 engine house. Fifteen-inch-deep steel columns support the roof trusses and a 20-inch-high horizontal girder that carries a 25-ton traveling crane. The 1905 filtration plant is visible in the rear on the left, and the circular wash water tank is visible in the center. United Water Resources

(see Figure 79). Initialed "W.H.L., 3/21/11" by the draftsman whose earliest known work for the water company was the 1898 engine house addition, the drawing illustrates the company's blending of the site's traditional details with modern industrial features. The design specified a three-story brick exterior with a hipped roof to complement the earlier sections of the engine house, but the interior was completely open to accommodate three bays of VTE pumping engines.

Hering & Fuller's design for the filtration house clothed modern technology within traditional exterior proportions and details. In contrast, the 1911 engine house exterior combines traditional nineteenth-century components with some early twentieth-century ones. To harmonize with the early

Figure 84: *No. 7 Allis-Chalmers pumping engine in the 1911 engine house, 1911. This vertical triple expansion (VTE) pumping engine, built and installed by the Allis-Chalmers Manufacturing Company of Milwaukee, displaced 607 gallons of water with each revolution and could pump 20 MGD. Through the opening to the 1898 engine house on the right, the Nos. 5 and 6 VTE pumping engines manufactured by the Edward P. Allis Company, the predecessor to Allis-Chalmers, are visible. United Water Resources*

sections of the engine house, the designer placed individual double-hung windows and double doors with the site's traditional brickwork and date medallions on the first story, and paired double-hung windows, like those on the 1898 section, on the second story. On the third story and on the roof dormers, the designer placed triple windows with steel-frame sashes, which was the first use of modern factory windows on the site. The design for the eaves included wooden "outlooker" rafter extensions on the steel trusses to simulate a traditional wooden roof on the exterior.

In contrast with Hering & Fuller's detailed designs for the filtration plant, the 1911 engine house drawing illustrates only the basic design of the building and leaves the details to be worked out by the water company and its contractors. Specifications on the drawing, such as "Roof

Figure 86: *No. 8 and No. 9 Allis-Chalmers pumping engines, installed in the north end of the 1911 engine house, c. 1912. These pumps, rated at 7.5 MGD, brought the total number of VTEs in the pumping station to five. The building's steel trusses and hollow tile roof panels dominate the daylight-filled interior. United Water Resources*

Figure 85: *No. 7 Allis-Chalmers pumping engine in the 1911 engine house, 1911. Measuring 36 feet long by 15 feet wide, and nearly 50 feet tall, the No. 7 pumping engine has cast-iron stairs providing access to five stories of maintenance catwalks. The traveling crane used to install and maintain the VTEs and subsequent pumps is visible at the top. United Water Resources*

Figure 87: *"Cage Plate for $7\frac{1}{2}$ million gallon pumping engine. Hackensack Water Company. Allis-Chalmers Mfg. Co.," c. 1911. Cage plates regulated the flow of water at the bottom of the cylinders. The ninety valves on this cage plate opened while the engine pulled water from the suction well and closed while it pumped the water into the distribution system. Frank Voposek*

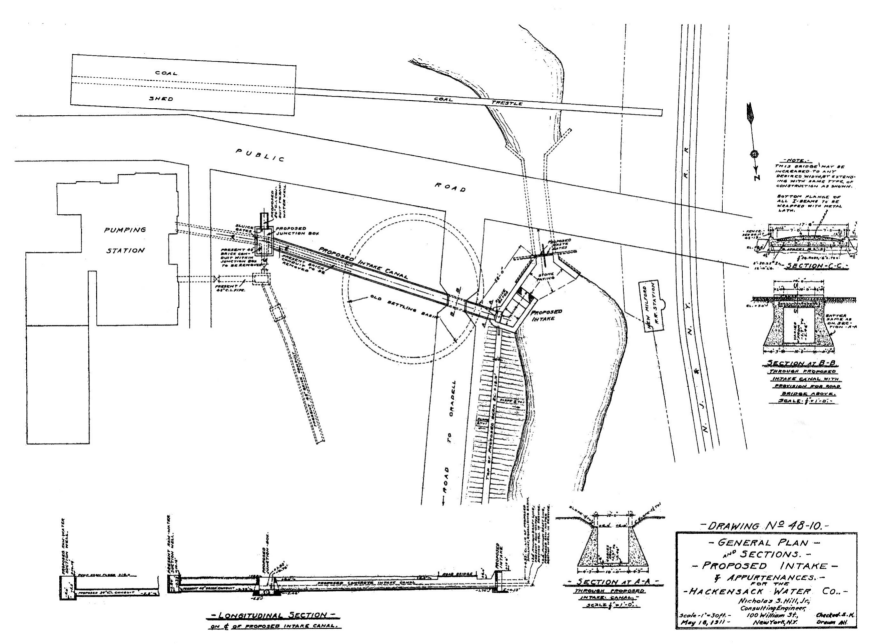

Figure 88: *"General Plan and Sections, proposed Intake & Appurtenances for the Hackensack Water Company, 1911." Nicholas Hill, a New York consulting engineer, designed the new intake system for the pumping station. His plan showed the outline of the old settling basin, constructed in the 1880s. The intake pond between Van Buskirk Island and the railroad, noted as an "Equalizing Basin," was reformed with a new berm on its east bank. United Water Resources*

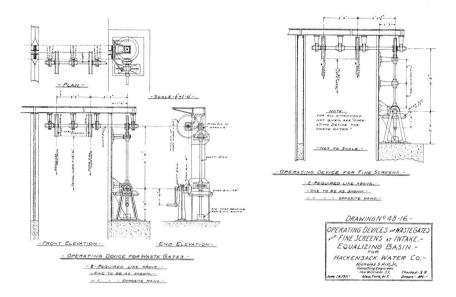

Figure 89: "Operating Devices for Waste Gates and Fine Screens at Intake Equalizing Basin for Hackensack Water Company," 1911. Nicholas Hill designed a series of cranks, "worm wheels," and shafts supported on steel frames to operate the waste gates and intake screens. Hill became president of the water company in 1936. His 1911 intake system remains intact today. United Water Resources

Figure 91: "Entrance to Intake Canal, Showing Screens, 4/21/34." Nicholas Hill designed the iron and steel sluice gates with retractable screens to keep debris from entering the intake canal along with the raw water headed to the 1882 engine house. United Water Resources

Figure 90: Intake canal construction, 1911. The new concrete canal brought water from the intake reservoir on the west side of Van Buskirk Island to the raw water pumping engines in the 1882 engine house. United Water Resources

Figure 92: The intake canal, c. 1912. The water company erected a wrought-iron fence around the completed intake canal and landscaped the banks with evergreens. The sluice gates on the other side of Elm Street are visible in this view west from the engine house. United Water Resources

Construction similar to that of the Filter House," illustrate the company's concern that the new construction should complement the existing buildings. A specification for the first-story windows notes, "To match old Building," that is, the design of the windows on Charles Brush's 1882 engine house.

As indicated on the drawings, the construction required a large excavation to accommodate all the piping and the concrete foundations of the building, the pumping engines, and the exterior suction well, a 12-foot-wide by 14-foot-deep well that extends the full length of the west façade (Figures 80 and 81, p. 84). The drawing specified that "Designs for all structural iron

work to be made and submitted to Mr. D. W. French, Supt., for his approval before any of the work is made." The roof truss design by the Fagan Iron Works of Jersey City illustrates the building's intricate steel roof framing over the 62-foot by 106-foot clear span (Figures 82 and 83, p. 85). Masons laid 20-inch-thick brick walls between and around the exterior of large steel columns that support the roof and a 25-ton traveling crane.

Superintendent French installed three VTE pumping engines—Nos. 7, 8, and 9—in the 1911 engine house. In 1901 the Edward P. Allis Company of Milwaukee, which had built the Nos. 5 and 6 pumping engines in the 1898 engine house, had merged with two other Wisconsin firms—the Fraser and

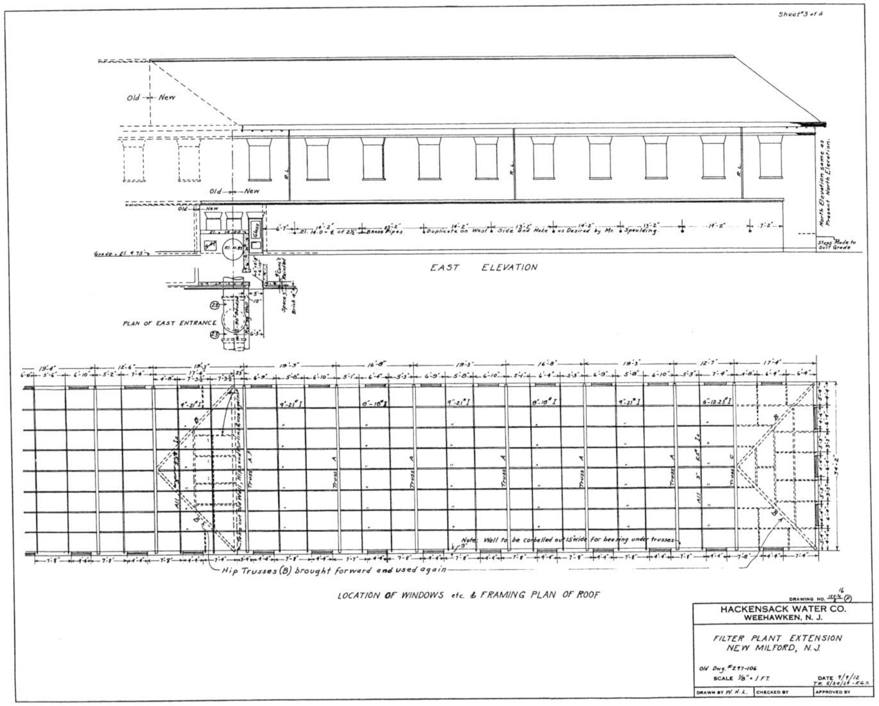

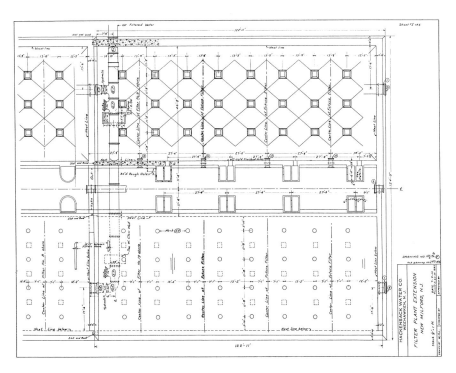

Figure 93: "Filter Plant Extension, New Milford, N.J.," 1912. Company staff designed the 1912 extension based on Hering & Fuller's design of the 1905 filter house. The east elevation and roof plan illustrates the company's penchant for reusing building components. United Water Resources

Figure 94: "Filter Plant Extension, New Milford, N.J.," 1912. The basement floor plan in the 1912 extension replicated Hering & Fuller's design of the 1905 filter house with only a few modifications, like the rectangular controllers in the pipe gallery between the clear wells. United Water Resources

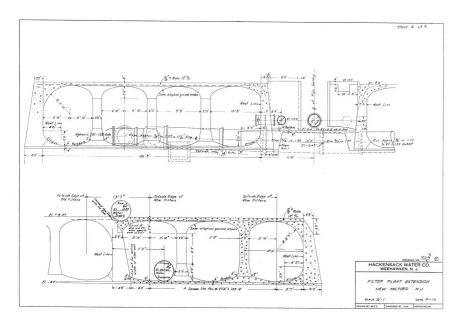

Sheet 4 of 4

HACKENSACK WATER CO.
WEEHAWKEN, N.J.

FILTER PLANT EXTENSION
NEW MILFORD N.J.

Figure 95: "Filter Plant Extension, New Milford, N.J.," 1912. The clear wells in the 1912 extension replicated the design of the 1905 clear wells (see Figure 49) and were built directly up against them. United Water Resources

Figure 96: Filter gallery, 5/19/35. The 1912 extension was indistinguishable from the original 1905 construction. The ends of the filters projected into the gallery to allow the operator to see the conditions of the water during filtering and backwashing. The operator controlled each filter from its adjacent operating table. United Water Resources

Chalmers Company and the Gates Iron Works. The combined Allis-Chalmers Manufacturing Company was a leading manufacturer of steam pumping engines in this country. Allis-Chalmers built and installed the three new VTEs for the water works, bringing the total number of VTEs on the site to five. The water company installed Pump No. 7 on the south end of the 1911 engine house and took up nearly one third of the interior space (Figure 84, p. 86). This pumping engine is 36 feet long by 15 feet wide and nearly 50 feet tall (Figure 85, p. 87). Through its intake pipe, the pump sucked filtered water from the suction well along the west side of the building. It displaced 607 gallons of water with each revolution and could operate at 22 rpm to pump a total of 20 MGD into the low-service portions of the distribution system. As Gerry Weinstein, a past president of the Roebling Chapter of the Society for Industrial Archaeology has observed, "This is a magnificent **engine repres**enting the height of American Steam engineering practice." As

a young man Ted Hoffman often visited the water works to see his father, who worked there as a machinist, and he recalls the sights and sounds of the VTEs on page 120.[157]

On the north end of the new engine house, Allis-Chalmers installed two smaller VTEs to supply water to the high-service portion of the distribution system on the slope and on the top of the Palisades (Figure 86, p. 87). The engines drew water from the suction well on the west side of the 1911 engine house and pumped it at a higher pressure than the low-service pumps in order to supply the higher elevations. Each engine had a capacity of 7.5 MGD and the duplication provided backup for the high-service system, which was smaller than the low-service system. Allis-Chalmers manufactured, assembled, and tested the pumping engines in Milwaukee (Figure 87, p. 87), disassembled them for rail transport, and then reassembled them at the water works. The five VTEs in the 1911 and 1898 engine houses provided impressive sights and

Figure 97: *"Hackensack Water Works, New Milford, N.J.," c. 1913. The Hackensack Water Works with the newly completed extension to the filtration house, left; and the 1911, 1898, 1891, and 1882 sections of the engine house, from center to right. This post-card view from the intersection of New Milford Avenue and Elm Street shows the roads unpaved and an iron fence along the lawn in front of the works, which were prominent because of the lack of trees on Van Buskirk Island. William Berdan and Alice Berdan*

Figure 98: *The Hackensack Water Works, c. 1915. 1905 filtration house, left; 1911, 1898, 1891, and 1882 engine house sections, center; 1882–1886 boiler house, right. While the boiler house (far right) was demolished in 1967, the rest of the historic complex has remained remarkably intact since its completion in 1912. Frank Vierling*

sounds within the pumping station, as Frank Vierling, the Oradell Historian, recalls on page 190.

In 1911 the water company hired Nicholas Hill, a New York consulting engineer, to design a new intake for the raw water pumps in the 1882 engine house in conjunction with the construction of the engine house addition. This was the start of Hill's long association with the water company that culminated in his service as president from 1926 to 1936. Hill's 1911 intake system included sluice gates with screens at the southeastern end of the intake pond, waste gates at the south end, and a 10-foot-wide intake canal leading to a new junction box that connected the old brick intake and canal to the engine house (Figure 88, p. 88). Hill's design included iron and steel operating devices for regulating the flow of water from the intake pond to the canal and to the river (Figure 89, p. 89). The Tierneys constructed the canal and the bulkheads of concrete, and the completed operating devices were prominent at the intersection of Elm Street and New Milford Avenue

(Figures 90 and 91, p. 89, and see Figure 183). They erected a wrought-iron fence around the canal and planted evergreens along it (Figure 92, p. 89).

"hip trusses brought forward and used again"

With the new engine house complete, the Tierneys concentrated on building the extension to the filtration plant. Hering & Fuller had anticipated the construction of eight additional filters on the north side of the filter house in their 1905 design (see Figure 41). Company employees designed the extension, with "W.H.L." serving again as draftsman. The 1912 "Filter Plant Extension" drawings were the first done in-house with the title block, "Hackensack Water Co., Weehawken, N.J."

The design continued the east and west elevations and replicated the original filter house's north elevation, which the extension replaced (Figure 93, p. 90).

Figure 99: Coagulation basin, 1911. The maintenance crew began the cleaning process by floating a raft with washing equipment onto the water. United Water Resources

It also continued the company's tradition of reusing building components as it erected new sections, as indicated by a note on the drawing, "Hip Trusses Brought Forward and Used Again." The designer copied the configuration of the clear wells, the filters, and the filter and pipe galleries from Hering & Fuller's 1905 building (Figures 94, 95, and 96, pp. 90–91). With a capacity of 3 MGD for each of the eight new filters, the water company doubled the total capacity of the filtration plant from 24 MGD to 48 MGD. The construction of the extension was timely, as production of purified water averaged 27.6 MGD when the first two filters in the extension came on line in 1913 (Figures 97 and 98, p. 92). As demand grew, the water company gradually placed the other six filters in service, and by the end of the decade, peak production approached 40 MGD.

Since Hering & Fuller's 1903 design of the coagulation basin had anticipated the doubling of the original filter house, the basin had no problem supplying the amount of water needed for the completed extension. The

Figure 100: Coagulation basin, 1911. As the water drained from the basin, the washing equipment settled on the bottom. The intake water conduit with its intake holes is visible midway up the interior embankment (see Figure 47). Stone paving is visible above the conduit and the concrete surface is visible below it. United Water Resources

Figure 101: Coagulation basin, 1911. The maintenance crew had to rake and hose the thick sludge by hand into the blow-off drain. United Water Resources

Figure 102: Superintendent D. W. French (front row, second from right) and his employees in front of the 1911 engine house, c. 1915. Left to right, front row: Frank Baxter, Paul Melrose, Sr., George Bell, George Bennett, Tom Finnerty, Ed Cole, William Mc Dermott, Mr. French, George Lebold. Second row: F. Phillips, Mr. Lockington, unknown, Vic Aldenetta, Tom Lally, Arthur Lockwitz, John Schmittner, Tom Keelan, Harold Newton, Will Brunning, George Cavanaugh. Third row: Earle Talbot. Rear steps: Joe Hughes, Ed Sullivan, Walter Boquist, and Emile Fricker. United Water Resources

higher production, however, required that the basin be cleaned more often, the frequency depending on the condition of the raw water. The colored or turbid water caused by heavy rains also required additional alum treatment, which resulted in larger deposits of floccs, or coagulated particles, at the bottom of the basin. Cleaning was a fairly arduous job that typically had to be done two to four times a year and could take up to a week.

The maintenance crew began the process by floating rafts with pipes and other equipment in the coagulation basin (Figure 99). They drained the water from below the intake and outlet conduits in the basin through the blow-off pipe that ran under the north embankment and into the river (see Figure 41). As the water drained out, the rafts and equipment settled to the bottom, revealing the

sludge that had accumulated on the concrete surface of the embankment below the water conduit and on the floor of the basin (Figure 100). The crew connected a hose to a pipe that supplied pressurized raw water from the engine house. The men took turns hosing and raking the thick sludge from the lower slopes and the floor of the basin where the flocc had settled, and they gradually pushed the sludge toward the drain (Figure 101). Raking the heavy sludge was hard work, handling the high-pressure hose was difficult and dangerous, and the disagreeable smell of the sludge made the job even more onerous. The sludge and wash water flowed through the blow-off pipe into the river, from where they had come except for the alum. Barry Schwartz, a former supervisor of water purification at the water works, recalls that the maintenance crew typically received some special compensation for this difficult work (see page 162).

Between 1882 and 1912 the water company had erected five engine house sections (1882, 1886, 1891, 1898, 1911), four boiler house sections (1882, 1886, 1898, 1906), and two filtration house sections (1905 and 1912). Charles Brush had employed classical proportions and industrial Romanesque details in his design of the original engine house, and the engineers and designers that succeeded him followed this precedent. Of the eleven historic buildings erected between 1882 and 1912, only the 1882–1886 coal shed and boiler house has been demolished. After overseeing the company's expansion and construction for fifteen years, Superintendent D. W. French was justifiably proud of the efforts of his staff (Figure 102). The Hackensack Water Works constituted an imposing presence on Van Buskirk Island (Figure 103).

Following rapid advances in steam technology, in 1915 the water company replaced the original raw water pump in the 1886 engine house with the first centrifugal turbine on the site, the No. 3 pumping engine, manufactured by the Allis-Chalmers Manufacturing Company (Figure 104). Jim Flynn, who worked as a watch engineer in the pumping station at the water works, believes that Allis-Chalmers developed this type of centrifugal turbine to pump flood water at New Orleans (see page 135). No. 3 is a cross-compound

sack water. In 1916 the water company had pumped an average of 29.5 MGD. In 1918 production spiked to 36.7 MGD. While the engine house and the filtration plant had the capacity to supply the required water, the water company had to install two additional boilers in the 1906 boiler house to power the extra production. To vent these new boilers the water company erected a 185-foot-high circular chimney with corbelled-brick detailing at its top, on the east side of the boiler house in 1917 (see Color Plate 29). A map of the Hackensack Water Works from October 1917 shows the full development of the site in its primary historic period of 1882–1917 (Figure 105).

"a severe economic blow"

pumping engine, with two horizontal reciprocating pistons powered by the successive use of a single blast of steam at high pressure in the first cylinder and low pressure in the second. While it is only a fraction of the size of the No. 7 VTE installed four years earlier, the No. 3 pump had nearly twice the capacity, 36 MGD. Part of this difference stems from No. 3's "low lift" work load; it only had to pump water from the engine house to the coagulation basin, whereas the No. 7 had to pump water at a considerably higher pressure into the distribution system. The configuration of the No. 3 pump with a reciprocating engine powering a rotating turbine is unusual.

The country's involvement in World War I significantly increased water demand in Bergen County. The army began constructing Camp Merritt in Dumont in August 1917 as an embarkation camp for troops bound for Europe. By the end of 1918 the camp housed 42,000 soldiers, all consuming Hacken-

After five hectic decades of increasing demand, the end of World War I ushered in a flat period for the Hackensack Water Company and its water works. As the Army decreased its use of Camp Merritt, the water company lowered production of filtered water for three years, to 34.2 MGD in 1921. As the economy recovered from its postwar decline, housing development in Bergen boomed again and by 1923 the water company had increased its water production back to a wartime level of 36.6 MGD. For the water company, however, this boom would be short lived. Anticipating the postwar boom, it had begun a second expansion of the Oradell Reservoir in 1921. It replaced the timber-crib dam with a modern and considerably larger concrete dam and dredged the lowlands along the river above Emerson. The enlarged reservoir extended back to Harrington Park and Closter, and had a storage capacity of 2.3 billion gallons.

Figure 104: *No. 3 Allis-Chalmers 36-MGD pumping engine, c. 1915. Considerably smaller than the No. 7 VTE, the No. 3 centrifugal turbine pumped nearly twice as much water at a lower pressure. This cross-compound pumping engine used a single blast of steam twice, first in the high-pressure cylinder on the right, and second in the low-pressure cylinder on the left. United Water Resources*

The cost of the reservoir expansion, wartime inflation, and criticism by the State Board of Public Utilities of the water company's wholesale rates for Hoboken, all prompted the directors to increase that city's rates when its supply contract expired in 1922. After considerable political and legal wrangling, Hoboken opted in November 1923 to buy water from Jersey City. The Hackensack Water Company lost its biggest customer and the revenue from millions of gallons of water a day, "for which millions of dollars worth of pipe had been laid and millions of dollars worth of collecting, filtering, and pumping capacity had been built. It was a severe economic blow . . . that caused many sleepless nights and in the end brought about a considerable reorganization of the top management." From its postwar peak in 1923 of 36.6 MGD, production of filtered water plunged in 1924 after the loss of Hoboken as the water company's primary customer to 31 MGD, and it wouldn't steadily exceed 36 MGD again until World War II.[158]

"standard in water systems throughout the world"

The end of the Hackensack Water Company's Hoboken era coincided with the passing of its first generation of leaders. After forty-five years as a director and forty-one of them as president, Robert de Forest retired in 1926 and passed the presidency to Nicholas S. Hill, Jr., a company director and its consulting engineer. Hill was an 1892 graduate of Stevens Institute and had worked as chief engineer of New York City's supply before starting his own engineering firm. He began consulting for the Hackensack Water Company in 1910 and was one of the primary engineers for the rapid development of Camp Merritt during World War I. By the 1920s Hill's engineering firm had an international reputation, with major projects in the United States and abroad. As the new president of the Hackensack Water Company, Hill

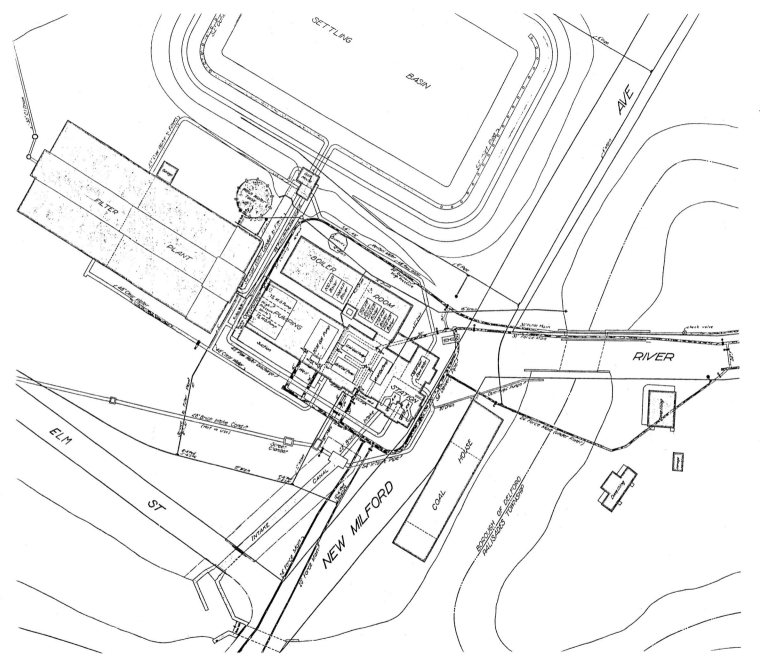

Figure 105: Hackensack Water Works, October 1917. During World War I the historic complex included the 1905 settling or coagulation basin, top; the 1905–1912 filtration house and wash water tank, left; the 1882–1911 engine house and 1898–1906 boiler house, center; the 1882–1886 coal house between the engine house and the Hackensack River; the superintendent's house and workers' dwellings on the south side of the river, right; the intake canal, bottom center; and the various force mains for distributing the water. When it built the filtration plant in 1905, the water company had moved the superintendent's house and the workers' dwellings across the river, right. The original location of these houses is visible in Figures 9 and 37. *United Water Resources*

brought in several new engineers to update its operation, including George Wieghardt, who had been the chief engineer of the Baltimore Water System, and Harrison Cady, a mechanical engineer from Swarthmore College who assumed supervision of the pumping operations. Bowing to the winds of change, D. W. French resigned after forty-two years with the company, nearly thirty of them as superintendent. Hill ushered in a new era of management that included organized activities for the employees (Figure 106).

While the filtration plant had successfully reduced the turbidity and bacteria in the Hackensack River water supply to acceptable levels, the filtered or drinking water was still plagued by unpleasant odors and tastes. During the 1920s George Spalding, the superintendent of the water treatment, and Paul Tamer (Figure 107), the chief chemist, conducted experiments in the laboratory and at various locations within the filtration plant to remove the tastes and odors. In 1929 Spalding reported to the American Water Works Association: "Experiments being conducted in the laboratories of the Hackensack Water Company at the New Milford purification works indicate that small quantities of activated char (carbon) in finely divided condition may be used in conjunction with the usual alum coagulation process thereby furnishing a means of removing odors due to micro-organisms, phenolic substances, and the ordinary odor producing substances present in surface water."[159]

While activated carbon, or char, was known to remove tastes and odors in water, efforts to use it in filter beds in place of some of the sand were

Figure 106: "*Basket-Ball Team—1928–1929, Hackensack Water Company, Weehawken, N.J.*" *Employees' participation in sports activities organized by the water company was prominent in the late 1920s. United Water Resources*

Figure 107: Chemical laboratory, second floor of the east wing of the coagulant house, c. 1924. In the 1920s, Paul Tamer (pictured), chief chemist of the company, conducted experiments with George Spalding, superintendent of the filtration plant, on using activated charcoal to remove odors and tastes from the drinking water. The process they developed became standard in water purification facilities around the world. In this view, the chemical laboratory had changed little since its opening in 1905 (see Figure 62). United Water Resources

disappointing. Spalding and Tamer developed a method of applying the material as a fine powder to water prior to coagulation. Despite some skepticism, Spalding demonstrated its effectiveness and Hackensack began using it in 1931. Spalding's process became "standard in water systems throughout the world," and his contribution to providing "pure and palatable water [was] so highly regarded in the waterworks industry that he was later given the American Water Works Association's George Warren Fuller Memorial Award." The association had honored Fuller by naming its annual award after the "father of sanitary engineering in the United States" for his many contributions to the water works industry. Barry Schwartz, who held Spalding's position several decades later, describes the use of activated charcoal on page 157. Ted Hoffman shares his recollection of Paul Tamer on page 187.[160]

The economic boom of the 1920s increased the population in Bergen County by more than 70 percent, and the construction of the George Washington Bridge, begun in 1927, promised even greater increases. By the end of the decade, production of filtered water briefly reached its previous wartime high of about 37 MGD. Nicholas Hill set the water company to planning a new reservoir that would be formed by a large dam in Rivervale and Old Tappan, in roughly the same location that Allen Hazen and Hering & Fuller had recommended thirty years earlier. The water company quietly began buying land for the new reservoir.

In 1929 the water company commissioned the site's first steam turbine from the DeLaval Steam Turbine Company of Trenton, New Jersey (Figure 108). The water company installed the steam turbine in the 1911 engine house at the New Milford Plant in the northern half of the center space between the No. 7 VTE and the Nos. 8 and 9 VTEs. The new No. 10 pump had a horizontal configuration, with one steam turbine driving two pumps at 77 rpm, for a total capacity of 30 MGD. It was considerably more efficient than the old VTEs and took up a lot less space, and it became the primary engine for pumping filtered water into the low-service portion of the distribution system.

Figure 108: No. 10 DeLaval Turbine. Manufactured by the DeLaval Steam Turbine Co. of Trenton, N.J., c. 1930. No. 10 is a horizontal pump and the site's first steam turbine. The turbine portion, bottom center, drove the two centrifugal pumps that had a combined capacity of 30 MGD. No. 10 took up considerably less space than the No. 7 VTE pumping engine, right, which had a capacity of 20 MGD. United Water Resources

Hill's anticipated continuation of growth in the 1930s failed to materialize. With the stock market crash at the end of 1929, the national economy plunged into depression and construction ground to a halt. The water company avoided layoffs and its employees were particularly thankful to have their jobs in light of the massive unemployment all around them. The opening of the George Washington Bridge in 1932 brought thousands of new automobiles to Bergen County but little in the way of new construction. Hill put major capital-intensive projects, like the proposed reservoir above

Figure 109: "Pumping Station, New Milford, 4/21/34." By 1934 the roads were paved and the water company had attractively landscaped the site. The sign on the 1911 engine house reads "Hackensack Water Company, Established 1882, Pumping and Purification Plants." United Water Resources

Figure 110: "Filter Plant, New Milford, 4/21/34." Shrubs and trees planted twenty years earlier along the filtration house contributed to the site's landscaped appearance. United Water Resources

Rivervale, on hold and focused the company's efforts on improving its existing facilities. In the mid 1930s the water company made a number of improvements to the now 30-year-old filtration plant. Supervised by George Wieghardt, these improvements provided jobs for idle construction workers, which was no doubt part of the company's motivation for undertaking them. The water company documented the appearance of many portions of the water works before, during, and after the 1930's construction with professional photographs that provide a detailed record of the work and much of the site (Figures 109, 110, and 111). During this time, the water company also started referring to the water works as the New Milford Plant.

"improvements to coagulation basin"

In 1933 the water company built some small additions on the east side of the filter house for a machine shop, a lavatory, and a garage (see Figures

Figure 111: "Intake Canal to Pumping Station, New Milford, 4/21/34." This eastward view toward the 1882 engine house shows the shrubs planted along the canal some twenty years earlier. United Water Resources

Figure 114: "Aerial View of New Milford Plant, Sept. 1935, Temporary Coagulation Basin under construction." The water company prepared the intake reservoir, lower right, along the west side of Van Buskirk Island for temporary coagulation use during a major renovation of the 1905 coagulation basin, upper left. This view toward the southeast shows the newly completed steel wash water tank at the northwest corner of the 1905 basin. By the mid 1930s, trees had grown large enough to cover the undeveloped portions of the island. United Water Resources

Figure 112: "Wash Water Tank, New Milford, 4/21/34." By 1934 the original concrete wash water tank designed by Hering & Fuller in 1904 was showing signs of age, and the water company had already removed its conical roof. (See also Figures 71 and 72.) United Water Resources

Figure 113: "New Sluice Gates 5/23/34." Contractors rebuilt the sluice and waste gates in the intake reservoir to prepare for the renovation of the 1905 coagulation basin. United Water Resources

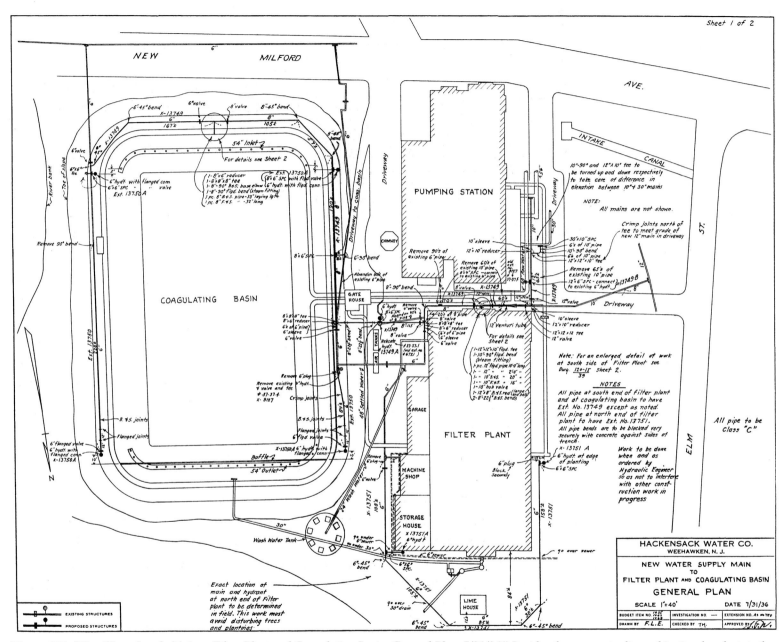

Figure 115: *"New Water Supply Main to Filter Plant and Coagulating Basin, General Plan, 7/31/36." Besides the new water lines, this site plan depicts the 1933 additions to the filtration house and the 1935 wash water tank, bottom center, plus a "baffle" wall installed along the north end of the coagulation basin to skim flocculant as the water flowed to the outlet conduit, bottom left. United Water Resources*

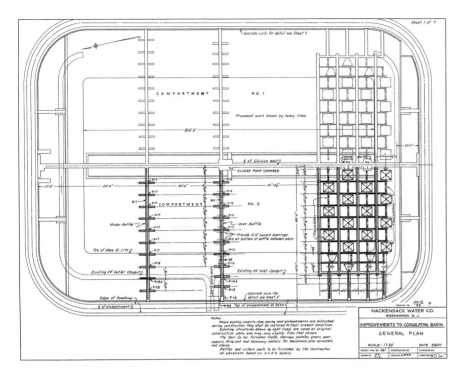

Figure 116: "Improvements to Coagulation Basin, General Plan." To simplify mainte-nance and improve the performance of the basin, company engineers developed a plan to divide it into two compartments with mixing chambers at each end, where wooden paddles called "flocculators" would increase the interaction between the raw water and the treatment chemicals. The drawing date of 3/8/37 postdated the start of con-struction in 1936. United Water Resources

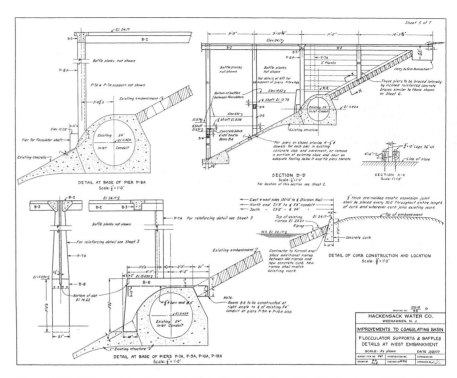

Figure 117: "Flocculator Supports & Baffles, Details at West Embankment." The floc-culators hung on concrete frames with removable wooden baffles to regulate the mixing rate in the four mixing chambers in each compartment. The drawing date of 3/8/37 postdated the start of construction in 1936. United Water Resources

115 and 152). The machine shop enabled the water company to make parts on site for the old pumps, an important consideration as many of the parts were no longer available from the manufacturers. In 1934 the water com-pany erected a new steel wash water tank by the northwest corner of the coagulation basin to replace the 1905 concrete tank, which was showing considerable signs of age (Figure 112, p. 101). That same year George Wieghardt prepared for the renovation of the coagulation basin by convert-ing the intake reservoir between the plant and the railroad tracks into a temporary coagulation basin. Contractors rebuilt the intake and waste gates

to improve the control of water flowing to the plant and to the river (Figure 113, p. 101). The water company built a temporary diversion dam to empty the intake reservoir and then lined its bottom to enable its temporary use for coagulation (Figure 114, p. 101). It installed new water supply mains link-ing the pumping station, the filtration house, the coagulation basin, and the new wash water tank (Figure 115).

To improve the operation of the coagulation basin, George Wieghardt and other water company engineers developed plans to divide it into two com-partments separated by a north-south division wall, so that one side could remain in operation while the other was being cleaned (Figure 116). To speed up the coagulation process, they designed mixing chambers for the south end of each compartment with a series of 14 "flocculators" made of wooden and steel paddles on concrete supports (Figure 117). By stirring the mixture of raw water and treatment chemicals as it entered the basin through the inlet conduit from the gate house, the flocculators sped up the coagulation process to increase the yield of treated water and to reduce the use of chemicals and the resulting sludge. To preserve the company's independence from electric power failures, the engineers installed Pelton water wheels, which were driven by pressurized raw water from the engine house, to turn the flocculators. The water company had earlier installed Pelton

water wheels in the filtration house machinery room to power the backwashing machinery.

The basin renovation plans also called for subdividing each compartment into three sections separated by curtain walls with removable wooden baffles to regulate the flow of water from the south or inlet end to the north or outlet end of the basin. To remove the sludge that accumulated in the middle, the engineers designed a sludge pump chamber in the center of the division wall. The pump sent the sludge to an outlet pipe that emptied into tank trucks, which took the sludge to lagoons on the east side of Madison Avenue just below the south bend in the river. After the sludge in the lagoons dried, the residue could be removed to an appropriate location.

Figure 118: *"Co-ag Basin from South Side, looking north, 1" Water in Basin, 6/16/36." The equipment raft used in washing out the residue has settled on the bottom in the northwest corner. The skimmer baffle wall, an earlier improvement to the basin outlet, is visible on the north end, center right. The new wash water tank can be seen beyond the basin in the center, and the gate house is visible on the left. United Water Resources*

Figure 119: *"Co-ag Basin from S.E. Corner, looking west, 1" Water in Basin, 6/16/36." The interior embankment wall of the basin included the concrete conduit with inlet holes in the lower left. Beyond the basin, the pumping station is on the left, and the filtration house is on the right. The gate house is visible on the west embankment, right center. United Water Resources*

Figure 120: *"Co-ag Basin, from west side north of Gatehouse, looking toward southeast corner, 8/23/36." The contractors cut through the top of the embankment on the southeast corner of the basin and built ramps on each side to provide access for construction equipment and materials. United Water Resources*

Figure 122: *"Co-ag Basin, 9/8/36, W. W. Gutteridge giving grade for cutoff walls." The tall cutoff or division wall that would create two compartments in the basin required a large footing down the center. Wesley Gutteridge, standing on the new footing, later became superintendent of the Spring Valley Water Company, a subsidiary of the Hackensack Water Company (see Figure 133). United Water Resources*

Figure 121: *"Co-ag Basin, Taken from N.E. corner looking southwest, 9/30/36." The original construction of the basin embankment consisted of stone paving along the upper slope to prevent ice damage, a concrete inlet conduit along the middle, and concrete on the lower slope below it converging with the concrete bottom. The access cut and ramp in the southeast corner are visible on the left, and the cut for the new division wall is visible on the right. United Water Resources*

105

Figure 124: *"Co-ag Basin, Taken from N.E. corner looking southwest, 9/30/36." The construction of the division wall to create two compartments in the basin is underway on top of a wide footing. The pumping station is visible on the upper right. United Water Resources*

Figure 123: *"Division Wall Construction, Coagulation Basin, 9/30/36." The wall construction included a web of reinforcing rods, right center, and wood forms, left center, in preparation for pouring the concrete. United Water Resources*

Figure 125: *"Co-ag Basin taken from south center looking N.E., 11/19/36." Constructing the concrete frames for the curtain walls in this view and for the mixing chambers in the south end of the basin required elaborate wooden forms (see Figure 117). United Water Resources*

Figure 126: *"Flocculators in west compartment of Co-ag Basin, Taken from S. end of division wall looking west, 6/19/37." Driven by Pelton water wheels powered by pressurized water from the engine house, the flocculators increased the mixing rate of the raw water and chemicals in the mixing chamber at the south end of each compartment of the renovated basin. At the top are the pumping station, left center, and the filtration house and gate house, center right. United Water Resources*

Figure 127: *"Inlet side of east compartment of Co-ag Basin Taken from S.E. corner of Basin looking S.W., 6/10/37." With the renovations complete, raw water treated with chemicals in the gate house entered the mixing chambers where the flocculators below the surface increased the mixing rate of the water and chemicals. United Water Resources*

This was an improvement over the old method of flushing the sludge into the river.

The complicated renovation of the coagulation basin took about ten months and the water company documented the entire process. It began the construction in August 1936 by draining the basin (Figures 118 and 119, p. 104). To get inside the basin, the contractors cut through the top of the embankment in the southeast corner near the New Milford Avenue Bridge over the Hackensack River (Figures 120 and 121, p. 105). The contractors began building the division wall by installing a wide concrete footing, and then they erected a frame of reinforcing rods and covered it with wooden forms (Figures 122,

123, and 124, p. 105–106). In the center of the division wall the contractors built the sludge pump chambers, through which the sludge would be pumped out of the basin (see Figure 116). When the division wall was complete, the contractors erected the concrete frames for the curtain walls (Figure 125) and for the flocculators in the mixing chambers on the south side of each compartment. The Dorr Company furnished the "shafts, bearings, paddles, gears, gear support, drive unit, sprockets, chains and anchors" for the flocculators (Figure 126). The water company put the east compartment of the basin in service in June 1937, and the west compartment shortly thereafter (Figure 127).[161]

Figure 128: "Pump Station and Filtration Plant, 4/10/38." 1905–1912 filtration house, left; 1898–1911 engine house, right. The wrought-iron fence in the foreground enclosed the intake canal, visible through the bottom of the fence that brought the raw water to the 1882 engine house. United Water Resources

"a new standard of excellence"

Nicholas Hill passed away in 1936 while the water company was renovating the coagulation basin. An engineer with a strong personality, Hill was no doubt personally involved in developing the plans for all the major improvements to the water works during his tenure, and the condition of the facility reflected his attention to detail (Figure 128). To succeed him, the directors elected Henry de Forest, the son of Robert de Forest, as the chairman of the company. Henry de Forest was a lawyer like his father, and at the water company he "limited his activities largely to matters of broad policy." The directors appointed Charles Alfke as vice president and manager to run the company's affairs. This arrangement was "reminiscent of the years in which

Mr. de Forest's father was President and D. W. French was Superintendent in charge of active operations." While the arrangement worked for many years, Nicholas Hill's engineering knowledge and broad experience were sorely missed. Three of his associates, George S. Buck, William Seifert, and Charles Jost, eventually took over Hill's engineering firm under the name of Buck, Seifert & Jost. George Buck and Charles Jost soon joined the water company as directors, and Buck eventually became president. Buck, Seifert & Jost became the company's consulting engineers, and continue in this capacity today. In 1938 the directors promoted George Wieghardt to chief engineer.[162]

As part of the upgrade of the filtration plant, George Spalding and Paul Tamer developed plans to modernize the water quality laboratory in the coagulation house. The plans included the complete rebuilding of the second floor interior in the east wing. The original chemical and biological laboratories (see Figures 62 and 107) were combined into one large lab. The modernization included ceramic tile floors and walls to maximize sanitary conditions and all new lab equipment (Figure 129). The water company put the new lab in service in 1937 and printed a pamphlet indicating the extent of analyses at New Milford that "set a new standard of excellence" in water testing (see *Laboratory Control*). By this time the water company was supplying 400,000 customers.

In 1937 the water company installed Pump No. 4, a 40-MGD DeLaval centrifugal pump powered by an Ames uniflow steam engine, on the south side of the 1891 section of the engine house. It replaced the original No. 3 pump, the 10-MGD Worthington installed in 1891. When the United States entered World War II, the army set up Camp Shanks as an embarkation facility in Orangeburg in Rockland County, New York. In a repeat of its World War I experience with Camp Merritt in Dumont, the water company quickly extended pipes to supply the camp with Hackensack River water. To meet the wartime demand, the water company installed two Worthington turbine pumps in New Milford in 1941: the No. 11 pump on the north side of the 1891 engine house, and the No. 12 pump on the north half of the central space in the 1911 engine house between the No. 10 turbine and the No. 7 VTE on the south end and the Nos. 8 and 9 VTEs on the north (Figure 130). During the war demand for filtered water at New Milford exceeded 40 MGD for the first time, but the plant had no problem meeting it: "Despite the wartime shortages of both men and materials, Charles Alfke and the other operating officials of the water company maintained its services without the slightest interruption throughout the whole period of the war."[163]

Figure 129: *"New Milford Lab, 4/14/38." To upgrade its analytical capacity, the water company combined the old chemical and biological laboratories into one large space with sanitary floors and walls and modern equipment, including several vent hoods. In this view toward the southeast corner, Paul Tamer, the chief chemist, is at the microscope on the left; Ernest Schmidt, the lab's dishwasher, is at the rear; and Germaine Munding, the assistant chemist, is on the right. United Water Resources*

Figure 130: *No. 12 Worthington turbine pump, 1961. To boost capacity in the early years of World War II, the water company installed the No. 12 pump, rated at 10 MGD, just north of the No. 10 pump, left, in the central portion of the 1911 engine house. Like No. 10 (see Figure 108), No. 12 had a steam turbine, right center, which drove two pumps, bottom center. United Water Resources*

Laboratory Control

No large water works could operate efficiently and economically without the services of a chemical laboratory. Every detail of operation from the sanitary control of the watershed through the purification and pumping processes to delivery of water at the householder's tap is under the watchful eye of the chemist with his test tubes and microscopes. The laboratories at New Milford, equipped with the most modern apparatus for water testing, are believed to set a new standard of excellence in such work. Records of the tests made in a single year clearly show the scope and importance of laboratory control.

Tabulation of Laboratory Tests for 1937

Bacteriological Tests for Filter Plant Control	*8418*
Chemical and Bacteriological Tests for Distribution System Control	*4056*
Chemical and Bacteriological Analyses for Watershed Control	*10200*
Examination of Samples from House Services	*254*
Complete Mineral Analyses for Industries	*18*
Chemical Tests for Filter Plant Control	*32844*
Special Analyses	*257*
Microscopic Investigations of Samples from Reservoirs	*484*

At the end of each month tabulated reports are prepared which show the results of analyses for each day. These reports are sent to the State Department of Health at Trenton and to each of the fifty-one communities supplied by the Hackensack Water Company.

Pure Filtered Water for Four Hundred Thousand People in Bergen and Hudson Counties, *Department of Filtration-Sanitation, Hackensack Water Company, 1938.*[164]

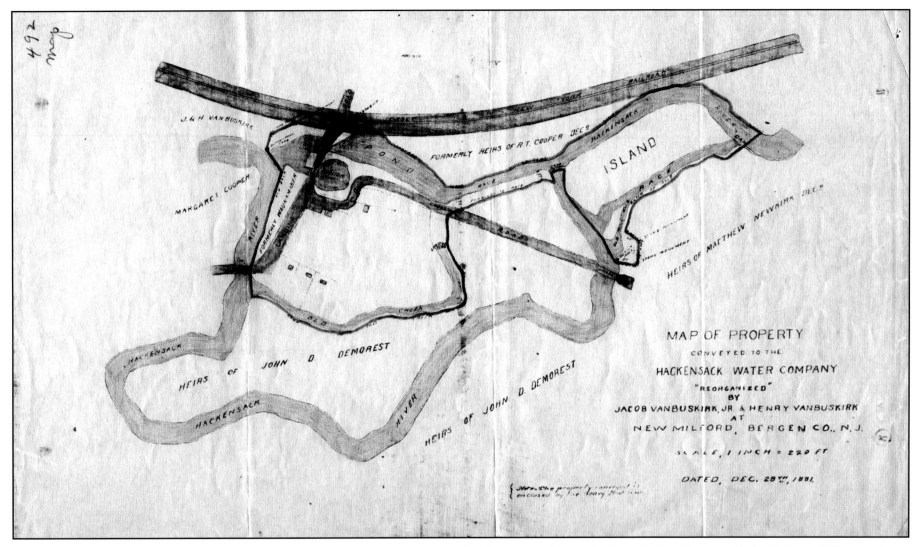

Plate 1: *Van Buskirk Island, December 28, 1881. The survey shows the original portion of the island acquired by the Hackensack Water Company for the Hackensack Water Works, with the Van Buskirk Mill and the "Old Dock" on the south side of Landing Road (currently New Milford Avenue), just west of the New Jersey & New York Railroad. The conveyance included a mill pond, a slough or tidal pond, two mill races controlled by dams west of Crossing Road (currently Elm Street), and several buildings and the "Old Creek" with a "Limit of Tide" at its head on the east side of Crossing Road. United Water Resources*

Plate 3: *"Hackensack Water Co Filtration Plant, New Milford, N.J. 1906." The company celebrated the opening of its innovative filtration plant with a pamphlet illustrating for its patrons how filtration made their water supply "pure and sparkling." United Water Resources*

Plate 2: *"Hackensack Water Works, New Milford, N.J.," 1906, west side. This hand-colored postcard depicts the 1905 filtration plant (left), the 1906 boiler house (center), and the 1898-1891-1882 sections of the engine house (right). New Milford Avenue extends from the foreground to the right, and Elm Street from the center to the left. Frank Vierling*

Plate 4: *New Milford pumping station, southwest corner, 1998. From the south side of New Milford Avenue, the incremental growth of the engine house is visible from the 1882–1886 sections (right), through the 1911-1898-1891 sections (left center). Water Works Conservancy*

Plate 5: *New Milford pumping station, south side, 2002. In developing the station over four decades, company engineers designed hipped roofs, gable roofs, a "ventilating turret," ventilating roof monitors, hipped dormers, and shed dormers. This view from Madison Avenue shows the 1882–1886 engine house (left), the 1898–1906 boiler house (right), and the 1891-1898-1911 engine house (rear center). Ron Jautz*

Plate 6: *1882 engine house, south façade, 2001. The company erected the original building of the Hackensack Water Works on Van Buskirk Island as a little temple of water supply, and it remains remarkably intact today. C. W. Zink*

Plate 7: *1882 engine house, south façade, 2001. The Industrial Romanesque design and late nineteenth-century craftsmanship of the original engine house established traditions that the company followed through four decades of construction at New Milford. Chip Renner*

Plate 8: *1882 engine house, south side and roof, 2002. For the original engine house, company engineers designed a complex geometry of hips and gables for the "ventilating turret" that exhausted excess heat and flooded the interior with daylight. The company carefully maintained this remarkable example of nineteenth-century craftsmanship for over 110 years. Dave Frieder*

Plate 10: *Pumping station, west façade, 1997. As steam technology developed in the 1890s, new vertical pumping engines required large spaces. For the 1898 two-story addition (left), company engineers replicated the designs, materials, and craftsmanship of the original 1882 engine house (right). Dave Frieder*

Plate 9: *1886 engine house, west end, 1988. In 1915 the company installed a 36-MGD Allis-Chalmers centrifugal steam pump in the first addition to the engine house, and meticulously maintained it for 75 years. As former president, George Haskew recalled, "We tried to keep New Milford pretty spotless." Gerry Weinstein*

Plate 12: *1898 engine house, west end, 2002. The two-story 1898 engine house addition housed the plant's first vertical pumping engines, which were installed and maintained with the traveling overhead crane supported on a steel frame within the brick building. Ron Jautz*

Plate 11: *1898 engine house, west façade, 1997. With its original doors, windows, and Romanesque brickwork intact, the façade of the 1898 engine house addition illustrates the remarkable preservation of the New Milford Plant. According to laboratory technician Pat Hoffman, "All the guys that worked there sensed they were in an historic place." Her husband Dan Hoffman, the plant manager, "knew it had historic significance right from the beginning, and his attitude was always 'Don't do anything to these walls!'" Dave Frieder*

Plate 13: *Pumping station and filtration house, 1997. The design and construction of the 1898 engine house addition (right), the 1905 filtration house (left), and the 1911 engine house addition (center) replicated the Industrial Romanesque details and craftsmanship of the original 1882 engine house. The company built the 1911 addition three stories tall to accommodate three enormous vertical pumping engines. In this photo the third floor and dormer windows have been boarded up. The company installed the bulkhead doors in the 1970s for flood control. Dave Frieder*

Plate 14: *1911 engine house entrance, west façade, c. 1988. While maintaining the site's traditional appearance, company engineers designed large window and door openings to fill the interior of the 1911 addition with daylight, and removable doors for bringing in the prefabricated parts of the vertical pumping engines. The condition of the woodwork and paint finishes illustrates the company's commitment to maintenance and the preservation of the original fabric while the plant remained in service. Gerry Weinstein*

Plate 15: *1911 engine house addition, west side, 2002. Company engineers combined traditional materials and window patterns with a steel frame and roof trusses to provide a huge volume of open space for the three vertical pumping engines installed in 1911. At the bottom are the Nos. 13 and 14 DeLaval electric turbine pumps that the company installed in the late 1950s to replace two of the original pumping engines. Ron Jautz*

Plate 16: *1911 engine house addition, south end, 1996. To house the No. 7 Allis-Chalmers VTE pumping engine, company engineers designed the steel-frame 1911 addition with a clear span 60 feet wide, 100 feet long, and 44 feet high. Workers used the overhead traveling crane to install and maintain the three original steam pumps, and ultimately to replace two of them with electric turbines. Jeff Wells*

Plate 17: *No. 7 Allis-Chalmers pumping engine, northeast corner, c. 1999. Representing the height of steam engineering technology based on marine engines that had developed over several decades, the No. 7 VTE pumping engine in the 1911 engine house addition could pump 20 MGD of finished or purified water into the company's distribution system. Chip Renner*

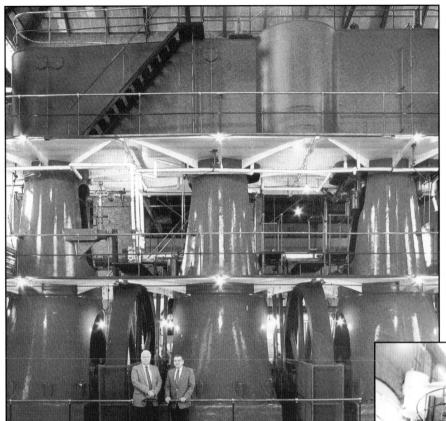

Plate 21: *No. 7 Allis-Chalmers pumping engine, south side, 1997. Frank Vierling of Oradell often visited the plant as a young boy and recalled the big pumps in operation: "It was always an awesome sight. The giant machines with their great spinning flywheels, their plunging cylinders, and hissing steam were exciting and thrilling, and at the same time a bit scary to little boys." Chip Renner*

Plate 20: *No. 7 Allis-Chalmers pumping engine, south side, 2002. Five stories of catwalks with cast-iron stairs provide access to all parts of the pump for maintenance. Ron Jautz*

Plate 23: *No. 7 Allis-Chalmers pumping engine, northwest corner from the basement, 2002. The 1911 No. 7 Allis-Chalmers illustrates the elegant beauty of industrial design during the machine age. Dave Frieder*

Plate 22: *No. 7 Allis-Chalmers pumping engine, basement level, 2002. The 15-foot diameter, cast-iron flywheels weigh 21 tons each. Chip Renner*

Plate 24: *Filtration house (left) and engine house, view east, 1988. The 1905 filtration house and the 1911 engine house addition were designed with brick walls and divided-light windows to complement the 1882 engine house and its 1898 addition. An underground network of pipes between the buildings connected them to the gate house and coagulation basin beyond. Gerry Weinstein*

Plate 25: *Filtration house, southeast corner, 2002. The south end of the filtration house was known as the coagulation house because of its four-story tower that was used for mixing chemicals for treating the water. The chemical solutions were conveyed to the gate house through the elevated pipe on the right. In 1905 the company installed chemical and biological laboratories on the second floor of the east wing, and in 1975, as environmental regulations increased, it expanded the laboratories to the second floor of the west wing. The east wing first floor housed machinery for backwashing the filters, while the west wing provided storage space for chemicals and equipment. Jaime Laga*

Plate 26: *Filtration house filter gallery, view north, c. 1974. In this view from the 1905–1912 sections toward the 1955 section, the original hydraulic controls are visible on top of the filter operating tables. The filter operators monitored the backwashing process by looking into the end of the filter tank that projected into the gallery on either side of the knee walls. Barry Schwartz*

Plate 27: *Filtration house filter gallery, view south, c. 1976. In the 1970s the water company installed computers to operate the 1905 filters, which former company president George Haskew considered "a fascinating marriage of the centuries." Barry Schwartz*

Plate 28: *Engine house valve wheels, 2002. Cast-iron valves on the west side of the 1911 engine house addition (right) controlled the flow of filtered water from the clear wells in the filtration house (rear) through an underground suction well from which the distribution pumps drew water (see Figure 83). Chip Renner*

Plate 29: *New Milford plant chimney stacks, 1997. The 1898 chimney, foreground, is 110 feet tall and has a 13-foot-square base and cap; the 1918 chimney is 185 feet tall with an 18-foot wide octagonal base. The distinctive brick corbelling of the caps displays the chimney builders' art. Chip Renner*

Plate 31: *Coagulation basin, view west, 2002. In 1937 the company installed concrete and wood partitions to create flocculation chambers within the 1905 coagulation basin, in order to increase the mixing rate of treatment chemicals with the raw water. Pressurized water from the engine house powered the steel flocculation baffles at the bottom of the chambers. Chip Renner*

Plate 30: *Waste gates, 2001. Installed in 1911, the cast-iron waste gates controlled the flow of water from the intake pond to the Hackensack River. The adjacent intake gates controlled the flow of water into the intake canal for the pumping station. C. W. Zink*

Text on map:

HACKENSACK WATER COMPANY

Watershed of Hackensack River
above New Milford Pumping Station

H U D S O N   R I V E R

Labels on map: Macquapsink Creek, Oradell, WESTWOOD, Woodcliff Reservoir, Breakneck Brook, Watershed Area, NEW YORK, VALLEY, POMONA, Oradell Reservoir, NEW MILFORD Purification and Pumping Plants, Holdrums Brook, PEARL RIVER, NANUET, Watershed Area, HAWORTH, OLD TAPPAN, Hackensack River, NEW CITY, Hackensack River, Tenakill Creek, TENAFLY, CLOSTER, Dwarskill Creek, NEW JERSEY, BLAUVELT, ORANGEBURGH, TAPPAN, Congers Lake, Rockland Lake, Watershed Area, Watershed Area, PIERMONT, NYACK

Plate 32: *"Watershed of the Hackensack River above New Milford Pumping Station," c. 1950. The watershed that formerly supplied the water works straddles northeastern Bergen County in New Jersey and southeastern Rockland County in New York. It currently supplies the Haworth pumping station on the east side of the Oradell Reservoir (left), which was built in stages in 1902, 1911, and 1921. The Woodcliff Lake Reservoir, opened in 1905, is visible left of center near the top. Today the watershed includes the DeForest Lake Reservoir (1957) in Rockland County and the Lake Tappan Reservoir (1967), straddling the Bergen Rockland border. United Water Resources*

Plate 33: *New Milford pumping station, c. 1985. Formed by an oxbow in the Hackensack River, Van Buskirk Island (lower left) includes the New Milford pumping station, the southern terminus of Elm Street, and the northern terminus of Madison Avenue (lower center). New Milford Avenue runs east-west across the southern side of the island. United Water Resources*

Part II

They Were Great People

This history of the Hackensack Water Works after World War II shifts from documents to voices. The oral histories of the six people who worked on the site or visited it frequently contain descriptions and insights unavailable in written or graphic sources: sights, sounds, smells, attitudes, feelings, opinions, and more. Their words describe how circumstances and experiences shaped their lives, interests, and careers. Brief recollections from two additional employees and one longtime Oradell resident illuminate individual experiences of the water works. All these oral accounts also depict engaging aspects of work in New Jersey in the second half of the twentieth century.

George Haskew is an engineer who worked for the water company from 1965 to 1996. Before that he worked in the engineering firm of Buck, Seifert & Jost in New York on water industry projects. He started working at the Hackensack Water Company as assistant to the president, George Buck, and ultimately retired as president himself. His engineering and management perspective provides an overall view of the operation as well as a personal account of working with the people involved in it.

Jim Flynn joined the staff of the pumping station as an assistant fireman in the boiler house in 1966, progressed to watch engineer in the engine house, and shifted to a supervisory role in the filtration plant. Jim's firsthand accounts of the equipment, the buildings, and the processes involved in operating the New Milford Plant bring its machines and spaces to life, and illuminate the relationships of the people who kept the water flowing.

Ted Hoffman of Paramus taught math at Pascack Valley High School for 32 years and retired in 1999. His father, Frank Hoffman, served as the plant machinist at New Milford from 1956 until his death in 1983 at the age of 66.

Ted often visited his father at the water works and early in his career he worked for Kuchar Brothers of Montvale on water company construction projects. Ted's account brings his father's creativity and his dedication to his work and his coworkers to life, and his recollections of the water works and its crew provide a vivid account of the place and their work.

Barry Schwartz of Hillsdale is a chemist and sanitary engineer who developed an interest in science at an early age, and after college and the service he went to work for Buck, Seifert & Jost on water quality projects. George Haskew hired Barry as chief chemist at the water works laboratory in 1968 and he worked for the water company for the next thirty-two years, retiring in 2002 as the director of water quality and regulatory affairs. Barry's discussion of the scientific work of the lab, and the operation of the filtration house and the coagulation basin provides a scientist's perspective on the design and operation of these facilities, and his recollections of the people and the place provide a firsthand account of the efforts necessary to ensure the purity of municipal water.

Pat Hoffman went to work in 1974 at the office of the Spring Valley Water Company, the subsidiary of the Hackensack Water Company in Rockland County, New York. Seeking greater challenges, Pat became the first woman sample collector among the men who collected samples around the watershed for testing at the New Milford Plant laboratory. Intrigued by the lab during her visits to drop off water samples, Pat returned to school to take science courses and in 1976 she joined the lab staff. Her recollections portray utility work at a time when women had limited opportunities for advancement. In 1992 Pat married Dan Hoffman, the former superintendent of the New Milford Plant, who died in 1996. Her description of Dan's forty-eight years with the water company at the New Milford Plant illuminates his dedication and enthusiasm for the work, the place, and the people.

Miles Kuchar was born in 1921, the same year his father and uncle started a construction company in Montvale. Growing up in the business, he became interested in the water works when his father contracted for jobs there. After college Miles joined the family firm and worked on Hackensack Water Company projects over several decades, from pump installation and lab renovations to dam construction. Miles recalls how hard people worked in years past and how they overcame complex challenges to get the jobs done.

Jesse Jones, who started as a laborer with the water company at the New Milford Plant in 1966 and retired in 2003, shares his experience working his way up through the ranks. MaryFrances Schwartz, who became a technician in 1967 at the New Milford water quality laboratory, where she met her future husband, Barry Schwartz, recalls her experience working for a close-knit organization like the water company.

Frank Vierling, the Oradell Historian, was born in 1923 on Maple Avenue in Oradell and grew up within a mile of Van Buskirk Island. His reminiscences about his frequent boyhood visits to the site convey the marvel of the place and the machinery, as well as life before World War II, when much of Bergen County was still undeveloped.

Chapter 5

That's Why We Did It That Way

After World War II ended, war housing construction in Bergen County began to boom again and the water company directors reactivated plans for a new reservoir. In 1948 George Wieghardt upgraded the pumping station with some new boilers and pumps. He hired Kuchar Brothers of Montvale to demolish the four 50-year-old coal boilers in the 1898 section of the boiler house (see Figure 30) and the two 30- and 40-year-old coal boilers in the 1906 section. In the 1898 section Kuchar Brothers installed two oil-fired boilers in the space formerly occupied by the four original coal boilers.

In 1905 D. W. French had installed two 24-MGD horizontal Allis-Chalmers steam pumps in the 1882 engine house to supply raw water to the new coagulation basin. These pumps, which had replaced the site's No. 1 and No. 2 Worthington pumps from the 1880s, were by now obsolete and unable to meet the increasing water demand. Wieghardt replaced them with a DeLaval pumping engine that consisted of a steam turbine driving two centrifugal pumps, each with a capacity of 40 MGD (Figure 131). Kuchar Brothers installed these new No. 1 and No. 2 pumps, the last steam-driven pumps installed at the water works. Miles Kuchar began working for his father's construction company on the installation of these pumps, the first of his many projects for the company.[165]

> *My father started his company, Miles Kuchar Incorporated, the year that I was born. When he started taking out the first coal burning boilers in '48 I was going to college at Stevens Tech in Hoboken. I started out in general engineering and ended up with a mechanical engineering degree. You could get your master's*

Figure 131: *No. 1 and No. 2 DeLaval pumps, c. 1961. Installed in 1948 by the Kuchar Brothers of Montvale, each of these raw water pumps, right, had a capacity of 40 MGD and both were driven by one steam turbine, center. DeLaval designed the pump drive so that the pumps could operate in tandem or independently. These were the last steam-driven pumps installed at the water works. United Water Resources*

> *degree in a year in almost any engineering you wanted to specialize in. Then in 1949 my father installed the steam turbine pumps for raw water in the 1882 engine house. Unfortunately, in 1949 he had a heart attack and he couldn't work. When he was working on the steam turbines I started working and I worked on water company projects for over fifty years.*

When I began working at the water company, they had coal carts going on a rail line from the coal shed right to the main line of the railroad [Figure 132]. They would dump the coal into the carts underneath the coal car and at once the car would be pulled by cable up into the coal house. The coal house was just like a big, old barn; a big, big barn [see Figures 8, 19, and 24]. They dumped the coal and the carts kept going back and forth to empty the coal car. I remember Danny Hoffman, the maintenance fellow at the time, telling me when he started he used to shovel coal and all that was left in the coal car. From the coal house they put the coal through a hopper onto the conveyor, which took it to the boilers. The old conveyer was over the road at first and then they put it under the road.

Figure 132: "Coal House, Cable Car on River Crossing, New Milford, 5/23/34." The steam-powered cable car ran on a wooden trestle that extended from the New Jersey and New York Railroad siding on the west bank of the Hackensack River to the 1882–1886 coal shed (see Figure 88). The operation of the cable car provided a fascinating scene for children and adult visitors to Van Buskirk Island for several decades. United Water Resources

When I first walked into that big pump station it was unbelievable with those big three-stage pumps in there. They were just lined up one alongside the other. There were five of those vertical pumps in there. The rooms were full of them [see Figures 35, and 84–86]. Big No. 7 was still running. I remember Danny Hoffman starting No. 7, and they'd be running around turning dials and whatever they had to do. It took a lot of work. Steam would fly out all over and the check valve would close with a big noise and things would shake, but they kept working. It was a marvel to watch them work.

A friend of mine lived in Glen Rock and he owned a company that manufactured the sluice gates on the Oradell Dam. He almost treated me like his son. He told me when he was young he went to a plant in York, Pennsylvania, which at the time was owned by F. Morgan Smith [and] was later bought by Allis-Chalmers. He told me how he saw them start making the casting, pouring the castings in molten metal, machining the castings [see Figure 87], and then taking them up and assembling a whole pump, like pump No. 7, and running through all the tests to make sure they operated properly. . . . and then they'd disassemble them and bring them up to Oradell. Those pumps were shipped all over the United States. And this was back in the late 1800s, early 1900s. It's hard to visualize all the physical labor that went into that to assemble the pumps and take them apart, and ship them and reassemble them. They were great people.

At the middle of the century, most of the directors and employees of the water company could look back at their accomplishments over several decades (Figure 133). They were particularly proud of the Hackensack Water Works, which many of them had been instrumental in developing (Figures 134 and 135). But many of them were also nearing the end of their careers. After four decades with the company, George Spalding retired in

Seated L. to R.: John C. Schlicht, Earle Talbot, George Spalding, Henry L. deForest, Charles J. Alfke, Emile J. Fricker. *Seated Second Row, L. to R.:* Joseph Domas, Victor Aldoretta, Thomas Adams, Anthony Zoeller, Lawrence Hogan. *Third Row, L. to R.:* Adolph Damiano, Archibald Lyle, Thomas Mitchell, Wesley Gutteridge, Peter Pallo, M. Warren Cowles, Harrison Cady, Adrian C. Leiby, George MacCoubrey, John N. Miraglia, Joseph Liccardi, Samuel W. Zerman, George J. Schmidle, George Cavanaugh, Arnold Staub, John W. Lipinski. *Fourth Row, L. to R.:* Edward Walasyk, Walter Brown, Walter H. Boquist, Charles Jost (Buck, Seifert & Jost, Consulting Engineers), Julius Von Scheidt, William Block, Henry Hein, George F. Wieghardt.

Figure 133: *"Executive Staff, 1949." The mid-century marked a turning point for the company, as many senior staff members and directors retired, and their successors laid plans for a major period of expansion. Adrian Leiby,* The Hackensack Water Company 1869–1969. *United Water Resources*

Figure 134: *"New Milford Pumping Station, 1950." In this view from the west side of the intake reservoir, the 1911 engine house is visible in the center, and portions of the 1882 engine house and the 1905 filtration plant are visible on the right and left, respectively. United Water Resources*

Figure 135: *New Milford Plant from Madison Avenue, c. 1950. The 1882–1886 sections of the engine house are on the left, with the roofs of the 1898–1911 sections visible beyond. The 1898–1906 boiler house is in the center, and a fuel oil tank for the 1948 oil-fired boilers is visible on the right. Frank Vierling*

1949, and Peter Pallo, a sanitary engineer, assumed the supervision of the filtration plant. After fourteen years as president, Henry de Forest retired and the directors appointed George Buck as president, putting the reins of the water company back in the hands of an engineer. In 1954 George Wieghardt retired as chief engineer, and the water company appointed Adolph Damiano, the assistant engineer, to replace him.

After George Buck was graduated from the University of Pennsylvania's engineering school, he had joined Nicholas Hill's engineering firm and helped design water supply projects around the United States and in South America. Upon Hill's death, Buck and two other Hill associates, William Seifert and Charles Jost, formed Buck, Seifert & Jost to take over their mentor's business. Buck had been the water company's consulting engineer for more than twenty-five years and had also served as a director for many years when he was appointed president. While Buck was particularly well suited to guide the water company in its next period of expansion, the start of his term as president was marked by controversy surrounding the construction of its new reservoir in Rockland County. After the water company announced its plans for the reservoir in early 1951, opponents formed the Anti-Reservoir Association to fight it. Despite the vigorous opposition, the New York Water Policy and Control Commission approved the plan. When the water company completed the reservoir in 1956, it named it DeForest Lake in honor of Henry de Forest, for his role in getting the project underway.[166]

"the scientific purification of the water"

Between 1950 and 1955 the demand for water rose 25 percent. In 1951 Buck, Seifert & Jost designed a new filtered water basin and a new coagulation basin for the land west of the water works on Van Buskirk Island. This construction would have required the abandonment of Elm Street, and the plans were soon dropped. In 1952 production of filtered water reached the nominal 48-MGD capacity of the filtration plant, and the water company began planning for an addition to the filter house on its north side.

Buck, Seifert & Jost designed the addition in 1953 and 1954 to house six new filters. To power the extension and to prepare for the electrification of the pumping station, the consulting engineers developed specifications for an electrical substation on the east side of Elm Street. The addition required the demolition of the north wall of the 1912 filter house extension but left the rest of the building intact. The engineers designed the addition in a modern style, with horizontal aluminum windows, but they created a symmetrical north end with a hipped-roof tower (Figures 136 and 137) to complement the symmetry and basic form of the 1905–1912 filter house (see Figure 54). They also specified red brick for the exterior to match the other buildings in the complex (Figure 138).

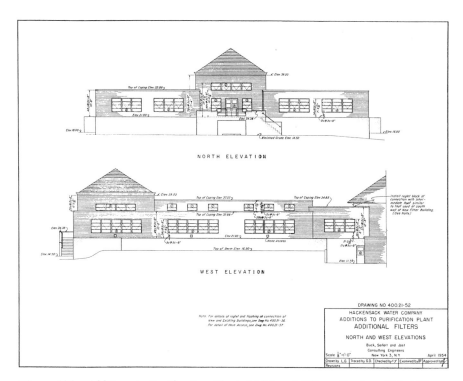

Figure 136: "Additions to Purification Plant, Additional Filters, North and West Elevations, April 1954." Buck, Seifert & Jost, the company's consulting engineers, designed the 1955 addition to the filter house in a modern style with horizontal windows. They included a small tower on the north end to relate it to the 1905 south end of the filter house. United Water Resources

The layout of the addition was similar to that of the original filter house, with an operating gallery between two rows of filters (Figure 139). While the operating gallery in the old sections provided a view of only the ends of the filters (see Figures 66 and 96), in the 1955 addition the filters were completely open so that the operator could better observe the filtering and backwashing processes while controlling the filter at the operating table (Figures 140, 141, 142, and 143, and see Figure 201). For the interior walls the engineers specified glazed blocks, which gave the extension an antiseptic appearance. The addition included a control room in the southeast corner where the operator could monitor conditions in the new filters (Figure 144).

Figure 137: 1955 filter house addition, c. 1956. The 1955 addition, as seen in this view of the northwest corner, includes a full story with windows above the filters, in contrast with the covered filters in the 1905–1912 sections of the filter house. United Water Resources

The basement in the addition contained a pipe gallery in the middle and clear wells on each side (Figures 145 and 146, p. 120), just like the earlier sections (see Figures 56 and 94). A major Buck, Seifert & Jost improvement was the use of concrete settled water influent conduits along the south, east, and west sides of the basement story to supply the filters. This separated the influent and wash water systems, which were crammed together in the 1905 and 1912 pipe galleries (see Figure 63). While the basic filter design followed the originals, the engineers made several other improvements, including larger gutters for removing the backwashing water and "Wheeler Bottoms," a new type of collecting block, at the base of the filters (see Figure 145). The design also included a different configuration of gravel and sand with a more elaborate grading of gravel sizes. It increased the working room and simplified maintenance in the pipe gallery (Figure 147, p. 121). The improved filter design enabled the engineers to eliminate the air component of the backwashing system.

Figure 138: 1955 filter house addition, c. 1956. The large horizontal windows on the east, above, and west sides of the addition provide daylight over the filters, in contrast with the dark cover over the 1905–1912 filters. The two smaller windows on the left provide daylight to the control room. United Water Resources

The six new filters increased the capacity of the filtration plant by 45 percent to 70 MGD. When the water company put the filter house extension in service in 1955 (Figure 148, p. 121), filtered water production was nearly 53 MGD. Within four years it increased by nearly 20 percent to 63 MGD, and the water company had to begin planning for more capacity. The postwar boom fueled a growth in water demand resembling that of the water company's first four decades. To help customers understand their water supply, Peter Pallo, the supervisor of the filtration plant and a skilled draftsman and artist, drew a schematic rendering in 1957 that illustrated the flow of water from the reservoir to the consumer and its "scientific purification" along the way (Figure 149, p. 123).

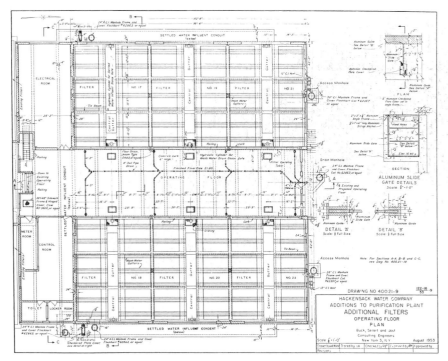

Figure 139: "Additions to Purification Plant, Additional Filters, Operating Floor Plan, August 1953." The plan resembled the earlier sections of the filter house, with filters on either side of an operating floor or gallery. Buck, Seifert & Jost included an electrical room in the southwest corner and a control room in the southeast corner. United Water Resources

Figure 140: 1955 filter house addition, c. 1955. This view of the operating floor looking north shows the open filters on each side. Buck, Seifert & Jost specified glazed block for the interior to maximize the sanitary conditions. United Water Resources

Figure 141: 1955 filter house addition, c. 1955. In contrast with the 1905–1912 sections of the filter house, the operator in the 1955 addition could look over the entire filter while controlling the filtering and backwashing processes. In this view of the east filters, the operator is controlling filter No. 18 in the southeast corner of the addition. United Water Resources

Figure 142: 1955 filter house addition, c. 1955. From the operating gallery, the operator could observe the conditions in the entire filter, as seen in this view of filter No. 17 in the southwest corner of the extension taken during backwashing. United Water Resources

Figure 143: 1955 filter house addition, c. 1955. During backwashing, the wash water pumped through the bottom of the filter floated the accumulated residue and overflowed into the concrete gutters, which drained the dirty water to a waste outlet. When the water became clear, the operator stopped the backwashing and restarted the filtering. United Water Resources

Figure 144: "New Milford Filter Gallery, Modern Controls, 1960." From the control room in the southeast corner of the 1955 filter house addition, the operator could monitor the conditions in all the new filters. United Water Resources

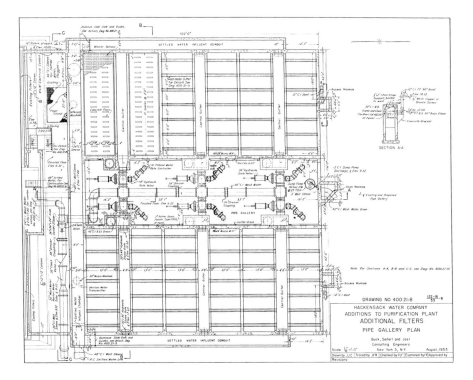

Figure 145: "Additions to Purification Plant, Additional Filters, Pipe Gallery Plan, August 1953." Improving on the design of the 1905–1912 filter house, Buck, Seifert & Jost shifted the settled water influent to the outsides of the filters, which simplified the piping in the pipe gallery. United Water Resources

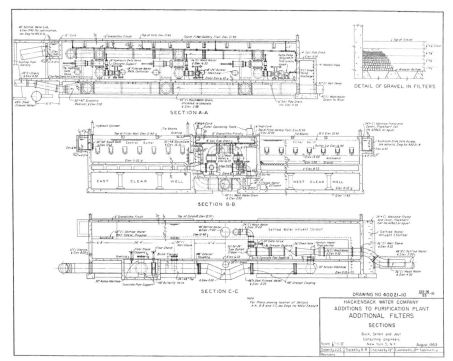

Figure 146: "Additions to Purification Plant, Additional Filters, Sections, August 1953." In contrast with the elaborate groined arches and elliptical bottoms of the 1905–1912 clear wells, Buck, Seifert & Jost designed rectilinear clear wells with square columns for the 1955 addition. Improvements like the layering of gravel, upper right, enabled the elimination of the air scour used in backwashing the 1905–1912 filters. United Water Resources

"a cacophony of sound, but always rhythmic"

While the water company had improved the filtration plant, most of the pumping station was still running on old technology. Electric motors were prevalent in the water supply industry, but the New Milford pumping station was still running on steam, and most of its pumps were forty or fifty years old. While steam power isolated the plant from electric power outages, the old pumps were inefficient and required a lot of maintenance, and many parts were unavailable. Keeping them running required licensed operating engineers and firemen around the clock, plus mechanics and machinists.

Many of the men had learned their trades through firsthand experience at the plant.

Ted Hoffman, a resident of Paramus, says that he practically grew up at the water works and he remembers the old steam engines and the work of the plant vividly.[167]

I can remember witnessing three of the old Allis-Chalmers steam engines at New Milford working in harmony to pump out water in the summer [see Figures 34 and 84–86]. One of the first or second times I had gone out to the plant with my mom, my father wanted to show me the whole plant, what it was all about. He was very

Figure 147: Pipe gallery, c. 1955. Because the cramped conditions of the 1905–1912 pipe galleries made maintenance and changes particularly difficult (see Figure 63), Buck, Seifert & Jost designed the pipe gallery in the 1955 addition with considerably more working room by placing the settled water influent conduit on the outsides of the filters. The 36-inch cast-iron pipes in the gallery supplied wash water to the bottoms of the filters. United Water Resources

Figure 148: New Milford filter gallery, c. 1955. The 1955 addition increased the filtration house capacity from 48 MGD to 70 MGD. This northward view shows the seamless integration of the 1905–1912 filter house and the 1955 addition beyond. United Water Resources

proud of being able to work there. So he took me through and we watched those machines. There was a rhythm to them. Boom-boom, boom-boom. It would just continue. That 21-ton flywheel would move around [Figure 150, p. 124, Color Plates 17–22, and see Figure 84]. It was balanced. With all of those machines working in that plant you could hear an echo because of the vast expanse. There would be a cacophony of sound, but it was always rhythmic. There was a melodious type of rumble through the plant that always reminded me of Jules Verne's Twenty Thousand Leagues Under the Sea—Captain Nemo—when you looked at

those pumps. That's what I would think about as a young kid looking up at them. It was just unbelievable. The staircase that went up to them was interesting because it all fit together in pieces [Figure 151, p. 124]. It was like an erector set. It always fascinated me when I looked at them.

With those large boilers going to create the steam to run those pumps, it was always hot in the boiler room. I don't care whether it was the middle of winter or the middle of summer. Middle of summer was like hell. I think you'd call it winter purgatory, but it was not a good place to be. It could be 20 degrees out and it would be going to town in there. They had these large windows and doors that went up on tracks in the boiler room. They'd just leave them wide open. At night, you could drive by at midnight and the windows would be open, the steam would be coming out. The lights would be on in all of the different areas. The area where men were would be brightly lit. The pump area would be lit but not as bright as the boiler area. Then there would be lights in the filter gallery. There'd be lights all over the place and then there'd be lights on the outside on the building. It would always be lit all night. From the outside the only thing you could hear would be some of the steam going off. Only in the plant there was an echo in that large area.

The old steam engines had to be oiled on a twenty-four-hour basis, so a man would start on his shift at one point and would oil the machine and by the time he got to the final destination of where he had to oil them, he would have to start again and re-oil them. They had to be constantly cared for and were definitely maintenance-heavy, but in terms of running they were always very dependable. You had your oilers, your mechanics, and your machinists. Some of the guys would take something apart before [my father] would get there and they'd come over to the shop with this barrel of parts and he'd go crazy. It was like a jigsaw puzzle—now how does this go together? You're looking at parts that may have been seventy-five years old. How are we going to put this thing back together again? That was one of the things that used to drive him crazy.

Because the pumping machines were so old, they had to make the parts. Some of the machinery dated from the turn of the century. Many of the companies were out of business and there would be no way of getting parts. Some of the bearings were Babbitt bearings, which had to be cast and then cut. He would cast them. . . . My father would basically be in the machine shop manufacturing parts, but frequently he would be out of the shop to take measurements to see what was broken, to have some of the mechanics take parts apart and bring them in. You never could tell

where he would be, but, predominantly, he was in that shop cutting. There were other guys there that could cut, but I believe that he was the only machinist with that title.

The machine shop where my father worked was around the back of the filtration house [Figure 152, p. 125, and see Figure 115]. You would have to go in through the front gate, pass in between the office and the laboratory, turn left, go all the way in the back and it was in a flat-roofed building that's right on the side of the filter gallery. Originally the flat roof of that building was flooded in the summer so that it would cool the building off, because it would be very, very warm in there. I know when my father first started working there he was laughing because they still had the pulleys on the ceiling that would operate the belts that would run those antiquated machines that he had to work on. He said in some cases

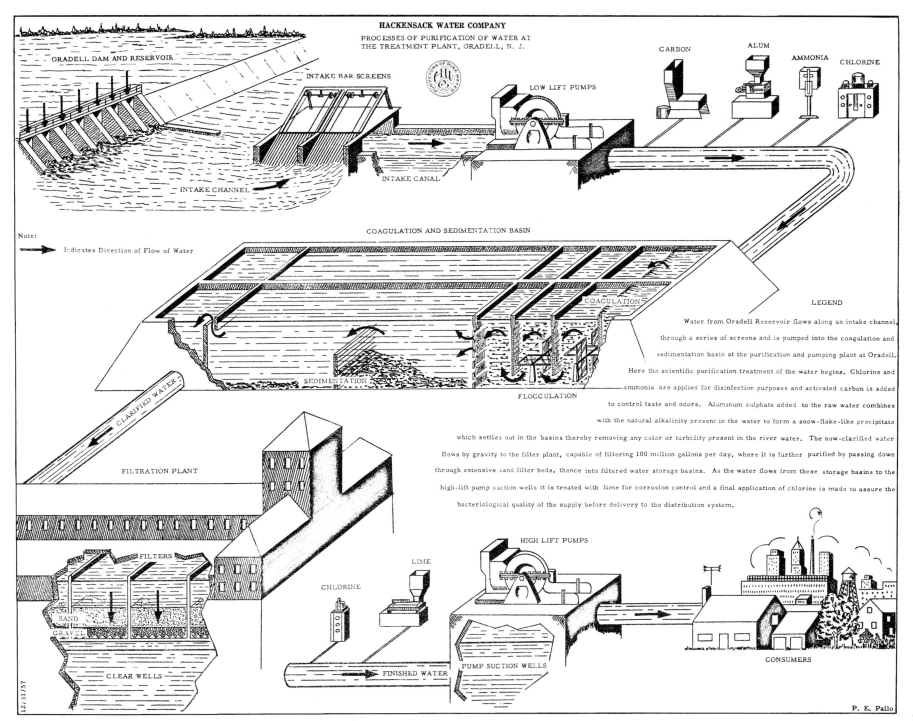

HACKENSACK WATER COMPANY

PROCESSES OF PURIFICATION OF WATER AT
THE TREATMENT PLANT, ORADELL, N. J.

ORADELL DAM AND RESERVOIR

INTAKE BAR SCREENS

LOW LIFT PUMPS

CARBON   ALUM   AMMONIA   CHLORINE

INTAKE CHANNEL

INTAKE CANAL

Note:

Indicates Direction of Flow of Water

COAGULATION AND SEDIMENTATION BASIN

COAGULATION

SEDIMENTATION

FLOCCULATION

CLARIFIED WATER

LEGEND

Water from Oradell Reservoir flows along an intake channel, through a series of screens and is pumped into the coagulation and sedimentation basin at the purification and pumping plant at Oradell. Here the scientific purification treatment of the water begins. Chlorine and ammonia are applied for disinfection purposes and activated carbon is added to control taste and odors. Aluminum sulphate added to the raw water combines with the natural alkalinity present in the water to form a snow-flake-like precipitate which settles out in the basins thereby removing any color or turbidity present in the river water. The now-clarified water flows by gravity to the filter plant, capable of filtering 100 million gallons per day, where it is further purified by passing down through extensive sand filter beds, thence into filtered water storage basins. As the water flows from these storage basins to the high-lift pump suction wells it is treated with lime for corrosion control and a final application of chlorine is made to assure the bacteriological quality of the supply before delivery to the distribution system.

FILTRATION PLANT

FILTERS

SAND

GRAVEL

CLEAR WELLS

CHLORINE

LIME

HIGH LIFT PUMPS

FINISHED WATER

PUMP SUCTION WELLS

CONSUMERS

12/31/57

P. E. Pallo

Figure 150: *The 1911 No. 7 Allis-Chalmers VTE pumping engine in the 1911 engine house, 1999. Each of the two cast-steel flywheels on the first level weighs 21 tons. Dave Frieder*

Figure 151: *Cast-iron stairway, No. 7 Allis-Chalmers VTE pumping engine, 1999. Cast-iron stairs provide access to five levels on the pumping engine in the 1911 engine house. Dave Frieder*

waterpower drove those machines originally. They were converted to electric, but most of the machinery was very old. It was old, old stuff.

My father knew a lot of the pumping machines in New Milford by the sound. I can remember him saying to me that he could hear it when they were not working well. I remember one day in 1956 we were walking in and they had just started to shut down one of the old vertical pumps because the flywheel had cracked. It was the old No. 5 or 6 in the middle, the 1898 part [see Figure 34]. Basically the whole plant started to rock in a different way. There was a different sound and they knew something had cut loose. It took time to shut it down because it wasn't a matter of just stopping them. That was it for those machines. They started to replace those monsters with electric-powered pumps because they could

get more capacity out of them. The company also upgraded because of demand. The population explosion in the area demanded more and more water during those days, so they upgraded the pumps. They realized that the Allis-Chalmers pumps could not stay forever.

"we had to rig them through the big door"

A few years before the flywheel cracked on one of the 1898 VTEs, the water company had directed Buck, Seifert & Jost to develop plans to

Figure 152: *Filtration house, east side, 1997. In 1933 the water company added garages, a machine shop, and a storage house on the east side of the 1905–1912 filter house, right (see Figure 115). The water analysis laboratory was on the second floor of the coagulant house, left. Chip Renner, "The New Milford Plant of the Hackensack Water Company," National Register Nomination*

electrify the pumping station. The cracked flywheel propelled these plans forward. The water company removed the Nos. 8 and 9 VTEs at the north end of the 1911 engine house and replaced them with the site's first electric pumps: two 30-MGD DeLaval centrifugal pumps driven by electric motors manufactured by the Ideal Electric Company (Figure 153). The water company hired Kuchar Brothers to install them. Miles Kuchar remembers installing the No. 13 pump in 1956 and the No. 14 pump in 1959 (Figure 154).

> *The DeLaval Pump Company made top-of-the-line pumps in Trenton. . . . when it was one of steel making's main places. They shipped them all over the United States and the world. The company people went down there to DeLaval to work out the specifications . . . for whatever needs they had, like the size of the*

> *motors. They worked everything out with DeLaval and bought the pumps directly from them and then we installed them.*

> *The pumps weighed 11 tons each and the 2,000-hp motors weighed 16 tons each. As part of the job we put in a 48-inch case valve that weighed 11 tons. We had to pour concrete slabs to support the electric pumps, and we had to push them through, rig them through the big door to get them in there. Once we got in the door, we used the traveling overhead crane to slide everything. We put the frame in first and then the pump and then the motor, and then we had to connect it to the 48-inch pipes under the floor. We brought them up and connected them to the pumps. The bolts were big, around 3 inches, because of the high pressure. The labor part was fairly easy, we just had to assemble everything. We had the welders there as the piping on the main flow work was all steel and most of it was welded in the field. We also had steamfitters working on that job. It took about six months to install each pump.*

The electric pumps were much simpler to operate than the early steam pumps, and they were more reliable. The water company scrapped the Nos. 5 and 6 pumps in the 1898 engine house, but it continued operating the Nos. 1, 2, 3, 10, 11, and 12 steam-driven pumps until it closed the plant. It kept operating the No. 7 VTE in the 1911 engine house into the early 1960s. Ted Hoffman remembers the debate about scrapping No. 7, and Gus Carlson's role in saving it.

> *We really owe Gus Carlson a thanks for keeping that last vertical pump, No. 7. He wanted to keep it as a backup or a historic piece, and he did not go along with taking No. 7 out. He wanted to hang onto that one. They didn't need it and he kept it.*

George Haskew remembers the company's attitude toward No. 7 after it was taken out of service.[168]

> *Removing No. 7 would have been a costly thing to do. It would have to be cut up and taken out of there and it wasn't in the way,*

Figure 153: 1911 engine house with No. 13 and No. 14 DeLaval centrifugal pumps, driven by the site's first electric motors, 1961. United Water Resources

so it was just kept and we decided to make it look good. It was pretty dirty and messy so our own people painted it. The colors that are there are as close to the original colors as we could come. We looked under the paint layers to try and find the original colors and we used them in the repainting.

"we augmented the system in all these ways"

By 1960 the water company was supplying 700,000 people and 11,000 fire hydrants with an average of 64 MGD. It operated three water supply reservoirs, four water distribution reservoirs, and eight water distribution tanks. (see *Water . . .*). As water demand continued to rise with the development

Figure 154: No. 14 DeLaval pump, 1911 engine house, 1961. Kuchar Brothers of Montvale installed the No. 13 pump in 1956 and the No. 14 pump in 1959 at the north end of the 1911 engine house, in place of the former Nos. 8 and 9 VTE pumping engines, to pump filtered water into the distribution system. The 2000 hp electric motor, behind the operator, drove the centrifugal pump, left, which had a capacity of 30 MGD. United Water Resources

boom of the early 1960s, George Buck and the directors and officers of the water company were increasingly aware that they needed to expand their pumping and filtration capacity. Since Van Buskirk Island had too little land for a major expansion, the water company began planning a new pumping station and filtration plant about one mile upriver on 40 acres of land on the east side of the Oradell Reservoir in Haworth. Buck, Seifert & Jost designed the Haworth plant with a capacity of 50 MGD and considerable room for expansion. This was the beginning of the end for the Hackensack Water Works. The water company opened the Haworth facility in 1964 with half of its initial capacity and brought more filters and pumping equipment on line as demand grew. By 1968 when Adrian Leiby wrote his history of the Hackensack Water Company, the New Milford and Haworth plants were together supplying water at an annual rate of nearly 90 MGD.

While the water company began developing additional capacity with its Haworth plant, a severe drought gripped the region. Average rainfall had been below normal since 1955, "and in the years 1963, 1964, and 1965 it was so far below normal as to threaten the area with disaster." In June 1965 Governor Richard J. Hughes "declared a state of emergency imposing restrictions on the use of water in the four northern counties of the state." George Buck led the water company's response to the drought by focusing resources on contingency plans for emergency water sources. He brought in George Haskew, a young engineer at his consulting firm, Buck, Seifert & Jost, to lead this effort at the water company. Haskew stayed with the water company for twenty-eight years and retired as its president, the position held by his mentor when he arrived (Figure 155). Haskew remembers those years:[170]

> I was first involved with the New Milford Plant and the water company in 1964 in the fall, when I still worked for the consulting firm of Buck, Seifert & Jost. I was there on a detached assignment in connection with the drought at that time. Then in the spring of 1965, I was brought over to the company as a full-time employee, first as an assistant to George Buck, the president, and then in the fall of 1965 when the chief engineer Adolph Damiano retired, I became chief engineer, and I was there until I retired in 1992. In between I had been promoted to vice president in engineering, senior vice president, executive vice president, and then eventually to president.
>
> In the 1960s Mr. Buck could see that this drought situation was going to be bad. We wanted to try to maximize the capabilities of the Hackensack River and the water supply area. We built a

Water . . .

"... supplying the Village of Hackensack and places adjacent thereto with sufficient water for extinguishing fires, culinary and other family uses, watering the streets, and such purposes as may conduce to the health and comfort of the citizens." This was the expressed purpose of the Hackensack Water Company as set forth in the corporation papers in 1869. From this modest beginning the Company has grown to become one of the largest private water supply utilities in the nation, serving 700,000 persons in 56 communities of Bergen and Hudson Counties.

To meet this ever increasing demand, the water comes from a watershed area of about 113 square miles, encircled by hills and drained by numerous streams and brooks which constitute the upper tributaries of the Hackensack River and the Pascack Brook. In this watershed area are three storage reservoirs: De Forest Lake; which impounds 5,600 million gallons; Oradell Lake, with a capacity of 3,000 million gallons, and Woodcliff Lake, which has a capacity of 900 million gallons . . . Uniformed inspectors continually patrol the watershed area, collecting samples for analyses from more than ninety points on various streams and investigating any possible sources of contamination. . . . In the laboratory at the purification plant . . . about fifteen thousand samples are examined yearly, involving some 90,000 separate chemical, biological and microscopic analyses. All of this work is done in strict accordance with the rules and regulations of the State Health Department of New Jersey.

Continuous and uninterrupted pumping operations are essential in serving the public. At the pumping Station in Oradell, steam and electric driven pumping units, with a combined rated capacity of 180 million gallons daily, are used to pump the water through more than 1,500 miles of water mains.

The residential and industrial expansion of the territory served by the Hackensack Water Company cannot proceed without an adequate water supply. By careful planning, utilization of sound engineering and scientific principles and adoption of modern processing methods, the Company will continue to meet the ever increasing demand for a potable and palatable water delivered in sufficient quality at adequate pressure.

Water: How The Hackensack Water Company Serves 700,000 People, 1960.[169]

Figure 155: *George Haskew in the New Milford filtration plant water quality laboratory in 1975. United Water Resources*

diversion station in Herschfeld Brook behind the New Milford
works and put a temporary dam in there, and I built one on the
Saddle River in Paramus that's still there. We rented wells from
farmers, like Tice's Farm in Montvale, where we had a big main up
there. We rented the wells at the golf courses in Paramus and put in
a chlorinator and laid pipe on top of the ground and tapped the

main and diverted the well water into it. There were a couple of
swim clubs years ago in Paramus that had well points. We took
water out of the sand there and put in diesel engine pumps to
repump that water and put it into the system. We augmented the
system in all these ways.

We were going to, as a last resort, take water out of Saddle
River and filter it. There was an old mill in Paterson and I bought
their filter plant, which was a pressure filter with steel tanks and
piping. I bought the whole thing: valves, pumps, tanks. We started
to move them to Paramus to set them up to filter water without a
building, just in the open if it got really bad. We never finished
that, as it didn't have to go into action.

Bergen and Hudson residents and businesses weathered the drought
"thanks to their own conservation of water and the company's long-term
planning and huge capital expenditures for reservoirs." Thanks to the company's DeForest Lake Reservoir, Rockland residents went through the
drought with practically no restrictions. Haskew credited George Wieghardt
for his foresight in building the DeForest Lake Reservoir in the 1950s:[171]

Wieghardt was the chief engineer who went to Henry de Forest
with a reservoir plan and really put his whole job and life on the
line in a way to push that, because the Thruway was coming in,
and he recognized that . . . the Thruway would just make a reservoir impossible because development would start and there
wouldn't be an opportunity for a reservoir in the future. De Forest
and the board people bought his argument. They saw the wisdom
of it and they went forward with the reservoir. Otherwise, DeForest
Lake never would have been there.

After George Haskew had consulted on the Hackensack system for a few
months, George Buck wanted his help full time at the company:

Mr. Buck took me to lunch with Adrian Leiby, who was a partner in
the Leiby law firm and secretary of the company; Bob Moraney,

who was with the de Forest law firm and board chairman of the company in later years; and Parker Ames, who was president of a company in Rockland County. They were the executive committee and that's where I was interviewed. I worked in the Weehawken office, which was the main office for everything in those days. Mr. Buck brought me on in the spring of 1965 as assistant to the president because the drought situation was worsening and he wanted help. I spent a lot of time in court because a lot of things we built, we didn't have building permits for. We went out and did them because they had to be done, and I spent a lot of time on the witness stand in the first year.[172]

The 1960's drought convinced George Buck that it was time to build the long-contemplated reservoir on the Pascack Brook above Rivervale. Allen Hazen and Hering & Fuller had first identified the potential of this area at the turn of the century, and Nicholas Hill had overseen the acquisition of much of the required land in the late 1920s before the Great Depression forced the water company to shelve its plans. With the state of emergency declared by Governor Hughes in 1965, there was virtually no opposition and the water company began excavating the site. It hired Kuchar Brothers to build the dam. Miles Kuchar remembers the work involved:

One big job we did for the water company was building Tappan Dam up in Rivervale. Before they bought the property in Old Tappan, it was a nudist colony. We had to put a berm up to divert the Hackensack River. We only poured three quarters of the dam first, and then we diverted the water through the dam part that we finished. Plus we built the new bridge. We started in 1965. It was quite a project.

The water company opened the reservoir in 1967 and named it Lake Tappan in honor of the Native American tribe that had originally inhabited the river valley.

In 1967 the water company tore down the old coal house, designed by Charles Brush and built in 1882 and 1886 as the original boiler house and coal shed on the south side of New Milford Avenue (see Figures 8, 19, and 24). The construction of the Haworth plant took some of the pressure off the New Milford Plant and enabled the water company to retire the old No. 7 Allis-Chalmers pumping engine. The rest of the plant remained fully operational and still predominantly steam powered.

Jim Flynn began working at the New Milford Plant in 1966 and stayed there until it closed twenty-three years later, when he went to work at Haworth (Figure 156). Flynn remembers the old machines and what it was like running them.[173]

I went to Bergen Technical and Vocational High School in the program for stationary engineering, and I had my license when I graduated from high school in June of 1965. I worked a few other jobs and then I went to work at the New Milford Plant for the water company in February of 1966. Fred Schelhas came to work there in April. He lived in the same town that my wife lived in and my in-laws knew his family. My father-in-law used to go fishing with his father, and I became very good friends with Fred. After I got married, Fred was the one who helped me get my first apartment and also helped me fix it. We worked at New Milford together all those years, and Fred left a year before I did. He's the best mechanic I ever met.

I was hired as an assistant fireman, and I worked my way up to assistant engineer and then to watch engineer, and from there I moved into management in the purification department. There were four people running the pumping station. There was a watch engineer, assistant watch engineer, a fireman, and an assistant fireman. The fireman's job was to run the boilers; his responsibility was to keep the steam pressure up. He had to be licensed by the state to

run the boilers, and the assistant fireman was to assist him in that capacity. My job responsibility as an assistant was to do what he needed done, cleaning the burners, adding chemicals to the boiler feed water, and other little things like keeping the place clean. When you're generating steam, you're going to get scale on the metal tubes and on the water side of the boiler. You add chemicals to eliminate scale as much as possible. We had 185 psi, twenty-four hours and 365 days a year. That would be considered medium pressure. High-pressure systems would be like the old Public Service generating stations. They were up at 1,100 or 1,200 psi.

I was an assistant fireman for probably two years, and then I moved into the engine room as an assistant engineer. The engine room had all the steam engines and the electric pumps, and I went to assist the watch engineer, whose responsibility was to run and maintain water pressure in the distribution system, and my job was to assist him in that capacity. The watch engineer used whatever tools he had, which were the different size pumps you had in the New Milford Plant, and after 1964 you also had the Haworth Plant, and you could put those pumps in service up there.

The watch engineer's office was in the engine room, and when I first came there it operated on lease lines supplied by the telephone company [Figure 157]. Lines would go into your pumping station, your booster station, your tanks, and that information would come back electronically to an instrument that you could read. All of that information came back into that office. You had instrumentation for the whole system telling you what pressures were in different areas, where your tank levels were, where your reservoir levels were, your finished water reservoir levels, and as the pressure started to come up in the system, then you would start cutting back on your pumpage. Of course, you didn't want the

Figure 156: Jim Flynn in front of the 1911 engine house, 2003. James Hogan

130

Figure 157: 1891 engine house, c. 1961. The watch engineer operated the pumping station based on pressure and water-level information that came in from key points around the system. The No. 11 Worthington pump is in the foreground. A portion of the No. 3 Allis-Chalmers pump in the 1886 section is visible through the doorway. The water company later enclosed the instrument area in a small office for the watch engineer. United Water Resources

pressure to get too high; otherwise you'd start blowing mains up throughout the whole system. The watch engineer's primary task was to make sure you maintained the system with the pumps you had available.

"Tuesday morning wash load"

Operating the system involved maintaining a balance among all its various components, and Flynn described some of the intricacies and nuances the engineers had to deal with on a daily basis:

We could tell when the demand was going to be high and when it was going to be low, just by historic information. . . . Your demand would increase in the summer because of watering grass, watering all the landscaping, increased shower usage, filling swimming pools, and so forth. We also had what we called the "morning load" that would start at 6 o'clock . . . when everybody's getting up to take a shower. Then it would die down for a little while, and then years ago we had what we used to call the "mid-morning load." That's when all the stores would start to open, and all the big stores would turn on their air conditioners, which used water for cooling. When I first started there we also had what they called a "Tuesday morning wash load," when most of the housewives would start to wash their clothes on Tuesday morning. Our next load would be the "supper load," in the evening, after 6 o'clock. Everybody would be washing dishes and taking showers, and that would last for a couple of hours, depending on where you worked.

As a watch engineer you had to be ready for all this. You had to have your tank levels up for those loads because you wouldn't want to go through the trouble of putting a big 2,000-hp motor in just to maintain that pressure for a couple of hours and then take it out. It's not cost effective to do that. In the summertime we knew in certain areas at 2 o'clock in the morning the sprinkler systems would go on around different, large offices. Since you knew that was going to happen, you would have the Franklin Lakes tank up high before 2 o'clock in the morning to meet that load condition.

The sound level in the engine room depended on which engines and which turbines you were running. You had a low growl to a high whine. If you were using the No. 12 turbine [see Figure 130], which was a high-rpm turbine, the reduction gear used to whine quite a bit. If you were running No. 10 [see Figure 108], which was a large 2,000-hp turbine, she would growl but nothing to bother you. It was a nice sound. The same was true with the No. 11 turbine. It was very quiet and when you didn't hear that noise you'd say "Uh-oh." The other steam turbine, with raw water pumps Nos. 1 and 2 [see Figure 131], she used to growl quite a bit too because of the reduction gear, but we all just got used to it.

A good watch engineer could always tell that there was something wrong, just by the sound. When I first went into the engine room, I worked with an engineer by the name of Bill Willis and he was breaking me in on the operation of all this equipment, and he was very good. One night he said to me, "we're going to show you how to get No. 11 turbine up and get it online." Before you started one of these turbines, you had to start an auxiliary lube oil pump, to pump oil all through the system before you could start turning over the turbine. He told me to get that lube oil system running on it, which I did. It was a little steam pump that would just pump the oil around. Then we went out and made our rounds, and after we came back he was sitting in there and he got up and he said, "Something doesn't sound right." I said, "What do you mean?" He said, "Something doesn't sound right," and he walked out and came back and he said, "Oh, yeah, that's right. I told you to start that little pump." Even with all the other noise in the area, he heard something that was different and that was something that I learned. A guy who was there for a while and had the experience, he could walk by a piece of equipment and say, "Something's not right."

"they said it was a maintenance nightmare"

While the No. 7 pump, manufactured and installed by the Allis-Chalmers Manufacturing Company in the engine house in 1911, was taken out of

service shortly before Flynn began working at the water works, it remained as a monument to the era of big steam engines, as he recalled.

When I first started there, No. 7 was not being used anymore [Figure 158]. I believe the last time they used it was in 1963 or 1964. No. 7 was cleaned up and not restored to running condition, but it was restored to the point that it was all cleaned and painted. All the brass parts were shined up and so forth but it was not run. Most of the engineers at that time had run No. 7. They were there quite a long time. I would hear stories about how No. 7 would operate. With a big steam engine like that, its top rpm was 20, so it moves very, very slowly, and you wouldn't want to see it go much faster than that. Those two flywheels weigh 21 tons each [see Color Plates 20–22), and if it went too much faster, they would take off on you. It could pump around 18 or 20 million gallons of water a day.

No. 7 is a vertical triple expansion reciprocating engine driving the pump. When you make steam, you're compressing steam. The higher the pressure the more compressed it would be. In a triple expansion steam engine, you're using the steam three times. It's a three-cylinder engine, and you first use the high-pressure steam in a small cylinder. As you trap the steam in there and as it starts to cool, it expands and pushes down the piston and the rod. That's where your power comes from. It's a positive displacement pump, which means whatever water comes in must go out. As the piston comes down, it's pushing the water out. As that piston comes back up, it's sucking water in. The engine side is like a car engine; you have an intake valve to let steam in, and you have to have an exhaust valve to let the steam back out after it's been used. One side of the pump is the suction side where the water comes in from the filter house through the suction well underneath, and the other is the discharge side where the water goes out into the distribution system.

Figure 158: *No. 7 Allis-Chalmers VTE pumping engine in the 1911 engine house, 1989. Dave Frieder*

From the first high-pressure cylinder the steam is exhausted into the intermediate pressure cylinder, and from there it's exhausted into a receiver and then to the low-pressure cylinder.

The first is the smallest piston because the pressure is higher. The second piston is larger, and the third is larger again. We're using the steam three times. After that low-pressure cylinder, it was pretty well down to nothing, and you would then exhaust that low-pressure side to a feed water heater, which would heat the water that went back into the boiler. The problem that you had with a piece of equipment like this is that it had to be oiled. All the pieces were moving and you had to oil them by hand or fill up oil cups and you had to do that every two hours. They said it was a maintenance nightmare and there was a lot of work that had to be done on it on a normal basis to keep it running.

"it was a beautiful pump to see running"

The No. 3 pump, manufactured by Allis-Chalmers and installed in the 1886 section of the engine house in 1915, was one of Flynn's favorites:

The No. 3 raw water pump was made by the same company that made No. 7, the triple expansion. No. 3 was a reciprocating cross-compound pump or double expansion engine, meaning it used the steam twice [Figure 159 and see Figure 104]. The steam went to the high-pressure side, then to a receiver, which would feed the low-pressure side. The high-pressure side, like any unit in the engine house, was 185 pounds. On the low-pressure side you were down in the area of 15 psi, and the lower the pressure the bigger the cylinder. The steam comes through the intake valves on each side of the piston in sequence, and as it cools it expands, and the piston slides back and forth with the cycle. The eccentric gives us the circular motion. After the steam gets used the second time, it goes into a condenser and again gets condensed back into water, and then it's pumped back into the boiler system. This pump could do about 36 million gallons per day. It operated at a low rpm, no when this piston is coming back if there's nothing there to stop it, it's going to hit the end plate. It has to be timed so that when you let the steam in, it's pushing the piston back one way. One valve has to open to let the exhaust out, then it has to close before the piston goes all the way, and another valve has to open to let a little steam in there to cushion it. Those adjustments were made by the mechanics that were maintaining all the equipment—your machinists and your maintenance mechanics.

Figure 159: The 1915 No. 3 Allis-Chalmers pump in the 1886 engine house, c. 1961. This cross-compound or double expansion uses a single blast of steam twice in high-pressure, left, and low-pressure, right, reciprocating engines visible on either side of the centrifugal pump, which has an outer housing reinforced by fins (see Figure 104). United Water Resources

more than 30 rpm. Like Nos. 1 and 2, we're looking to move volume, not pressure. It was a unique pump in that it had two reciprocating engines that would turn one centrifugal pump.

The engine portions of No. 3 have Corliss valves [Figure 160], named after the guy who invented them. Everything on it is timed. A steam engine has power on both sides of the piston, but there's also what we call cushioning. You've got to time the valve so that

Figure 160: No. 3 Allis-Chalmers pump in the 1886 engine house, c. 1961. The Corliss valve mechanism for the high-pressure reciprocating engine is visible on the right, and the centrifugal pump is on the left. United Water Resources

You had to oil every moving piece on No. 3 every hour. It had a lube oil system that fed the eccentric bearings through a flexible pipe, but you had to oil all your rods and valve gear by hand, and it took some experience and little tricks of the trade to learn how to do it. The watch engineer usually oiled No. 3, as opposed to the assistant. I have to give credit to Bill Willis; he was the one who showed me how to do it. You had to feel the crust heads and the eccentrics on No. 3 to make sure that they didn't overheat on you. You had to actually feel these parts while it was running. You had to watch the speed and put your hand on it. The eccentrics were tricky. You had to actually put your hand in there and feel it as it came around. You had to be good to oil it when it was moving. You took the oilcan and you moved it with the rod. Everything was actually by hand because you had to fill the cups. You also had to oil each one of the holes because there's a little bearing surface in there and what you would do is you'd wait for it to come back to you with the oilcan instead of chasing it. When you were good, you could just grab it and just move with it if you wanted to. You had to know what you were doing, or you could say goodbye to your hand. It was a little difficult.

We ran No. 3 right up until 1990, but that doesn't mean we ran it every day. In the wintertime, it wouldn't be used at all. To use the term that we used in there, it was last in, first out. As you were running and your demand became higher, you would put other pumps into service until it finally got to the point where you needed another one and you would use No. 3. Now when demand started going down, No. 3 was the first one coming out. So it did not run that often, only in the high-demand season, unless they had to do work on something else. But we had to keep it ready to go the rest of the year.

I was told when I started there that this type of pump was designed for the New Orleans storm water system. New Orleans is below sea level and any time it rains, all the storm water goes to these collection points and gets pumped out, otherwise New Orleans would go underwater. It was a beautiful pump to see running, all the valve gear and all the noises that you would hear from it. I ran that many times as opposed to No. 7, which I never ran. No. 3 was not that noisy. However, when you looked at this pump when it was going, you would stand there and look at it and go "Wow." I just don't want to see it go anyplace.

"No. 10 was a workhorse"

Flynn describes the steam turbines as less complicated than the reciprocating pumps, but they still had the intricacies of steam as a power source:

Nos. 1 and 2 DeLaval pumps installed in 1948 pumped 60 MGD of raw water, more than the other pumps in the plant [see Figure 131]. In our raw water we're looking to move a large volume at low pressure, maybe 10, 12, or 13 pounds. The unique thing about Nos. 1 and 2 is that one steam-driven turbine runs a reduction gear that drives two pumps. The intent when they built this unit was to be able to run one pump at a time. Each pump had a clutch on it, and the problem that they found was when you're running one pump, how were you going to pull the clutch in on the other pump when it is at a dead stop? It will break, so it was never run that way. It was always run as one unit, Nos. 1 and 2. That's what they called it, and the reason was in the early days they had the old Nos. 1 and 2 Worthington pumps in the same spot where the raw water came in, and the DeLavals replaced them.

On these turbines you're using steam to create a vacuum to fill up the chamber, to bring your water up into your pump. You have to have a vacuum on the engine because you're coming in under pressure and it's pushing it through and when it gets down to the other side, you're below 14.7, which is atmospheric pressure. Now you have to pull the steam out, so that's why you have to have a vacuum on the turbine. Once you finish using the steam, it goes into a condenser. The condenser is under a vacuum that the turbine produces, and you're cooling the steam down to water, to pump it back to the feed water to be used in the boiler again. We used the raw water as a cooling medium, so we'd pull the raw water through the condenser. On our finished water units we pulled the finished water through the condenser.

The No. 10 pump made by DeLaval in 1929 has a steam turbine that drives two pumps, which can pump out 30 MGD at about 125 psi [see Figure 108]. The physical space it takes up is a lot less than No. 7, which could do 20 million gallons a day on a good day, they told me, really pushing it. No. 10 was used during heavy demands. I ran this unit many, many times. It's a powerful unit, its 2,000 hp. The steam turbine is on one end and that's your drive unit. The power from the engine is transferred to the pumps through a gear reducer in the middle that reduces the rpm to the two pumps that pump the water out. The pumps ran at around 700 rpm. The turbine was doing about 3,600 rpm. You didn't want the pump to go that fast, so it's reduced.

The suction comes into the first pump and then it's discharged into the second pump and then it's pushed out to the distribution system. It has a cone valve, shaped like a cone that protects it from the pressure of the distribution system. Once the pressure of the pump is greater than the distribution pressure, then the cone valve will open and will allow the water to go out. It's regulated by a hydraulic cylinder that has water pressure from the distribution system. If the pump slows down, the valve can close automatically.

At the bottom there's a separator to take water out of the steam. With a rotating turbine, the steam has to be dry. You don't want to have any water particles in there because it can damage your cups on your turbine wheels. After the steam is used, it goes down into a condenser and the water that we are pumping is pulled through one side of the condenser, and on the other side the used steam gets condensed back into water. Then a pump sends the condensed water back up into the feed water heater, which goes back to the boiler. Usually No. 10 was a workhorse that would go in service and you would leave it in all summer.

The No. 12 Worthington turbine pumped 18 million gallons a day [see Figure 130]. At one time in the New Milford Plant they used to have a high-pressure system and a low-pressure system. The high-pressure system was 240 psi for the high-service area in the higher elevations, to push the water up over the hill on the Palisades, up to Fort Lee and Englewood Cliffs to go down into Weehawken. The low-pressure system was 120 psi for the low-service area in the lower elevations. No. 12 was a high-pressure pump, and in the north end of the engine house they used to have two uprights just like No. 7 that were high-pressure pumps. You had the high-pressure pipes and low-pressure pipes out in the street. It was a dual system that was hard to maintain and they wanted to eliminate it.

Around 1954 or 1955, they eliminated the high-pressure system and they put a booster station on Hillside Avenue in Alpine. We pumped the water from New Milford up to a tank on Hillside Avenue, and we had other pumps, electric pumps, that would then pump it up over the hill. Before that, in the original No. 12 configuration, you would pull through one pump at 120 psi, and discharge through the second pump, and then you would pump out at 240 psi. When they went to a low-pressure system only, they made it into two separate pumps; they eliminated going from one pump to the other and both pumps pumped out at 120 psi. They could have changed the reduction gear, but that was very, very expensive, so this was the route that the company took at that time. No. 12 made a lot of noise—the reduction gear whined a lot.

"a centrifugal pump is a little safer to operate"

The electric pumps took a lot less work to operate and maintain, as Flynn recalled:

The Nos. 13 and 14 DeLaval pumps were driven by Ideal Company electric motors; each one is 2,000 hp [see Figures 153 and 154]. They ran at 4,160 volts and pumped 30 MGD each. You're going to have maintenance on any piece of equipment, but there was less maintenance on the electric units. You had to periodically change brushes and clean them. It's like anything else that creates heat. You're going to have wires that fail, that have to be taken care of. It's like on your car, your alternator or generator has to be rewired once in a while. The impeller rings, sitting on all the bearings, would wear—we actually call them "wear rings."

The water came up through the bottom, went into an impeller in the middle, and then it was pumped out the other side. In centrifugal pumps, as the impeller is turning it's creating a vacuum in the middle of the impeller—a negative pressure—and the water rushes to it. As the impeller throws the water out, that's where you get your pressure and your volume. The faster it goes, of course, the more you're going to pump. These were constant-speed pumps, and the way you control it is you would pull down on the discharge valve in the back and let water go out. The reason why centrifugal pumps were used instead of positive displacement pumps, like No. 7, is that

whatever comes in the positive displacement pump goes out, and the pressure is always pulsating. If you start the pump up and the outgoing valve is closed, it's just going to build up pressure and something's going to break. Usually positive displacement pumps are used when you want metering or when you want a chemical application.

A centrifugal pump is a little safer to operate. As you start it up, it has slippage. If you're not pushing the water out, nothing else is going to come in. It'll build up pressure and once the pressure is built up, the cone valve opens again, and the water goes out into the system. You read how much water is going out through meters on the main line outside. The water from Nos. 13 and 14 went out to the main transmission line, and it all went through a magnetic meter out there, so all you had to do was a little math and you knew what was pumping what. The electric pumps were more economical to run. On a typical shift day you would usually have Nos. 13 or 14 running and one of the steam units, maybe No. 11, and these three would pump filtered water to the distribution system. Then you would have two raw water pumps, Nos. 1 and 2, pulling raw water in and pumping it up to the coagulation basin.

Several of the smaller pieces of equipment in the engine house are historic, like the DC generators in the 1882 section that powered the traveling cranes and some of the lights, and the two small Worthington steam engines in the 1886 section of the engine house. As Flynn recalled, the watch engineers had to know how to run all of them:

The small Worthingtons are single, reciprocating engines running two-stage air compressors. We would use these occasionally to supply extra air to the shops, the machine shop and the carpentry shop and so forth. When you had to turn over the basin, we had an air-operated gun, so you needed a large amount of air, and that's when we would use these. We would also run them when they were cleaning the boiler, because they would use an air gun to clean the *tubes. These were not run every day, only once in a while. At the time they had no electric air compressors and you always had two of everything for backup.*

"hard on your family life"

Work at the pumping station was demanding, but Flynn and the other men developed ways to compensate:

The engine room was a hard place to keep clean. . . . Each one of your assistant engineers had a pump or an area that they had to keep clean, dust, oil, and so forth. And the watch engineers had their little part that they had to take care of also. The heavy main-tenance was done by a maintenance crew, painting or scraping and all that stuff, but it was done in a clean way. Our management at that time used to say that we had a place where we were actu-ally giving something to people that they had to ingest, and if the place didn't look clean, then it would give the wrong impression. So one of the things we had to do was keep the place clean.

Most of the guys who worked in the engine room had to like to do it because it was shift work, hard on your family life. Every two weeks you would rotate to a different shift. One of the things we did learn is that it was better not to work with the same guy all the time. On my rotation I would work with one engineer for four weeks, another engineer for two weeks, and another engineer for

two weeks. After working four weeks with one engineer, you get to where you've discussed all you want to discuss, you get to where you talk about your personal life up to a point and you say, "Okay, that's it." You don't want to come in and say, "Oh, what a day I've had at home today." You don't want to talk about that, so you get to a point where you can come in and work the midnight shift and you look at each other and you don't say two words. So it was good working with a different engineer or, in my case, when I was the engineer, different assistant engineers because a little variety . . . was good. If you have the same partner all the time, it's not good.

I advocated that the assistant engineer who I worked with knew as much as he possibly could and I would teach him as much as I could because it was better for me then. It was easier to run a shift when a guy knew as much as you did if he could, because you'd be doing something and something else could happen and he would know what to do. And fortunately, we had good people working there, and most of us did know what to do when the guy wasn't there or taking care of another problem. You tried to make the eight hours go by and have a little bit of fun, as we say. You tried to make your job a little more interesting to each other. I know that at one time, we had almost every steam engine that was ever invented in that building, so it was a good education for young guys who wanted to get into that steam engineering part of the their life.

Chapter 6

The Consumer Is the Best Indicator of Water Quality

By the 1960s the laboratory in the filtration house had acquired a lot more equipment and more people worked there (Figures 161 and 162). While the New Milford Plant was predominantly a male workplace, women found opportunities for rewarding work in the laboratory. Peter Pallo (see Figure 133), the supervisor of water purification, sketched a layout of the lab that illustrated some of the complexity of the analytical activities performed on a daily basis by the staff (Figure 163).

Figure 161: New Milford Plant Laboratory, c. 1966. The water quality laboratory provided rewarding work opportunities for women in an otherwise male workplace. This view toward the northeast shows the distillation and extraction and the media preparation bench on the left, and the chemical and mineral analysis bench on the right in the rear (see Figure 163). The staff, from left to right: Chief Chemist Ed Mullen, Chemist Ann Willis, an unidentified assistant, Laboratory Assistant Mike Berado, and Laboratory Technician Louise Vandebeek. United Water Resources

Figure 162: New Milford Plant Laboratory, c. 1966. This view toward the southeast corner shows the chemical and mineral analysis bench (see Figure 161). Laboratory Technician Louise Vandebeek is on the left, Chemist Ann Willis is on the right by the mineral analysis equipment, and an unidentified assistant is in the center by the chemical analysis equipment. United Water Resources

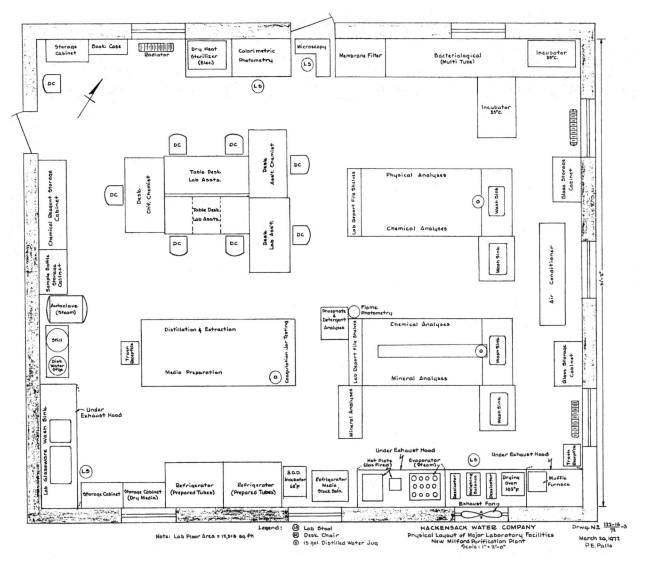

Inside the figure (floor plan labels):

Storage Cabinet · Book Case · Radiator · Dry Heat Sterilizer (Elec) · Colorimetric Photometry · Microscopy · Membrane Filter · Bacteriological (Multi Tube) · Incubator 35°C.

DC · LS

Incubator 35°C.

Chemical Reagent Storage Cabinet · Table Desk Lab Assts. · Desk Chf. Chemist · Desk Asst. Chemist · Desk Lab Asst. · Table Desk Lab Assts.

DC · DC · DC · DC · DC · DC

Lab Report File Shelves · Physical Analyses · Chemical Analyses · Wash Sink · Glass Storage Cabinet

Sample Bottle Storage Cabinet · Autoclave (Steam) · Still · Dist. Water Stg. · Air Conditioner · Wash Sink

Under Exhaust Hood · Distillation & Extraction · Media Preparation · Trash Receptacle · Coagulation Jar Testing · Phosphate Detergent Analyses · Flame Photometry · Chemical Analyses · Lab Report File Shelves · Mineral Analyses · Wash Sink · Glass Storage Cabinet

Lab Glassware Wash Sink · Wash Sink · Mineral Analyses

LS · Storage Cabinet · Storage Cabinet (Dry Media) · Refrigerator (Prepared Tubes) · Refrigerator (Prepared Tubes) · B.O.D. Incubator 68°F · Refrigerator Media Stock Soln. · Under Exhaust Hood · Hot Plate (Gas Fired) · Evaporator (Steam) · LS · Desiccator · Weighing Balance · Desiccator · Drying Oven 103°F · Under Exhaust Hood · Muffle Furnace · Trash Receptacle · Exhaust Fan

Note: Lab Floor Area = 12,318 sq. ft.

Legend: LS Lab Stool · DC Desk Chair · 13 gal. Distilled Water Jug

HACKENSACK WATER COMPANY
Physical Layout of Major Laboratory Facilities
New Milford Purification Plant
Scale: 1" = 2'-0"

Drwg. Nº 122-16-3 / 72
March 26, 1972
P. E. Pallo

Figure 163: *"Hackensack Water Company, Physical Layout of Major Laboratory Facilities, New Milford Water Purification Plant, March 26, 1972. P. E. Pallo." As superintendent of water treatment, Peter Pallo oversaw the operation of the water quality laboratory, and his floor plan illustrates the complexity of the analyses necessary to maintain water quality. United Water Resources*

When Ed Mullen decided to leave in 1968, Barry Schwartz joined the laboratory staff as chief chemist and continued working for the water company for thirty-two years (Figure 164). Like several other employees, Schwartz came to the water company through the engineering firm of Buck, Seifert & Jost. When Peter Pallo retired, Schwartz became superintendent of water treatment. In his twenty-two years at the New Milford filtration plant, Schwartz was involved with every facet of its operation and was responsible for complying with new regulations as the U.S. Environmental Protection Agency and the New Jersey Department of Environmental Protection assumed increasing roles in assuring water quality. Barry recalls his years with the company:[174]

> *I started working at the Hackensack Water Company on December 16, 1968. I had just come out of the army looking for a position, and I first started to work at the engineering firm of Buck, Seifert & Jost.*

. . . I worked in their laboratory in Englewood Cliffs for about a year and a half and a position opened up at the water company for a chief chemist and I was accepted for that position and stayed there for the next thirty-two years.

Figure 164: Barry Schwartz, New Milford laboratory, c. 1976. Barry Schwartz started working at the New Milford Plant as chief chemist in 1968, became superintendent of water treatment, and worked for the water company for thirty-two years, retiring as director of water quality and regulatory affairs. In this view in the recently expanded west wing of the laboratory, Barry is injecting a water sample into a gas chromatograph to analyze it for pesticides under newly issued water quality rules. United Water Resources

When I started as chief chemist in 1968, the lab occupied 1,200 square feet of the east wing of the building and there were about thirteen people involved in the lab: chemists, technicians, sanitary inspectors, and the laboratory assistants who prepared the chemicals for the bacteriological assays and kept the place nice and clean, and also made the coffee. As chief chemist I was in charge of the whole lab, including sanitary inspectors as well as the laboratory personnel. I was trained by my predecessor, Ed Mullen, who retired and afterwards consulted for Elizabethtown Water, and it took about a year for me to get comfortable in the position.

As chief chemist, I had the responsibility for the treatment chemicals and adjusting them as necessary to maintain the water quality. The filtration plant ran seven days a week, twenty-four hours. Back in the 1960s there were two people on shift in the filtration plant and four people on shift in the pumping station, there were six people employed, in each of three shifts a day. That's a total of eighteen people every day to operate the New Milford Plant. Then there were the managers, the patrol force, the laboratory people, and the clerical staff. Peter Pallo was the superintendent and he was my boss. My job included monitoring the plant process to determine if any changes or adjustments were needed in the treatment chemicals, whether it was the coagulant, disinfectant, or the pH adjustment.

On a typical day I would start by looking over the results of the filtration process from the previous day and making sure everything was properly maintained. Then I walked out to the filter operator's office, which is at the other end of the plant from the laboratory, and checked over the logs to see what the treatment was, what they were doing. Then I would go back to the lab and make sure the samples were being properly maintained and that everybody showed up for work. If there was anybody out sick, then you'd have to adjust the schedule. Then I would take a walk outside to the basin to make sure the flocculators were properly working. If it was a nice day, you always walked along the wall there, the parapet, and just checked that the settling was properly maintained. Then I'd go about my normal work of maintaining the logs, the records, ordering chemicals for the laboratory, and doing the general administration. There were also research projects going on, in terms of new processes, and I would oversee those as well.

Running the laboratory meant interacting with colleagues in the water industry and dealing with the public, as Barry recalls:

There was always a camaraderie between different utilities in terms of solving problems and answering questions. There was a good rapport among the people at the Hackensack Water Company, the North Jersey District Water Supply Commission, and the Passaic Valley Water Commission. We would all get together at these locations and talk, and if there was a problem you couldn't handle, you could ask for advice. It was also done through the New Jersey section of the American Water Works Association, which met routinely throughout the year, and you established the contacts and kept a rapport that way. There was a lot of communication of information with different utilities.

On occasion we'd have public meetings. There were rate hearings, when they proposed rate increases, and we would have to go to public hearings. We'd have public tours of the plant where people wanted to see the plant and we would have school groups. People were most of all interested in water purity and how it was maintained. We always emphasized that the water was safe to drink, even though today, you wouldn't say it anymore because of the potential liability. If there were college students from an engineering school, it could be Fairleigh Dickinson or Manhattan College, they would want to know everything, especially the plant process. The customers were more concerned about their drinking water. Why was the water cloudy? Why was it full of iron? What causes problems? Why does the pressure change? They would be more concerned about their individual need for water rather than about the process.

If there was a problem such as a large main break or a failure of the plant, then the press would come in. But then we had special people who would handle that, a public relations department. Once in a while they would ask me, when there was a question that was technical and they couldn't answer, they would say, "Talk to this reporter," and [I'd] tell him technically what the situation was.

We were doing a job for the public, producing a drinking water supply, so we were involved in something that was important. But on a day-to-day basis, it was like any other job. You'd have staff meetings that you'd attend and provide input and look at research. You followed through on what you had to do, like answering customer questions and complaints. I'd get several calls from customers on a daily basis. The CSB, our Central Service Bureau, handled all the leaks and customer complaints. If they had a tough one, they would send it to the laboratory. I'd talk to the customers. There were some people who wanted information on water quality, about hardness, about fluoride levels. Sometimes they wanted a report. Many companies were using water for processes, which we called process water, and they needed a monthly report on water quality, so we'd send it out with a cover letter each month as to what the water quality was and that was all done with a clerical staff who actually had to type up a letter. They'd use a real typewriter.

A full inspection of the steam engines was the highlight of the tours we gave. We actually would take people up all the way on top of No. 7 and walk around there. The steam engines required a lot of hands-on operation. The operators were always changing the speed, monitoring the vibrations. It required a lot more input on the operator's part than an electric engine does. You just push a button and an electric engine goes on, and that's it, you're finished. Steam engines required a lot more lubrication, monitoring, and they were much more interesting to observe. I always liked the steam engines when I was there. I never saw the triple expansions operate, but I did see the No. 3 pump operate and that was interesting to watch because every part of that engine moved. Every linkage, every arm was moving at that time, very slowly. There wasn't a high output of water, but it was very interesting to watch. In the old days, they would actually keep their coffee pot on the manifold because the condensed steam would keep it nice and hot. There were no hot plates back in those days. More recently they kept a pot of lubricating oil up there to keep it warm to make it flow easily.

"we basically followed the entire sequence of the water flow"

The water company's purification efforts involved the entire system: the water sources, the treatment processes, the distribution network, and the consumers, as Barry describes:

In purification we basically followed the entire sequence of the water flow. Raw water is essentially nonpotable water that's coming from streams and tributaries like the Hackensack River and Pascack Brook. It contains algae particles and silt that has to be removed, plus it contains some bacteria, which may be harmful. The process begins by removing these contaminants. It starts with the application of chemicals to coagulate and remove sediment and silt to clarify the water, and the addition of disinfectants, chlorine, and ozone today, to ensure disinfection. Then filtration removes any contaminants in the water supply left over from the coagulation process and produces high-quality, clear drinking water. The final treatment is to make sure the water is stable with respect to corrosion and scale forming. It's also to assure that the

water remains potable in distribution. Distribution water is drinking water and it has to be maintained, and as long as the water is under pressure it could not be contaminated from the outside, so as long as the integrity has been maintained in distribution, and the residual is present, the water is going to be very safe to drink. The residual chlorine level is very important to ensure water quality is being maintained. That's why a main break is a serious problem, because then you lose the pressure and the potential for contamination is greater. A main break has to be quickly repaired and restored to full service to assure that the water supply has not been compromised in terms of any contamination.

There were three major areas of collection of water samples for the lab. The first was the watershed, the raw water source for the water supply. The second was the plant process, the water that was being processed from the water source. Samples from the various processes had to be collected and tested to make sure that the treatment process was properly maintained. The third was the drinking water in the consumer distribution system. So the three areas were source water, plant water/process water, and distribution system water. The operators of the plant did their own collection of the plant and process samples. The sanitary inspectors collected samples from the watershed and the distribution system, so we could test it to assure that there was no contamination within the watershed and that the water was potable in distribution. Back in the early days of the water company, there was a lot of farmland in this area with outhouses that had to be inspected to make sure that the proprietors maintained them properly, and that was also the job of the sanitary inspectors. . . . All these things were done by the laboratory and the sanitary inspectors to ensure that the water supply was as good as could be.

The two main streams supplying water are the Hackensack River and the Pascack Brook and their tributaries. In those days there were about fifty-two samples that were collected throughout the watershed every week to ensure that the raw water supply was not being affected by any contamination or excessive runoff. The collection stations all had a series of numbers that referred to the different streams. The Hackensack River numbers started with 100, the Pascack Brook with 300, and the Tenakill Creek and its tributaries with 200. If the testing indicated a problem, then we'd do further inspection to try to locate the contamination. It could be an overflow sewer, a discharge from a septic tank in certain areas of Bergen County, or perhaps an industrial discharge that wasn't permitted.

Usually about thirteen sample bottles a day would come in from the watershed four days a week for a total of fifty-two. There were a series of bottles with different purposes, chemical, biological, and microscopic examination for algae, and these were analyzed according to a schedule. Each sample could typically be a couple of liters, depending on the particular assay needed. It was a big job and the cases were heavy; you had five or six gallons of water being collected and it was good exercise for the sanitary inspectors to go out. It was a nice job because it was all outdoors, when it was nice weather. Of course, when it rained or snowed, it wasn't a very nice job, but still they had to get the samples.

"if the complaints are very low, you know you're doing a good job"

Monitoring the distribution system was particularly important to ensure that the water quality was maintained from the filtration plant to the consumer, as Barry describes.

Back in the early days of my work there were maybe eighty-five different locations where the distribution system water was sampled weekly, and this was done under regulations by the authorities that required certain testing, especially for residual chlorine and microbiological factors, to ensure that the water was potable. You collected from places that were normally open: police stations, fire stations, stores, libraries. Places that were normally open during the week that you could get a sample without bothering people. The sanitary inspectors had a regular schedule on a daily basis and were known by the townspeople. They had to be warned in case anything happened to the water supply so they'd have to be able to answer those questions about what was occurring should there be a storm or hurricane, a broken pipe, a main burst, etc. They would have to be aware of that and would have to be able to respond to the people in the street as to what was happening. The meter readers [who] met the public also had to be aware of some major aspects of the water company in case they were asked questions. That, today, is kind of missing with automated meter reading. In the regular contact with utilities today, everything is done either by mail, Internet, or telephone with no personal contact.

When water enters the distribution system it is very high quality, but you get some deterioration as it passes through the mains and picks up some debris from corrosion, but it's very slight. One of the reasons for testing water in distribution is to make sure that if there are any problems with the piping, you can correct them by flushing the pipes or lining them with cement to ensure that the customer is getting the best possible water. One of the best indicators of clouded water is consumer complaints. If the complaints are very low, you know you're doing a good job. If the complaints start to increase, then you know something is wrong. So the consumer is the best indicator of water quality in terms of aesthetics.

The original distribution pipes were made out of wood of two types of construction. One was a thick piece of log with a hole through the center of it and the second was made of staves like a pickle barrel. In the barrel type, the planks were held together with wire and tarred to make it watertight. In the old days when the pipes were wood and they had a fire, they would have to go out and fight the fire with water from the distribution systems. They would find the wooden main in the street and actually drill a hole in it and use that water supply to fight the fire. Then they would put a wooden plug in the hole . . . and that's why we call a hydrant a fire-plug today. There are very few wooden mains left, but you can find a couple in some old areas, and they've probably lasted over 120 years. After wood came cast iron, then ductile iron, which is more flexible and doesn't crack as easy as cast iron when the ground shifts. Today when a cast-iron main or ductile-iron main is found to be heavily corroded, you can go in there with a mechanism and scrape out the corrosion and then apply a cement lining to that main to make it essentially good for another fifty years. In new piping today we're seeing a lot of plastics being used in distribution mains, like polyethylene and PVC.

"seasonal changes affect the water quality"

To monitor the water quality at the different points in the system, the lab staff conducted a series of tests on various conditions in the water, including tastes and odors, turbidity, and bacteria levels. Barry described how the lab tracked the variations as seasonal changes affected the water quality.

When the samples come into the lab, there are several water tests that indicate things about the quality of the water. We do what we call the T&O test, for taste and odor, which is a very important part of the testing program. There are very scientific procedures to determine the taste and odor levels of a drinking water. The lab staff had to be trained as to what the odors were, how to identify them, and the degree of level of the odor. Certain algae, for example, can give the water a certain odor, so by smelling the water, which was a typical task we did, you can tell if algae were beginning to appear in the water. A microscopic examination would then indicate the type of specie you had in the sample. The odor test is very important, especially since the consumer will easily detect an odor in the water.

Besides taste tests, there are taste contests in drinking water today among the water utilities. When the Haworth plant was first put on line, the Hackensack Water Company won an award for the best-tasting water. New York City has won because of their spring-like water and some towns actually bottle their own water and sell it because it's such good quality water. It's more or less a gimmick, but they are very proud of their water supply.

When I first went to work in the lab there were no computers, so everything was logged in manually onto a big log sheet that was put into a binder and kept as a record. You'd go back to refer to it and then at the end of the year, we'd do a compilation of the daily data into an annual log for the files. Once computers came along we got spreadsheets that made things much easier to maintain and track for trends in water quality.

Seasonal changes affect the water quality as well as the number of samples required for testing, and there are different seasonal water quality aspects that have to be monitored and treated. In the wintertime, you get ice covering the reservoir and algae can grow under the ice and produce odors that have to be carefully monitored. In the spring, the runoff from heavy rains increases the levels of cloudiness and turbidity in the water. In the summertime you may get heavy algae growths that would require additional treatment and monitoring of the treatment process. With the warmer water in summertime, taste is always more prevalent and customers can detect odors much sooner.

Algae are a major aspect for an assay in any surface water supply at all times of the year. Most algae are harmless, but they can create a treatment problem in terms of taste and odor as well as clarity. Some algae are coagulated and settle in the coagulation basin, but some have to be filtered, and they can clog a filter and require additional wash water to be used to cleanse it.

Turbidity is the cloudiness of the water, how clear the water is. A turbid condition can come from algae, small particles, silt, and debris in the water. Some types of dissolved air can come out of solution and create cloudy water, especially in the wintertime. Turbidity is measured by a particle deflecting light off its surface. Turbidity is heavily regulated by the EPA and is limited today to 0.3 turbidity units. When I first started working in the lab the limit was actually 5.0, then it went down to 1.0, then it went down to 0.5 and now it's 0.3. It became more stringent as the process of treating water became more and more advanced and was able to handle and produce waters with a lower and lower turbidity.

The water supply is normally turbid because it is raw water and it's silty. In a testing procedure, some of the particles may be digested to see exactly what they're made out of. For example, iron or manganese particles can be put into a solution to be able to analyze them. If you get turbid water in samples from the plant, maybe the filtration process is being affected by some factors, so you'd want to check that out. In distribution, turbid water is an indicator of some problem in the treatment process or some sloughing off of debris from the mains.

Monitoring for bacterial problems in the source, process, and distribution water was a key concern of Barry's and the lab staff, as he recalls:

Bacteria itself will not cause turbidity, and because it's such a minute particle, it doesn't actually reflect light. Because you can't see bacteria, assays for it are done by chemical means. You have to either grow bacteria to see colonies or go through a series of chemical tests to see how they react with different chemicals and to determine the speciation of the bacteria. In water treatment, there are two major areas of microbial assays for bacteria. The first is for coliform bacteria, which since the 1900s have been the indicator organisms for any pathogens. Coliforms are ubiquitous throughout nature; they're in the intestinal tracts of animals and they're an indicator of potential contamination. The second major test is the plate count. Plate count is a general indication of normal bacteria in drinking water supplies. You want less than 500 colonies, or bacteria, per milliliter of water supply. If you achieve that, then your water supply is probably a good quality and you're doing a good job in treatment. If the plate count exceeds 500 colonies per mil of water, it's not harmful per se, but it may indicate that something is amiss in the treatment process or in distribution, and this should be examined, and if necessary you can then take steps like flushing the area to make sure that the water supply is being maintained.

Coliforms are relatively easy to assay for. There are several different tests and it takes normally twenty-four hours to get a result. There's a whole host of bacteria that can be in drinking water, but the coliforms are the indicator organism and if they're absent, you can be sure that the water is potable. Drinking water is not sterilized, it's only disinfected, so drinking water does contain some bacteria, but these are harmless. Just like bleu cheese contains bacteria; nobody thinks twice about eating bleu cheese, although some people might. You test for bacteria in the raw water, and then in the filtered water you can see how effective the filtration was. The raw water is going to have levels of bacteria that are much higher than the treated water, and therefore you do a more sensitive assay or test on the treated water.

The main treatment for any pathogen organism in the water is the application of a disinfectant, whether it is ozone or chlorine. The first use of chlorine in drinking water supply was in Jersey City in 1908 and ever since that time the instance of deaths from cholera and typhoid have dropped precipitously, until the 1950s when essentially there was no more typhoid and cholera in the United States. The application of chlorine to drinking water is considered one of the most important public health benefits in the history of the world. Ozone is a form of oxygen that is very highly active and it essentially destroys all microbes. It's used now in the Haworth plant in addition to chlorine. So it provides another level of treatment to assure a level of quality not seen before. Ozone also assists in the clarification of water because it provides what is known as microflocculation, which is the ability to remove certain organic compounds in the water.

"women . . . were more dependable and stayed around"

The water quality laboratory historically provided opportunities for women that didn't exist elsewhere in the male-dominated water supply industry, and Barry appreciated their contributions to the quality and constancy of the lab operation.

About three quarters of the lab crew were women. All the technicians were women and the chemist that worked along side me was a woman. Mike Berado and the sanitary inspectors were the only men there. The company liked to hire women for lab positions because, I think, they were more dependable and stayed around. It was probably for them a second career. They were finished raising a family and they were living in the area and they tended to come to work every day. Because the lab was scheduled work, you really couldn't tolerate anybody with excessive absences. The clerical help were mostly women: secretaries, stenographers. I have to say that the staff there had very little absenteeism. The shift work was all men. That was more heavy work, though some women did try later on to work in maintenance.

MaryFrances Schwartz, who began working for the water company as MaryFrances Mangipane in 1967 and later became Barry's wife, recalled the prevalence of women at the lab.[175]

I went to work as a technician in the lab when I was around 25, after working in a hospital. The lab was an interesting place and the company liked to hire older women to work there because they were more stable. With regard to salaries, being a woman at the company was really not that much of a concern because there was a union. There were five lab women and we were a pretty close group. Anne Willis was a chemist and the four lab technicians [were] all women. Anne Willis was one of the first women to have a college degree in chemistry at that time [see Figures 161 and 162, and Figure 170]. Barry was the only man except for Michael Berardo, who was a laboratory assistant. Mike was interesting because he was a laborer in the construction gang and he got hurt and couldn't do his job any more so he transferred to the lab where he could do a job, and he stayed there many years.

Things changed as the technology become more advanced and they needed to hire chemists who could understand the chemistry behind the equipment, as opposed to just technicians. Then the lab expanded and the company hired male chemists like Louis Briganti, who started out as a chemist and then became a supervisor chemist and eventually chief chemist. The company doubled the lab in 1974 and added another wing in 1978.

"you can do almost anything if you set your mind to it"

In 1974 Pat Hoffman (Figure 165) went to work in the office of the water company's subsidiary in Rockland County, the Spring Valley Water Company, as Pat Herman. She soon joined the laboratory staff and worked there for sixteen years. In 1992 she married Dan Hoffman, the superintendent of the New Milford Plant (see Figure 181). Pat's recollections provide an interesting perspective of working as a woman in the male-dominated utility business.[176]

I started working . . . in 1974 in the office of the Spring Valley Water Company, which was a subsidiary of Hackensack Water. Spring Valley Water had a strong family atmosphere when I was there. Hackensack Water was also very family oriented, especially certain parts of it like the New Milford people. They really helped each other and worried about each other and

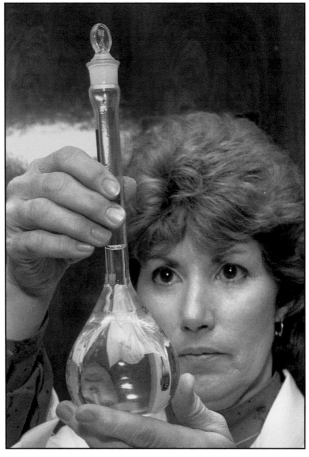

Figure 165: *Pat Hoffman, 1988. After collecting water samples from around the watershed, Pat became a technician at the New Milford Plant laboratory and worked there for over twenty years. This photograph of Pat examining a water sample appeared in an article on "unseen chemical contamination" in New Jersey's underground water supplies. Photograph by Richard Raska; Gordon Bishop, "Pollution on Tap,"* Newark Star Ledger, *May 15, 1988*

their families. Eventually it had to change because we were told that it shouldn't be family, that it was a business. But it started out very family and for the most part right to the end we still tried to keep it that way.

From the office there I just kept going into different jobs, and I ended up being a sample collector, and I went around to various wells and schools and businesses and collected water samples each week, each day, and brought them down to the lab. I also worked with the sanitary inspectors, but they did more of the emergencies or the special checking. I did the daily and the monthly sampling. The state requirements say that every area has to be tested regularly, so if you're supplying water from all these different areas, you have to take a sample in that area within a period of time.

At the company in those days the women mainly worked [in] the offices and the men did the other type jobs. It always seemed to be a man-dominated company. I would say that throughout the company they really tried to keep men in all the key roles. But things probably will be changing. They have to change. Women tried various jobs. Up in Spring Valley we had a woman that finally got to be out in the yard with the pipes and the supplies. She drove the big pipe trucks. I had started out in the office, and then I decided that the office didn't pay and decided to go for the outdoor collector jobs which paid more, but that was a man thing, too. I had to break into that. They really thought it should stay all men, so I had to show that I could do it.

Both the woman truck driver and I were new in these jobs. . . . We were union and we had seniority, so they really couldn't say no unless they took the job away. You had a right to try it. If you succeeded you could keep it, and luckily, we did, because we were determined that we were going to. A lot of women are happy in the office and that's fine, but I always wanted to do different things and learn more. I also was supporting a family by myself with no help, so I had to try and find jobs that would pay a little better and the outside jobs did. I got close to all the people there because I would do the job and others would be there to assist if they thought you needed it. I was determined, as other women were, that we were going to do it. And we did. You can do almost anything if you put your mind to it and set your mind to it.

"it was hard at first"

Pat found that collecting samples around the watershed was often challenging, as she recalls:

The collectors had to have two sets of bottles for bacteria types, and you did other tests from the wells. You had to collect various bottles for the various tests. Some were brown bottles that the chemists would use for different things. It depended on the test and where you took the sample. Some samples were more complicated than others. You did the wells once a month and you had to climb down into the well to get the samples. You had to make sure you took enough water for all the different tests that they might need. All the wells in Spring Valley were divided up into so many a week,

so that within a month's period you could test all the wells. A lot of Rockland County water is supplied by wells and we had a lot of them up there that had to be tested.

It was hard at first, but I had the cooperation of all the ones out in the field. . . . The hardest thing was learning where all the well sites were because they give you a big, black logbook and you had to try and find where you were going to go. They wanted me to prove that I could find them, and they were all in these sites that weren't obvious. The logbook would tell you whereabouts they were, and you had an area for the day that you knew it would be within a certain area. But you had to find them. It was okay after you got to know the wells, but they were down off of Route 202 down in the woods and all these outer areas like the Ramapo well field that was up in Hillburn. That was all the way back in the woods. So you wouldn't ordinarily know where they were.

There were times I felt unsafe going out to the woods, because they were full of snakes. You had copperheads and rattlers, especially in certain sections, and you had to be careful. The Ramapo well field was in an area that had drug people and stuff, so you'd see the needles there. You just had to be very careful. I think one of the big fears was if you went down into the wells that you would be shut in, because the Ramapo well field has all these great big cement vaults, and you climb down metal ladders and you'd be way down, and the guys used to say if anybody goes down there it could be the end, because you just weren't sure. Some of the places, if the guys were in the area they would check to see if I was all right and if I knew everything I had to. We had a patrol force that watched the watersheds and guarded the water company and all of us and made sure everything went all right around the plants. For the most part, we all worked very closely together.

"I felt that it was a very important job"

Pat saw the laboratory as an opportunity for interesting work and advancement. She and the other lab women took their jobs very seriously and the water company counted on their reliability to get the essential testing done:

After about two years as a sample collector there was an opening at the lab, so I took courses at Rockland Community College, and then I applied and took the test for a lab technician, and started down in the New Milford Plant. The lab was in the same building as the filtration plant, and they had a separate trailer attached to it because we had so much machinery and stuff that had to be used. We would go up the stairs in the filtration plant to get into the lab part, and we did some testing down in the trailer as well.

When I started in the lab it was at a time when women didn't have the key jobs. You could be a technician. Then it got so there were a couple of women chemists that had graduated and they got to work there. Toward the end, I was the only woman technician and there was one chemist that was a woman and one supervisor . . . Cheng Lusong. All the women really took their jobs seriously and wanted to do the best that they could, and I think they were very much into their jobs, and worrying about how the results would come out and how they had done the testing.

I felt that it was a very important job, and I felt that the samples had to be done right because a lot depended on it. You were supplying water to thousands of people, and you wanted to know that it was right, and as a sample collector, if you took the samples wrong, you might be jeopardizing people, and they needed the water, and schools needed it. So I took the job very seriously and wanted to do the best I could. And then going down into the lab being in the bacteria department I took that very seriously. Maybe

more so than the other departments there because I felt it was very important. Not that each thing you do with water isn't important, but if there was bacteria in it that could affect people's lives, and hospitals and other critical places are being supplied, so you want to be sure that everything is right. I maybe took longer than some to do those tests, but I wanted to make sure they were done right.

"there were times when we worked around the clock"

The laboratory work required a special dedication to meet all the testing requirements, as Pat remembers:

When we arrived in the morning everybody would greet each other. We all worked very closely that way, especially in the beginning. But you pretty much had to get to work because the work was always there, and you never knew what you were coming into and you didn't know what happened the night before, if there was anything special, so everybody pretty much started into work. When I started there were four technicians and three or four chemists. There were three supervisors—one main and two others—and there was one woman who handled the switchboard and the official paperwork that had to go in and out of the lab. Then the numbers went down and they didn't replenish them. We all just did the work. We were divided into departments. The samples first came into the pH department, and then there was the alkalinity department. There were the metals and bacteria departments, and then they had the chemists separate where they did the advanced tests. Normally you had a set area to work [see Figure 163].

If you worked in the other departments, which we rotated at times, and if somebody was out we had to fill in for maybe more than one area, or on holidays and weekends we did all of them.

The lab operated six days. On Sunday, if there were special tests in there, someone would go in to check them out. We each were assigned a holiday, and you did everybody's work for that day, and we stayed until it was done. We had to rotate a schedule so that one of the three or four technicians was there to cover the holidays.

The day all depended on what you were doing, where you were scheduled to work. I mainly worked in the bacteria section. In the morning you finished up whatever paperwork . . . you had, and then the samples started coming in. In the morning we would get all of the Rockland County samples and in the afternoon we'd get the Bergen County ones, so it was an all-day thing. There were like twenty samples alone for Rockland and about the same from Bergen, and you just spent all morning on Rockland and all afternoon on Bergen. In the afternoon, . . . the Hackensack River collector . . . would bring in all his samples, which you would then do. The samples came from the plants daily. You had to have the water brought down daily from each plant and tested. The New Milford Plant samples we would go and get ourselves and then bring them in and start testing them. When the lab was in the New Milford Plant we did all that ourselves.

Your distribution sites were once a month. Each week you had a different area that was brought in. The number of tests varied, but there were a lot every day. We were busy all day long. We never knew if special samples would come in. We tested some camp samples and different things that people needed tested like private wells, which they did as a courtesy. People would come in from camps and other places and you didn't know how many you were going to have that day or if there were any emergencies like water main breaks that had to be tested. Plus you did all the tests on the plants. They brought down big jugs of water and they were tested

for everything—bacteria, minerals, metals, the pH, the color. There was a whole series of things that had to be done on all the samples.

You had to do all the regular tests on the samples, and then you had to do various state tests that you had to keep up with, that you did in between. They would bring in the samples and they passed around so much water from each sample to the various other departments. You would test for color. You had tubes that you would compare them to, as to what color the water was. If it was high in color, then they would have to retest or find out why. You could tell by the odor if a sample was very "chlorine-y." Then you would do the chlorine test and the pH test to see how much registered and if everything was normal. And then the sample would go to the next department and so much of the water would go to the mineral department, and that would be boiled down and tested. I would get special samples for bacteria that had to be in sterile bottles that couldn't be opened until you were going to test the sample. Then the chemists got other samples to do other things on, to see that they all met the requirements.

I did all the bacteria testing, almost from the beginning. That was my job. To grow the bacteria we used special agar and special solutions, and when the samples would come in, we would fix all the samples. Danny DeSouza was our sterilization guy, and he also helped make the agar for me. He did all the special things. The agar is a gel that's hardened on a plate, and you would take some of the sample and put it on there, fix the sample to it. You would then set it into the refrigerator or the incubators for a set number of hours and then check it. Some took twenty-four hours, some took more, depending on what test you did, and you would tell if a sample was passable or not, if it cleared, and then you reported that. You could see the bacteria grow on the plates. And when it would grow in the bottles, it would turn yellow if you had a positive sample. It would turn from clear to yellow. If it was positive, then you had to have somebody sent out to resample that area so many times in a row until it came out clear, because that's the state rule. . . . Like if it was a school, it could be the internal pipes or something, but you still had to go back to test it three times in a row, to make sure that it wasn't the sample bottle or the sample collector that maybe influenced the sample into becoming positive.

All our samples and results had to be logged into the computer and we kept logbooks because we're inspected so many times within a year. Everything had to be visible and all results were sent to Mr. Leo Fong or another supervisor who had to approve of everything, and it had to be there for the state people to see. The state wanted the reports and things. We had state inspectors from New York and New Jersey, and they would spend at least a day and go around checking the various departments and see that our records were right and whether we did the test right. It was a tense time when we knew [the inspectors] were coming. They were there at least once or twice a year. That was so you could get certified. Otherwise you couldn't keep the lab open. You had to be recertified and checked.

There were times when we worked around the clock. We took turns to keep the lab going when we had the really bad main breaks and things . . . because it had to get done. We would see who would stay and who would come in later. We worked it out among ourselves. There was a big main break once right near the plant that was very serious. We didn't want anybody hurt, and we were working to try and keep up with all the samples that had to be done with that break. When anything went wrong with anybody, we all worried about each other. They were pretty conscious of the safety and nobody wanted anybody to get hurt, so everybody pretty much watched out for each other.

"if you had to work in there it was very hard"

Barry Schwartz's work as chief chemist and later as supervisor of water treatment involved him in all the operations of the filtration plant. His recollections of its design, processes, maintenance, and upgrading describe its role in the purification of Hackensack River water:

The operation of the filters was under my direction. When the treatment process was properly maintained, the filters would also operate properly, and they would have to be backwashed, depending on the head loss, about once a day. The old filters from 1904 and 1912 had sand on top of gravel. The new filters from 1955 were dual media with anthracite coal sitting on top of the sand bed. Anthracite coal was used because it's a very hard coal and it is not as friable nor would it decompose as soft coal would, and it's inexpensive. The coal was of a larger grain size than the sand, so you would filter from a larger to a smaller size media, which allowed you to filter at a higher rate and achieve less head loss, and therefore you can produce more water. The coal is lighter than the sand, and the 1955 filters had deeper beds so the coal wouldn't get washed out of the filter when you backwashed it. When you backwash, the sand regrades itself and restratifies with the coal on top. It was an innovation in filtering design but it wasn't developed at the New Milford Plant. The old filters were too shallow for a dual media.

The filter media was good for at least twenty years if the filter was properly operated. All filters tend to lose media during the backwash, so maybe every four, five, or six years you may want to top off a filter with additional sand. It was specially sieved sand that came from a sand quarry in Cape May. It wasn't beach sand, which is too fine. Beach sand is probably 0.2 millimeters. The filter sand was specially sieved to give you the proper size. There's a whole science to sieving sand and maintaining the proper gradient and size. You can order different sizes, around $\frac{1}{2}$ millimeter to 1 millimeter. Filter sand is normally 0.45 to 0.65 millimeters.

The old filters were refurbished probably every twenty years. At times they would [refurbish] two or three a year. It was a laborious process in which you had to take out the old sand and gravel, all by hand. Then the air grid with all its copper pipes had to be replaced, as the copper was probably corroded. It was heavy, hard work that took about four weeks per filter. It was a wintertime job, when the flows were low. It was never a pleasant job because it was cold in the filters and your hands would be all cut up from the gravel.

There's no heat in that part of the plant. It was never below freezing because it was all surrounded by water, but it was damp and cold. The worst part was the [1905–1912] pipe gallery, which was very crowded. They didn't allow for much work room. The old pipe gallery is very crammed with pipes and it was terrible to work in [see Figure 63]. When you had to go in there and repair the valves, you were on your back sometimes in an inch of water just working there. You're wearing rain gear, of course, but if you had to work in there it was very hard. You wouldn't build a plant like that today. You'd build it with some [way] for the maintenance people to work in there and get to the equipment with some ease and comfort.

The 1955 pipe gallery wasn't so bad [see Figure 147]. The 1955 filters didn't need air and the extra pipelines to produce it. They used a high-rate backwash. You just build the filter a little bit higher in order to use a higher rate of water wash. Today, they are going back to the air scour. Filter design sort of cycles. It went from air, to no air, to back to air now. Today air scour is seen as

more effective in terms of producing a better-cleansed filter than just a straight backwash with water.

The 1955 filters have what is known as Wheeler bottoms [see Figure 145], which are one-square-foot concrete pockets. It's an inverted, four-sided pyramid. At the bottom of the pocket is a one-inch hole, and there are hundreds of these throughout the filter, side to side, wall to wall. At the bottom of every pocket, a ceramic ball is placed, about the size of a baseball, that contacts all four sides of the pyramid, allowing water to flow through the bottom hole. On top of that are placed four equal-sized ceramic balls separated from each other by . . . nine smaller ping-pong-sized ceramic balls. On top of that you place gravel, different grades of gravel from 2 inch up to $\frac{1}{4}$ inch. On top of that, you now place your sand and your coal. The pocket allows only filtered water to go through. There was no difference, really, in backwashing a new filter and an old one. It was basically the same process, except you had no air line on a new filter so it was strictly a water wash.

"back in those days they preferred to do it visually"

In backwashing the filters, the filter operator had to monitor various conditions through several steps of the process, as Barry remembers.

Head loss is how fast the filter plugs up. As it plugs up, it will not filter as much water, and it builds up a head pressure. . . . When that reaches a certain value, you have to backwash the filter. Sometimes you can backwash a filter based on time as well as head loss, depending on the particular season. During the summertime when things were pretty hot and heavy, they would backwash the filters on a scheduled basis, so you knew what filters were out of service. If a filter is not properly serviced, it's not producing sufficient water to maintain the flow. There were gauges to monitor the head pressure. The pressure of the water from the top of the filter to the bottom of the filter was measured. You would tap into the pipeline at the bottom of the filter and also just above the filter media to get the differential, which is the head loss.

A clean filter wouldn't have very much head loss. You lose head because of the resistance of the flow. You'd have a foot of head loss initially, and as the filter media would build up with particles, you may get 5, 6, 7 feet of head loss. When it got to 8 feet, you would tend to backwash the filter. The actual height of the water in the filter would be determined by the height of the basin. The filter operators would call for more or less water, depending on the flow from the plant, because that would change on an hourly basis. The people in the pumping station would set their filtered water pump to meet the demand for drinking water, and that would essentially draw water from the filters and the basin. Then the filter operators would say, "I need more water" and the pumping station would put more raw water pumps on to get the basin level back up. So it was always a chess game, balancing the filtered water with the clarified water and the raw water.

The old and the new filters operated in basically the same fashion with the same type of valving. However, the old filters used what is known as an air wash or air scour, which would blow air through the filter to help cleanse some of the trapped debris off the media grains. The newer filters did not have the air wash. In the history of filter design, the Fuller design used air in the early filters because it would more effectively cleanse the media by disturbing it and shaking it up like clothes in a washer. The air flowed at about 3 psi. The height of the water in the filter was only about 8 feet and you didn't need much pressure to blow air

through the media. The air bubbled for two minutes to cleanse off the trapped debris. Then you'd stop the air and you'd allow the wash water to come forth and all that debris would be flushed out. The initial wash water would appear dark brown from all the trapped debris being washed out. The water would gradually clear as the filter was cleansed and you'd see the water clearing as it entered the gutter.

If you added both air and water at the same time, you would tend to lose media from the filter off into the gutter or the trough. It would be lost because the air would tend to make the sand more buoyant and you tend to lose it when you backwash, so you just use the air first followed by the water wash. The air scour normally took two minutes and the water backwash took about six minutes. After you backwash, you fill the filter back up with your treated water and you're back in service. You can do the whole process in fifteen to twenty minutes. All the valves were operated by hydraulic water pressure, so the operator moves the levers on the operating table to direct the water pressure to either open or close a valve.

The first thing the operator does to backwash a filter is to close the influent and effluent valves [see Figures 67–70]. Then he would open the drain valve to discharge all the water from above the filter to the receiving facility, which could be to a lagoon, clarifier, or the sewer. Then he would turn the air blower on [to] blow air through the submerged filter media. Then he'd shut the blower off, shut the air valve off, and open the wash water valve to bring in water to flush out the trapped debris into the gutter and out to the receiving facility. When the water cleared up, he would then shut the wash water valve, close the drain line, open the influent line, and fill the filter back up with treated water. When it was filled up to the proper level, then he would open up the effluent line to start the filtering. Back in those days, they preferred to do it visually so that they were sure of when to stop the backwash. You'd get some chlorine odors coming off the air scour, because it would tend to dissipate some of the chlorine in the water. We had filter masks to avoid breathing in that extra chlorine.

The most important job of the filter operators was monitoring the plant hydraulics as well as chemical treatment and water quality. On an hourly basis they had to watch the charts and keep the water in the basin within 2 feet of the limit. You didn't want to flood the plant, but on occasion it would tend to flood because of excessive water in the filters. You also didn't want to lose the hydraulics because then you'd have less water flow for the filters. Occasionally there was an operator error and a filter overflowed. You would wash the floors that way. It wasn't a major problem, but it was a little bit of an embarrassment because the water would flow down over the stairs and out the door back into the intake canal, and the person who was involved spent a couple of days hiding his head.

"water, water"

Pat Hoffman vividly remembers one of those times when a filter overflowed:

We would have to go back to the filter house on certain mornings and walk down the gallery to where the control operator was, and he would have the samples because he was in charge of that. One of the filters overflowed, and I remember walking down with this great big box that had the sample jugs from the basin, the raw and the purified water. I'm carrying it and I hear this noise, and all of a sudden I look back and the water was rushing over the basin and was coming after me, and I tried running with these heavy bottles

down this long hallway, and I'm running with these things and thinking, "Is this water going to catch up with me?" Previous to that, it had happened once before and one of the control operators got broken ribs because he fell.

I'm running with these bottles and I see some of the guys ahead and I'm saying, "Water, water!" That's all I could think of, and I couldn't get anything else out . . . and they're saying "Yeah, water!" like, "Yeah, we're working in a water company!" and I'm saying, "Water, water!" and they're looking at me like I'm crazy until all of a sudden the water starts barreling down the stairs at them, and they're out in the driveway and the water is pouring down. . . . I just managed to get up on one of the other steps on the side and I saved the water samples. I did not drop those bottles! Something must've stuck in the filter and the water just kept coming, and it went over the basin wall and down the gallery and it was just pouring down over the steps. That was a little scary. Afterward you can laugh.

"the water quality dictates when the filter would be washed"

Jim Flynn recalls overseeing and backwashing the filters from the operator's perspective:

In 1983 I moved from the engine room over to the filtration plant as a division foreman. The engine room and filtration plant had to work hand-in-hand. There were two people on watch in the filtration plant, a filter operator and an assistant. The filter operator's responsibility was to maintain chemical treatment to make the water safe, to backwash the filters, and to make sure that he gave enough water to the watch engineer so that he could pump it out to the system. You would constantly talk to each other—"I'm putting

*another pump in," "In two hours, I'm going to take a pump out,"
or something—so they could do what they had to do in response to
what you had to do. The filter operators knew their job and I
always reacted with them pretty well. The assistant helped by
going out and taking samples from different areas of the plant, by
doing water quality testing, and any other kind of assistance that
the filter operator needed.*

*The load on the filter would dictate when it would be washed. If
you had very dirty water, you might have to wash the filter every
twelve or fourteen hours. If you had good water quality, that filter
could go twenty-four or thirty-six hours. So the water quality dictates when the filter would be washed. To backwash a filter you
have to close the influent valve and leave the effluent valve open
until the water filters down to a set certain level in the filter, then
you would close your effluent valve to take the filter out of service.
You would open up your drain valve to get ready for the wash
water. The front sixteen filters from 1905 and 1912 you would first
wash with air for a two-minute period. The back six filters from
1955 did not have an air wash; they only washed with wash water.
Then you would wash the filter with wash water for a five- to six-
minute period. The water quality determined how much wash
water we would use. The filter would be clean at that point, and
then you would start reversing the process: close the drain valve,
open up the influent valve, let your filter start to fill up slowly, and
once it's filled up, you would open up your effluent valve and put it
back in service. It would take approximately fifteen minutes to
backwash a filter.*

*The operating tables for the filters were manual and made by a
company called Infilco. They had four-way valves for operating
the filters: the water inflow, the airflow, the wash water, and drain
gates, and so forth. . . . I worked hand-in-hand with Mr. Schwartz*

*and Mr. Hoven, and we set up a system where we automated those
valves, where it would operate on a simple computer system. It
was a tremendous leap forward [see Color Plates 26 and 27]. The
filter operator still had to make the decision on when the filter had
to be washed, but he didn't have to go out to the filter itself to do
the washing. All he had to do was give the commands on the computer system.*

"a marriage of the centuries"

George Haskew remembers the conversion of the valves from hydraulic
power to electric power and the introduction of computers as a fascinating
mix of old and new technology, and he recalls some unique aspects of the
filtration plant.

*The filters were originally controlled with what we used to call
three- and four-way valves, hydraulically. You operated a lever on
the filter table and that moved ports in a valve so that it opened
one section and closed another. Then the hydraulic pressure goes
to open or close a big valve and that makes things work. When you
called for the backwash, that started the Pelton water wheels [see
Figure 60], making augers run to pump the air. The wash water
pump was also water-wheel operated, which always fascinated me.
The old hydraulic valves got worn . . . so we replaced them with
electric solenoid valves, and our people programmed a Com-
modore computer so you could sit in the control room and operate
those electric solenoid valves. You could see a little computer
make an electric valve work to call a nineteenth-century water
wheel into action. I always said that was fascinating because it
was a marriage of the centuries.*

*The filter bottoms are Hering & Fuller's design. They called
them ridge and furrow, because they look like a plowed field with*

furrows in between ridges [see Figure 65] . . . and they had a specially designed brass strainer plate with a little hook and furrow
arrangement to put it in there. They're still there. We had, over the
years, replaced those, and had machine shops make the pieces just
as the originals were. It was pretty unique because they worked
extremely well. The Fuller plant had an air wash system and the
filters were backwashed upward by putting water in the under-
drain system and pushing it up to float the dirty material out.
Nowadays, air washing is very common . . . but this was a very
early application of that. The 1955 filters are modern, with
Wheeler bottoms [see Figure 145], which are hoppers with balls
and gravel. But the old plant kept running exactly as Hering &
Fuller designed it and we operated that way all those years. It
would still operate!

"that was built to last a thousand years"

The clear wells or filtered water reservoirs under the filters are remarkable but hidden parts of the plant. Only on rare occasions, when a well was
emptied for inspection, would anyone venture into the dark and mysterious
space, as Barry Schwartz recalls:

When they rebuilt the filters, they took a section of the filter house
out of service and went into the clear well below to examine it. You
wouldn't go down there that often unless you suspected that a filter
was losing media and there was not enough sand in the filter. Then
you'd want to get it out of the clear well. Normally you'd find some
sand down there. Some silt would migrate through the gravel and
go through the Wheeler bottoms and wind up in the clear well and
you'd find these little mounds by the piping from the outfall of the
filter. There were six clear wells, one on each side of the filter
house sections built in 1904, 1912, and 1955. They were isolated

one from the other, separated by valves, so you could take one out
and keep the other ones in service.

A clear well is really just a concrete chamber, but they were
very interesting. They were a Romanesque design with arches and
pillars [see Figures 63, 64, and 95], and it was very dark inside
there and you'd need bright lights to see where you were going. It's
kind of eerie inside there. It was so dark, you wouldn't even know
what you were looking at. You could see the four pipelines coming
from each filter, but there was nothing really to maintain down
there, as long as they weren't leaking. It was well built. Back in
those days, it was designed to last quite a long time. The filter
plant was all concrete construction and . . . they used a lot of
rebar and high-tensile-strength concrete. That was built to last a
thousand years.

"you essentially cleanse the water
of any taste and odors"

Barry described the powdered carbon treatment that was developed at the
New Milford Plant by George Spalding and Paul Tamer in the late 1920s
and used there until it closed:

George Spalding was the superintendent of water treatment and a
very astute engineer. He developed the introduction of powdered
carbon into the drinking water at the Hackensack Water Company.
The activated powdered carbon is a carbon black that was found
to be very effective in absorbing organic compounds that cause
odors and tastes in water. Powdered carbon is like talcum powder.
It's very finely pulverized to powder, so it sort of suspends itself in
water and [can] be mixed thoroughly with the water. By applying
this chemical to the drinking water, you actually allow the carbon
to adsorb these organic compounds that produce the taste and

odors, and this carbon would of course coagulate with the flocculant and precipitate out or fall to the bottom of the basin. You essentially cleanse the water of any taste and odors by the use of powdered carbon. Powdered carbon was applied in the gate house at the same point as the alum application and the chlorine. The powdered carbon, when I was there, was used routinely. It was always being applied as a safety factor, but then the cost of powdered carbon became excessive and to get some control of the cost, . . . it became used only when necessary. Today some plants also use granular activated carbon, which is more like a sand or a larger granular than powdered carbon, to control taste and odor.

They tell a story about [George] Spalding. He was always at the plant. People were on shift, and if it was a midnight shift people tend to get a little sleepy at times, and if the plant was properly maintained and operated, you might want to catch a couple of Zs. But of course it was a no-no to fall asleep on the job. If you were caught, you could be dismissed. Spalding, being a gentleman, would always ring the bell before he'd go into the plant to make sure the guys were up. He was always kind in that regard.

"gravity didn't cost anything, so you used nature"

The application of the coagulant chemicals changed over time as new materials and equipment became available, including improvements while Barry worked there.

When I started working in 1968, they were just switching over the old dry feeders to liquid alum. The old chemical treatment back then used powdered alum. They hauled the 100-pound bags of alum to the top floor on the hydraulic elevator, but then it required some heavy lifting of the bags to get the alum into the solution tank [see

Figures 58 and 59]. You would dissolve a certain number of bags into a certain amount of water to create a solution of the alum, which is then applied to the treated water in the coagulation basin. In the early days they were also using soda ash to adjust the pH in the water. Soda ash is a dry chemical, essentially baking soda, or baking powder—sodium carbonate. They mixed this in separate solution tanks. The solution tanks were filled with filtered water, since you would always use your best quality water for producing the chemicals needed in the treatment process. The original process used gravity to feed the chemical solutions from the third floor of the chemical or coagulation house. Gravity didn't cost anything, so you used nature to feed your chemicals, but as the solution in the tank dropped in level, the flow also tended to drop so you had to open the valve periodically to maintain the proper flow of chemical.

Later on, they acquired what was known as dry feeders. They would feed the dry chemical into a water stream and avoid mixing batches on a daily basis. This was done for many years until they went to what is known as liquid alum. They acquired alum as a solution from the manufacturer and were able to feed it into the water entering the coagulation basin. They built two 30,000-gallon storage tanks for the liquid alum in the boiler house. The liquid alum was much easier to acquire and feed than handling numerous bags on a daily basis. The liquid alum pump gives you a definite quantity of chemical in each stroke, so you get a much, much more effective and more precise treatment of a chemical than the old dry feeders, which were notorious for fouling up and producing poor dosages and hence poor treatment. In the old days you'd have to worry about miscounting the bags, or whether you put enough water in the tanks, and then you'd have to make adjustments to the treatment stream to compensate. Later on they also started using liquid caustic soda to adjust the pH.

The chemical treatment took place in the coagulation basin. Barry Schwartz describes the process:

In coagulation, a chemical produces a precipitate in the water, what they call a flocc particle. It acts as a magnet to attract other particles in the raw water, and these chemicals tend to clarify the water by absorbing, attracting, and coalescing some bacteria and algae or other particles. Coagulation is still a very important part of the treatment process. It actually aids in the filtration process because it makes the water more amenable to filtration without excessive clogging of the filters. You can settle particles first before you filter. One of the chemicals used is aluminum sulfate or what is known as alum. You can also use ferric sulfate. These produce a hydroxide precipitate. It's a very fluffy precipitate that is slowly mixed with the water. The slow mixing will actually adhere other particles to the precipitate in a coalescing process. As this occurs, it will clarify the water, and these particles will settle to the bottom of the basin, and then you draw the clear water to the filtration plant. So the clarification is a very important step in the treatment process, and normally it's the first step done in producing drinking water. Sometimes you may have a presettling facility such as a reservoir, which allows larger particles to settle naturally. Then you apply your chemicals for coagulation to coalesce the remaining particles that don't settle through gravitation, and essentially build up their bulk with coagulants so they will settle.

Flocculant is another name for the coagulant. They are essentially synonymous terms. The coagulant or flocculant is mixed in slowly with the water . . . to promote flocculation for about half an hour. Then the water would be allowed to remain quiet and the floccs would settle in long settling basins and produce what is known as a layer of sludge, which is the residual waste product that eventually builds up in the basin. Every three to six months you have to go into the basin, empty it out, and flush all this sludge, or residual waste, to a disposal site. It could go to a lagoon, or a sewage plant, that is, to some place to allow the waste to be removed. Then you put the basin back in service for additional settling.

The chemical solution went through a pipe to the gate house [see Figures 41 and 44], where it dropped into the raw water coming from the engine house, and it would mix at that point through turbulence. The treated water would then flow into the flocculation units at the head of the coagulation basin for further mixing. The Pelton water wheels powered the mechanism to turn the paddles in the three sections of flocculation units [see Figures 116 and 126]. After that, the water went through a baffle wall into the settling portion of the basin, which is a large, rectangular area that allowed the flocc or precipitate to settle to the bottom, and the clear water was taken off to the filter house. Some would settle in the flocculation area but not very much.

"that was a big operation"

As the coagulation process changed over the years, the water company introduced new technology to make it more efficient, including the flocculators added in the 1930s (see Figures 116 and 126). George Haskew explained why the water company upgraded the basin with the flocculators and the mixing chambers (Figure 166):

Originally the process was just plain sedimentation. The technology was improving over the years, and they had more knowledge about chemical coagulation and how to make it more effective.

Figure 166: *New Milford Plant, c. 1960. The coagulation basin with the machinery houses for the flocculators, foreground; pumping station, left; filtration house, right. United Water Resources*

They put what they called a flocculating chamber in the end of the basin, with paddle wheels to move the water. The chemical would form what we call a "flocc," or in other words, a precipitate. That precipitate swept through the settling basin and swept up the particles of the dirt and colloidal material and the like, and carried it downward to settle it out. Above you had clarified water that was drawn out to go into the filters. The filters were considered to be a polishing action. Now we know a lot more about filters than they did in those days, and we know that the filter is extremely important in taking out some parasites and insistent bacteria that are not as affected by the disinfectants.

It was a big job to maintain the coagulation basin [in] New Milford because it had to be manually cleaned. In order to clean it, the basin was drawn down and men were put in with fire hoses to flush the solid material off those sloping walls and the bottom to a drain [see Figures 100 and 101], and then it went to the lagoons over on the other side of the road and the river there where the so-called sludge or solid material was collected and settled down. In newer plants nowadays, basins are mechanically cleaned. There are scrapers that pull that material to a drain and you don't have to do the kind of work that they did at the New Milford Plant. That basin was very big, and that was a big operation. It was all mobilized with the fire hoses and fixed nozzles.

"we called it the cog basin for short"

When he worked in the filtration plant, Jim Flynn was involved in operating the "cog basin."

The filter operator was in charge of the water quality, so therefore the coagulation basin was his responsibility. To determine how high he would keep it . . . he would have to anticipate load conditions. He'd get his basin up high for when you would have a high demand in the morning or evening, and when he did that, he would have to adjust chemical dosages on what he was pumping into the basin and what was coming out of the basin.

In coagulation you're trying to take your particulates—which will not stick together—and you're trying to make them so they will stick together. When you coagulate the water, all the particles that you have in the water will now start forming together to make a larger particle, which will now sink in your basin. You want it to settle; that's why it's called a settling basin. So once you put your coagulant in, it starts immediately and then you have gentle stir-

ring with flocculators to get this stuff to start sticking together better, and then it moves slowly through the basin, and as it goes through the basin, the particles start forming larger flocc and then settle to the bottom.

We called it the cog basin for short. The cog basin would have to be cleaned usually twice a year: once in the springtime and once in the fall. You would take the basin out of service completely and you would add your coagulant chemicals up at the dam so the water would have its coagulation before it came into the plant, and then you would physically get down into the basin with hoses and wash all the sludge to a pit where we would pump it over to a lagoon where it would be dealt with at a later time. Sometimes when you started it was 7 or 8 feet high, and pretty thick. For thirty years I called it sludge and now it's water treatment residual.

"everyone was happy with that"

As superintendent of water treatment, Barry Schwartz supervised the operation of the coagulation basin (Figure 167), which included scheduling its cleaning.

The 1937 separation wall created the east and west basins, but if they kept only one side full of water, the pressure of the water against that wall was considered a little too much and they were afraid the wall might collapse. They emptied both sides to service the basin, which took about four days. The cleaning was scheduled way in advance on a calendar basis. I would set up the operational schedule to clean the basin, but it was actually managed by the maintenance force that was part of the pumping station crew. I would set the schedule up for the filtration operators to maintain treatment and then get the crews from maintenance to do the actual work.

Figure 167: *Coagulation basin, c. 1960. Water company staff on the baffle wall at the north end of the basin used a Seechi Disk to measure the clarity of the treated water. The gate house is to the right of center, and the pumping station is behind it. United Water Resources*[177]

They would drop the level of the water in the basin to the sludge layer [see Figure 100]. Then they would go in there with hoses and hose all that sludge to the sump. In the center of the separation wall was a pump house, and they would pump the sludge through a pipeline to the lagoons across New Milford Avenue. When the basin was being cleaned, they would feed the chemicals at Oradell dam and use the intake canal as a treatment settling area, and that water would clarify through the intake canal, and that would go directly into the filter plant. The gate house could be switched over so the water went directly from the gate house to the filter plant and bypassed the coagulation basin.

Hosing the sludge in the basin was a pretty bad job [see Figure 101]. It was smelly from algae and detritus in the water, especially in the summertime. When I was there, we did it four times a year, so that meant that sometimes you were there in cold weather and sometimes in hot weather. They would take a hose team, which required five people, one to operate the nozzle and four to hold the hose back, and they usually had two teams. It was laborious work wearing essentially waders up to your elbows, actually up to your hips, in sludge to start out with, but the level would drop as the sludge was pumped out. The consistency of the sludge was like mud. It was thick and gelatinous and required a hose to move it. Initially it flowed and then as the water would drain from it, it would get thicker, and you would have to use the hoses to move it. It was heavy, hard work, and smelly work. Back in those days you had people who understood that there was a need to do that, and the fellows would get lunch and some overtime, so there was some extra compensation for that work in the basin.

Later on, we switched over to other flocculants that required cleaning only twice a year. . . . Everyone was happy with that. We started using polymers to replace part of the alum, so you saved on the chemical addition, using less chemicals and producing less sludge. When you cut your chemical dosage by 50 percent, you cut your sludge by maybe 30 to 40 percent. Then we introduced into the basin a tractor with a scraper to move the sludge to the sump and avoid excessive hosing, and we could let the level drop quite a bit before the crews went in there with hoses [Figures 168 and 169]. The tractor was lowered . . . with a winch into the bottom of

Figure 168: *Coagulation basin, c. 1970. To make the basin cleaning easier, a supervisor named Donald Hoven came up with the idea of lowering a tractor in to the basin to push the sludge toward the sump where it was pumped out. Jesse Jones of the maintenance crew is driving the tractor. United Water Resources*

Figure 169: "Coagulation Basin Cleaning," c. 1970. During cleaning, the mainte-nance crew drained both sides of the basin. In this view Jessie Jones is climbing up the east embankment with the flocculant mixing chambers visible behind him. United Water Resources

the lagoon. One of my bosses, Donald Hoven, came up with that innovation . . . and that worked very well. It required just one man on a tractor.

"the beginning of a new era for water supply"

As regulations on water quality increased in the 1970s, the water company had to upgrade its laboratory facilities in the filtration house. Barry recalls the start of the new era:

In the 1970s the EPA came on board and . . . started issuing regu-lations, and there was a need to . . . establish how the company was going to comply with these regulations. Things had to be

changed in the laboratory as well as in the treatment plant process. It was the beginning of a new era for water supply in this country. . . . Before that time, the U.S. Public Health Service was responsible for establishing interstate drinking water standards, and these were essentially picked up by the individual states as their standards. But the USPHS did not have jurisdiction intrastate, so the EPA was created to have a national organization that had authority across and within state boundaries.

When I first got there, all the wash water was being discharged to the Hackensack River, so there was no treatment of it. The EPA . . . regulated the discharge of wastewater, so we had to put in treatment to effect the clarification of the wash water before it was discharged to the river. We built a clarifier for the wash water in back of the filter house with a small equalization basin. It actually took the wash water and settled it before we discharged it back to either the river or back to the head of the plant, and then the sludge was pumped over to the lagoon. So now we had two sources of sludge: the wash water sludge and the basin sludge.

We just had to make sure that if the wash water was returned to the head of the plant, there weren't too many suspended solids in it, so it wouldn't affect the water quality. You use about 2 percent of your treated water for backwashing your filters, so if that 2% . . . had too much of a high solid content, it could impact the treat-ment process as it was recycled back into the raw water supply. So you want to make sure that your clarifier in the wash water treat-ment was properly operating.

George Haskew remembers expanding the laboratory so that the water company could comply with the new regulations:

The laboratory at New Milford had started out [in] 1905 as a little over half of the east side [see Figures 61 and 62], and then it was expanded to include the whole east side as one lab room. . . . And then I took over the office section which was on the west side of the building and converted that to a laboratory because we didn't have room in the old place to put modern equipment. We were getting [to] where we had more electronic equipment and things that I thought we needed to have to keep current and to do what we had to do properly . . . so we increased the laboratory to take over the whole floor.

To renovate and expand the lab, the water company hired Miles Kuchar, who remembers the project as complicated because the lab had to remain in operation during the work:

We renovated the existing laboratory, the old one, and then across the hall on that same floor they had offices, and we renovated that area to a second lab. We put tile on the walls and so on. It took about six months because they had to maintain that lab and keep testing the water quality.

When the water company completed the renovation and expansion of the New Milford laboratory, it held a dedication ceremony for directors and invited guests (Figures 170, 171, and 172). The expanded laboratory included new equipment that modernized the staff's analytical capabilities.

"you knew it was coming"

Van Buskirk Island had always been subject to flooding when high tides coincided with exceptionally heavy rains, causing the Hackensack River to overflow its banks. The water company had been dealing with these conditions from its opening of the water works in 1882. The New Milford crew knew when a flood was coming and had a number of procedures to prepare for it and to keep the plant in operation. George Haskew recalls the installation of bulkhead doors (Color Plates 11, 13, and 14) to make it easier to keep the floodwaters out of the plant.

Flooding was always a big issue. The flooding got worse over the years because with more development upstream, you had a more rapid runoff and the floods would increase. We put those ship-type steel doors on the plant to keep any high water out of the buildings. Those bulkhead doors were built gasketed as in a submarine or ship, so when we were expecting high water, we would close those flood doors. Otherwise we had to squeeze the sandbags in before we put those doors on and that was only effective up to a point. We made the doors; our maritime guys were used to doing that kind of stuff. They were watertight, so they kept the water out of the building. That made it effective and we could stay in there. . . . As long as we didn't have water in the building, we were okay. It didn't flood any equipment, any machinery, and we were just fine. There was leakage, however, in the foundation and in the pumping station. A couple of times we used the old fire engine that Oradell had with a big bell on the front, because it was a suction pumper that could lift the water that high, with a piston pump. But other than that, we could sit there and keep going, and let the water go around.

I used to be down there when it flooded, and the water would be whistling in that alleyway between the filter plant and the pumping station [Figure 173]. Water went through there and I used to wear knee boots in it. They would almost pop up sometimes in the current, but that was about as deep as it usually was.

Fred Schelhas worked at the Hackensack Water Company from 1956 to 1990, and retired as the foreman and assistant manager of the New Milford Plant. Fred recalled flooding at the plant:[178]

Every time we had a flood, we always notified the Oradell Fire Department that we might need them. We never did, but they used to bring their old fire engine down and we used to put it by the old

Figure 171: *Laboratory west wing dedication, 1975. George Haskew is in the middle with the striped tie between Walter Lucking, Hackensack Water Company president, left, and Robert Mulreany, chairman of the board. United Water Resources*

Figure 170: *Laboratory west wing dedication, 1975. Expansion of the laboratory into the west wing provided space for additional instrumentation to meet new regulatory requirements. Georgiana Wavle, a laboratory technician, is at the far left; Ann Willis, a lab chemist, and Louise Thomson, another laboratory technician, are in the center foreground. Frank J. deHooge, the superintendent of the Passaic Valley Water Commission at Little Falls, is wearing glasses and facing the camera in the center. United Water Resources*

Figure 172: *Filtration house, 1975. Entrance to the coagulation house from the filter gallery. The photographic exhibit for the west wing dedication illustrated the changes in water testing over the decades from the original small 1905 laboratory on the east end of the east wing of the coagulant house, to the 1936 expansion of the lab to occupy the entire east wing second floor, to the 1975 lab that occupied both the east and west wings. United Water Resources*

Figure 173: *New Milford Plant flood, c. 1970. View east toward the coagulation basin. 1905 filtration house, left; 1905 gate house, center; and 1906 boiler house, right. Prior to the installation of bulkhead doors, the New Milford crew sandbagged the door openings to keep out the floodwaters. United Water Resources*

boiler room to give the firemen drafting practice. We did it because it was tradition. They had to bring the water up into the old fire engine and pump. That old fire engine, being as historic as it was, the firemen always wanted to run it. They never brought any other piece of equipment because they wanted to operate that old fire engine to keep it running and train some of the young men for their annual firemen's competition. The head of the old Oradell DPW was involved in the fire department, and he and Dan Hoffman, the plant manager, grew up together. So they used to help

each other. When the firemen needed transportation for their old pumper, we would put it on our old flatbed and transport it to the annual firemen's contest.

The fire department always sent men down there with that fire engine every time we notified the town that we might need assistance. They were only pumping out the coal pit beneath the floor of the boiler room. There used to be a pushcart bringing coal over from across New Milford Avenue. Then we opened an underground conveyer under the roadway and it was still open to a pit under the boiler room. From the pit another conveyer would take the coal up to the boiler room. The fire department used to pump out that pit.

The boiler room was still operating and dry. You could walk around in the boiler room and it was bone dry. There was no way that we ever needed to wear any kind of boot inside the plant. Our pumps always took care of any water seepage. You might need small boots, all the way in the lowest point of the building under the electric clear water pumps, Nos. 13 and 14. That cellar drains into a pit with a large electric sump pump in there, and it would handle any water it needed to. We wore boots because if you went outside, you would need the boots, so we never bothered to take them off when we were inside.

The reason the watertight hatches are at the level they are, is because they are at the window level. If the hatches went any higher, it wouldn't be useful, as the water would be pouring into the windows anyway. The new Madison Avenue bridge that the County recently rebuilt has eliminated some of the obstruction problem that held flood waters back. We never before had a 200-hundred-year flood like "Floyd." It never flooded inside the building all the years I was there.

Jim Flynn also remembers that flooding never shut the plant down while he was there:

Even though we had floods, we were never washed out, because everybody just pitched in. You didn't care what job you had. You just pitched in and made sure you got everything going. Flooding would get into the cellars or into the fire room. I can actually remember the first flood that we had that the firemen were standing on benches and the water was almost up to the burners. That was one of those 100-year floods that you saw every ten years. The only thing that stopped the flow of water was broken supply mains. We had a few of them.

When there was a flood, the laboratory increased its testing to monitor the water conditions and the water company typically increased chlorination as a precaution. Barry Schwartz recalls how the laboratory staff coped with flooding:

During floods the plant internally tended to stay dry. The area around the plant did flood many times when I was there because it is on Van Buskirk Island. It would only flood, of course, when the tide was coming in and heavy rains were going out. Water would cover the ground around the plant, . . . but there was never any real problem with the contamination of the clear wells because they were essentially sealed. You might get some water in the clear wells, as nothing of that size is ever watertight, but then you increased the chlorine level to a certain point and it would solve any problems. We would be testing the potability of the drinking water all that time to make sure there was no contamination, and [we would] increase the chlorine levels as necessary. Every time we did that, we never saw any impact from any contamination. The floodwater would be turbid but essentially it's so diluted that there's no real chance of contamination from a health point of view. Flooding was never really considered a hazardous situation, just an annoyance.

During a flood we'd be able to walk . . . from building to building wearing hip boots. You could get the people in from outside; they would actually meet at the top of the hill by Jay's Pharmacy and be taken down in a large truck, which could drive through the water into the plant. Then they'd enter through the window to get into the laboratory or plant to do their work. The plant was essentially dry because it was higher and the doors had bulkheads and were sandbagged. You'd just see water around the building . . . circulating back to the river.

When I was there, it flooded maybe six times in thirty-two years. Some times you were close, then the tide would go out. The tide would save you. But, it was never a flash flood. You always saw it coming. . . . You could tell by the elevations of the reservoirs and the river stages. You'd have the hydrograph, so you knew what the elevations were at the reservoirs . . . It occurred very slowly, so if the staff wanted to get out, they could move their cars uphill in plenty of time and be driven back to the plant. Then when the shift changed, they could wait for the truck to come by and take them up. Or they would use waders or hip boots and walk up the hill to their car . . . Nonessential people could leave if they wanted to.

"because the work had to get done"

Pat Hoffman remembers how the crew kept working during one flood:

One time the island around the New Milford Plant got flooded out, and they had all these floodgate doors, which saved a lot of the place . . . We heard on the news that they were flooded and called to see if we had to go to work, and of course Mr. Schwartz said "Yes! Come in!" They met us at St. Joseph's with the flatbed trucks and trucked us in, and took us . . . and flung us over the gates to get in. They said, "Don't fall. Make sure you hold on to everything and don't fall, because you wouldn't want to get in this water." It was really gross! So they literally threw us over the gates, into the trailer. They had to tie down all the things to the trailer—the stairs and everything—because everything was floating. Fish were hopping, and the water was up to the stop sign.

The guys were worried about saving all their stuff, but at the same time there was some comedy in it. We spent the day in there, looking out at all this water and working, of course, because the work had to get done. They threw us over some pizza at lunchtime, over the doors, and when the water finally subsided, which took a while, you saw these fish on the grass on the front lawn in little puddles, and they were jumping, and I think they tried to save some of them. It was a comedy! It was good and bad. I mean, for the women trying to hop up and down on these trucks, it was a little embarrassing at times, and we had a Boy Scout troop that came to help us off the trucks over at the school, and you're thinking "Oh, geez, old women," and these little kids are looking up to help you.

"it wouldn't have been practical"

As water demand increased in the 1960s and 1970s, the water company had to figure out how to add filtration and pumping capacity. The age of the New Milford Plant, its restricted location on Van Buskirk Island, and increasing water quality regulations all contributed to limiting its potential to continue as a water works indefinitely (Figure 174). The water company had continued operating with steam at New Milford because it was an independent and reliable power source when there were few alternatives. George Haskew remembers the deliberations:

The steam equipment always provided a backup for power failures. The electric pumping equipment wouldn't run if there was a power failure, but the steam equipment would. There were also some generators there, small generators by today's standards, that were steam operated, so the plant was a valuable thing to maintain because it was independent. They had converted from coal to oil long before I was there, and the steam operation was perfectly serviceable. The only thing that wasn't running was No. 7. No. 3 was a Corliss engine and a unique piece of steam equipment that was kept in service much longer than an engine like that was, I

Figure 174: *New Milford Plant, c. 1965. This summer view of the engine house west façade shows the 1905 filtration plant, left, and the 1911-1898-1891-1882 engine house, left to center, and the 1882–1886 coal house, right. United Water Resources*

believe, anywhere else. The engines were big and noisy, but the steam was just fine. In fact, I remember we had an ice storm one year that knocked all the power lines down. The only thing that kept us going was the steam plant at New Milford because we had no electric power at Haworth. . . . The whole area was out of power [but] we were still pumping water at the New Milford Plant.

I was always very, very careful in trying to analyze anything. When you have an old system, with old processes and equipment, it's very easy when you ask a question, like "Why is this?," . . . for someone to say, "Well, we always did it that way." For me the question was . . . "Did you always do it that way because you always did it that way, or is there really a scientific or engineering or fundamental reason that it has to be done that way?" And so I would always try to analyze things before I ever got into thinking about . . . changing anything to make sure that there wasn't some real reason it had to be that way, that it was always someone's idea that got carried through the years. . . . You know, like I trained you and you trained him, and so on and so on, and that's how he knew it had to be done that way.

In the 1970s we got into the problem of enlarging Haworth. First of all, we had to analyze, should we enlarge New Milford? Should we enlarge Haworth? Should we enlarge each one a little bit or one a whole lot and then maybe we don't have to have the old one? We analyzed that and then we researched this idea of ozone, which we have in the Haworth plant now. I went to Europe to some of the installations there to analyze ozone as much as possible and to talk to operating people before we fixed on that and went ahead with it. We were one of the earliest ozone plants in this country at that size.

We started running pilot ozone plants in 1975. We built a pilot plant at New Milford. It was down in the bottom of the filter plant, in the gallery [where] we had some space. That was a batch plant, where we hauled the water down from the reservoir and batched it in. The pilot plant worked; then we built one up in Haworth later on and we ran the actual water with small ozone generators, and we piloted the treatment steams to see how they worked and whether one thing was better than another before we went at the final design. We did it over a full year so that we had cold water, warm water, hot water, and so on, so that we wouldn't get tricked by a seasonal problem.

In analyzing New Milford we were looking at cost. . . . It wouldn't have been practical to carry on into the future with the old steam equipment there forever, so we had to look at all of that. At some point back then, I tried to convert New Milford to natural gas to get away from oil so that I'd have the gas in there to run backup generators and the like. My scheme was that the gas pipe lines could go right through company property, and run up on the reservoir property, so farmers could, in the old days, get permission to tap a line and take service. So I said, "It's on our property, I can get the permission from the government to take service and all we have to do is run the pipe down." That's when the power company people came in and enlightened me that it was possible, the only problem was that they couldn't supply the loads that we would want. So that scheme went down the drain. I was going to convert the boilers first, and then we'd have the gas in there and we could go to a new generation of equipment for power.

As we were looking at how best to meet the future at New Milford, the drinking water regulations were coming more and more into the front . . . from the EPA and they . . . were increasingly severe. That meant we needed a higher grade of treatment and the old water works would have to be changed, in any event. We had people study whether we should convert New Milford to a standby *electric power station as a backup to Haworth. By the time we put the addition on Haworth, there was sufficient natural gas to handle gas turbines up there to provide electric power in an emergency.*

We looked at all of the various combinations of things that might be done, . . . and the most economical seemed to be to redo Haworth with more modern technology to increase the capacity up there so that New Milford wouldn't be needed in the future. Since it all started in New Milford way back with their pumping station from the 1880s, the hub of the entire piping system was New Milford, and everything emanated from there. Haworth was connected into that hub originally, and in later years we added a bigger connection to take water north from Haworth, but everything going southerly and east and west had to work out of New Milford.

To temporarily increase New Milford's raw water pumping capacity, the water company erected a small engine house in 1979 south of New Milford Avenue on the site of the 1882–1886 boiler house and coal shed. George Haskew obtained two used electric-powered centrifugal pumps for this installation.

The pumps in there were very slow speed pumps, about 250 to 300 rpm, because we had electric motors made especially for them. I bought those pumps from a secondhand junk guy down in Hudson County. They were fantastic pumps, built for drainage and . . . originally run by diesel engines. . . . We had them refurbished by the original manufacturer and they were sitting around for a long time, and we then put them in that station. They worked great. They fit the head condition just right.

The 1979 engine house marked the end of major improvements at the Hackensack Water Works.

Chapter 7

If You Stay Here Five Years, You'll Never Leave

Working in the water business instilled in people a remarkable sense of duty and dedication to keeping the water flowing. People commonly put their work above their personal needs, and in some cases sacrificed even their health to get the job done. For many people, working at the Hackensack Water Company during the second half of the twentieth century was like being in a family business. They watched out for each other, knowing that they needed each other to be able to deliver pure water to the public. Their stories of the paths that led people to their careers and the workplace interactions that shaped their lives are compelling reminders of life in the last century.

"I started with a pick and shovel"

George Haskew followed in his father's footsteps into the water supply industry, and remembers the circumstances well (Figure 175):

My father started with the Plainfield Union Water Company on a construction job in 1913. Plainfield Union served twenty towns in Union County, New Jersey, and he was there for some forty-five years. He was a self-trained engineer and surveyor, and he had a professional engineer's license. He later became superintendent and chief engineer, and retired in 1958. He put me to work at Plainfield Union when I was fourteen. Since I had some pull, I started with a pick and shovel, and I literally can say I've done everything in the business, I think, from there on up. I did all kinds of things after the pick and shovel work and later on. . . . when I was able to drive, I used to fill in for vacation people in the

Figure 175: *George Haskew on the Madison Avenue Bridge by New Milford Avenue, 2003. The 1882–1886 engine house is behind him on the left, and the 1898 boiler house is behind him on the right. James Hogan*

summertime, like meter changers and jobs like that, and I worked in the office sometimes at the commercial department.

Haskew went into the army in 1945 and afterward went to MIT, like George Warren Fuller and George Spalding had done decades earlier.

I couldn't get into school when I first got out of the service in '46. I ended up going to Williams College in Massachusetts on the G.I. Bill for a term because they had a cooperative arrangement with MIT where you got a bachelor of arts and a bachelor of science after five years. You spent three years at one, and two at the other,

171

or something like that. I entered in a January term with a group of veterans, and we were supposed to catch up over the summer and be in sync with other classmates in the fall. Before the end of that term, I began to realize that I was in the wrong place. It was moving too slowly in the areas that I had interest, so when we had some kind of holiday, I took a train to Boston, went over to MIT, and put in an application and was accepted for the fall of '47.

When I went to school there was a very diverse population of students because we had students in the same class who had started in the '40s before they went into the service and then came back and picked up again. And I was at the other end, where I was in the service first and then started as a freshman when I got out, so we had people that were all different ages and different levels of experience. I did my bachelor's work in civil engineering, which is a basis for other things. Some people went into sanitary engineering from chemical engineering and civil [engineering]. When I did my graduate work, I majored in sanitary engineering. We had a very good, complete, general course in sanitary engineering. We did a lot of work in bacteriology, in chemistry, organic chemistry, things that other engineers don't usually get involved in but are necessary for understanding and dealing with some of the water and wastewater problems.

When I was in school it was like the old cartoons where the lightbulb comes on, because I knew how to do some things, but I didn't know the theory behind it. When you started to learn the theory in engineering school, there was that lightbulb. "Bing!" I said, "Oh, that's why we did it that way." I got my bachelor's in '51 and my master's in '52.

After school I started out working in the wastewater and water field, which was sort of a natural because I had hands-on experience in so many things, and I could see that was pretty important when

I started working in an engineering office. Many design people, when they're designing piping systems, really don't have much feeling for how heavy something like a valve is. I knew because I had to lift them, and those were the little things that really helped. Lots of times when you saw a plant, you could see the hangers and the supports were inadequate because somebody didn't really know what the weights were.

"you wish you had another twenty years to work with someone like that"

George recalls the inspiration of working for dedicated and creative engineers:

In 1952 I went to work for Buck, Seifert & Jost. We were in New York City in those days. That was still in the time when consulting engineering firms, especially in New York State and in most other states, were partnerships. They weren't allowed to be corporations. I don't know when that came about, but nowadays professional corporations among lawyers and doctors and engineers are permitted by law. But the old way provided very, very good training because, since they were partnerships, the partners were fully involved. Nothing ever went out of the office that one of the partners didn't see and examine and whatever. . . . I think that was very good training because you always had superior oversight. There wasn't anything [like] an office boy drawing up some plans at lunch hour that became a project. Couldn't happen.

Buck, Seifert & Jost were involved in water and wastewater treatment, and also in financing and bond financing, where there usually has to be a feasibility report by an engineering firm in addition to the financial feasibility aspect. The engineering report was usually incorporated into the bond documents, and we did a *lot of that kind of work. That was very good experience and . . . I also did a lot of rate work. The partners were very unusual in some ways and an excellent mix. William Seifert was the financial rate specialist. Charles Jost [handled] the design aspect, and George Buck was the head partner and he was a very brilliant man. I learned so much working for him. It was the kind of experience that you wish you had another twenty years to work with someone like that because every day there was something you could learn.*

George Buck and the other two partners originally worked for Nicholas Hill. In the old days, an engineering firm had the partners and the people at the next level were called associates—worker bees—so the three of them were associates in the Hill firm. When Mr. Hill died, they mortgaged their houses and did whatever they had to do to take over and carry it on, which they did. They knew me when I was hired because they had done rate work for Plainfield Union Water Company many years before, so they knew something of my background. They knew that I had hands-on experience, which most of the people coming to a firm didn't have.

"I learned early that water company work is a full-time job"

George Haskew's years growing up in a family with a father working in the water business instilled in him a strong sense of duty about work:

My father's position certainly prepared me for when I came to Hackensack because I learned early that water company work is a full-time job. When there's an emergency, the phone rings at night and you're involved! I always felt like it was my business, in a sense, and it was important for me to be involved. It wasn't just something that you turned off when you went home at night. It was something that went on because I always thought that our job was

providing our customers with an ample quantity of safe water. That's what water companies do, and it kind of puts a focus on being involved. When there's a problem, it puts a focus on trying to be there to make sure that people are taken care of. If there's some reason why an area has to shut down and people have no water for a period of time, then the thing was to make some arrangements so that water could be furnished to them by connecting hoses in a hydrant or, in later years, we had tanker trucks and we could deliver water.

When you had a main break, and the guys are out there at two and three in the morning in the middle of winter, down in a hole in the mud and water, that takes a little bit of dedication. I don't care whether you're union, supervision, or what you are. And they did it. Everybody was dedicated to getting a job completed. We all worked toward one purpose. It's just something you did, that's all.

The company had this . . . policy of reaching out for people of expertise. Spalding was brought in early on for the New Milford filtration plant because of his expertise. They wanted to be sure that the plant would be well run and that things worked right. The company also had a history there of bringing in maritime people as chiefs at New Milford . . . because of the steam equipment. We had a fellow name Jack Schwartz, and then we had Gus Carlson after that. When maritime people are out on a ship and something breaks down, you can't get to the hardware store very easily, so they have to make a part and they have to make do and they know how to fix things. Well, that was a super combination for a plant like New Milford, where we were using steam machinery and old equipment that was perfectly serviceable, but you couldn't call up a manufacturer and get a part, necessarily. We always had a machine shop for that reason.

I remember Carlson complaining about something like a ther-mostat or some kind of electrical gadget, and he'd always be griping. I'd say, "What's a matter, Gus?" And he'd say, "Well, I'm trying to get parts for that thing, and the manufacturer said, 'You should see our new model.'" We're getting into this age of organized replacement—obsolescence—throw it away and get another one. One thing that always characterized the U.S. engineering and plant people, they walked around with a screwdriver and wrench in their pocket, and their first inclination when something didn't work was to fix it . . . to keep it going, make it work.

"we tried to keep New Milford pretty spotless"

George remembers the significance of maintaining the water works for both workers and visitors:

The maintenance was always the thing that we focused on, so they tried to take care of things. The cupola in the front part of the original 1882 building was rotted out years ago, and we replaced the beams up there and fixed that up so it looked the same [see Figure 7 and Color Plate 8]. There wasn't any big reason to change windows and things like that around the plant because heat was never a problem. We always had a lot of white steam, so heat was a by-product of what was going on. . . . If the plant was running, we had heat.

We tried to keep New Milford pretty spotless. It wasn't an easy place to keep that way, but that, again, was the old way of doing things. I remember as a kid, [at] the steam plant we had at the Plainfield Union Company, the brass was always polished. The operating and engineering people that were on every shift; they didn't sit down all the time . . . they polished the brass and

cleaned. The wooden floors were varnished, and they had a rubber mat you walked on and you'd be reluctant to step off the rubber mat because the floor looked so shiny, you might mess it up! It was an industrial operation, but that's the way it was. And in New Milford, the same thinking was there. It wasn't as easy to keep it looking real good because of the building and the changes that took place over the years. But keeping it clean showed that things were being taken care of.

The company was always open to people coming, like school groups. They used to sit on the floor, and the staff would talk to them and try to explain things. It's pretty much a big mystery to everybody where your water comes from! You open the faucet, it comes out, but what happens? So we always considered tours a good thing to do. I remember one time Pete Pallo [see Figure 133] built a model of the gate house, which was a very intricate and interesting structure. It was complicated; it wasn't just something where you had a pump for water coming in and one for water going out [see Figures 44–46]. When kids came on a school tour or something, he could take this thing apart and pull out slides and the gates, and they could see how the water flowed.

"there was a real professionalism about the work"

Barry Schwartz became interested in chemistry through a chemistry set he received for his birthday, and he developed that interest into a career in the water business (Figure 176).

I went to City College of New York and attended NYU for my master's in environmental health science. I had an interest in chemistry and science at an early age, and I sort of migrated into the chemistry part of science. I got a chemistry set for my birthday

Figure 176: Barry Schwartz in the laboratory at New Milford with equipment used in analyzing volatile organic compounds in water samples, 2003. James Hogan

when I was about ten or twelve, and that helped push me into the chemistry area. Chem Craft was the name of the set, and it came with a bunch of chemicals that you could use to make ink, which was about the only thing you could make with those chemicals. . . . That piqued my interest, and I continued from there.

In the service I was sent to the U.S. Army Environmental Hygiene Agency, located at Edgewood Arsenal in Maryland, and there we worked on army industrial complexes doing sanitary surveys, mostly to meet the discharge requirements for wastewater. So I got interested in sanitary chemistry through the army and used that experience to get a job at Buck, Seifert & Jost.

I started at the water company when some of the old-timers were there from the 1940s and 1950s. Utility work at that time was a

dependable, reliable job. People stayed in the job for a long, long time, and many of the executive engineers had worked their way up in the company. There was a real professionalism about the work that was done there, and a great deal of rapport and camaraderie among the staff. There was a work ethic back then among the old-timers. If they had a good job, they knew it was a job they needed to support their families and get their kids through college. It was a dependable job. In exchange for the dependability, they provided the necessary work to accomplish the job. It was a different work ethic in the old days regarding employment, where today people tend to move around jobs more than they did back in those days.

"I was interested in science when I was growing up"

Figure 177: Pat Hoffman, 2002. Reed Gidez

Pat Hoffman's background illustrates how she acquired an interest in learning and the determination to succeed at difficult tasks like those she experienced at her sample collection and laboratory jobs with the company (Figure 177).

I took science courses to better acquaint myself with everything. I was one that . . . always wanted to learn, so I kept on . . . and I took all my jobs seriously. I put myself into all my jobs, because . . . I felt that everybody was needed in a job, where . . . no matter what job you had it was important. The water was very important because people use that every day and need it, and it had to be done right.

I was interested in science when I was growing up. I originally had three scholarships to go to nursing school, and I went to Fairleigh Dickinson and Hackensack Hospital School of Nursing, and unfortunately when you're younger and you don't think things through, I got married to my first husband and I quit school, which was probably the most stupid thing in my life. I did it to help support my children. . . . I went back to school into occupational therapy while I was at the water company, but then I couldn't do the fieldwork because I couldn't get enough time off from the job to go and finish that.

As a child I dreamed of being a nurse. That was my thing. You either became a nurse or a teacher back in my day . . . I always wanted to help people and I worked as a candy striper and a nurse's aide through school. I worked in hospitals and always wanted to become a nurse, so anything to do with science seemed interesting.

My father, William Drummond, was very intelligent. He was born and had grown up . . . in Scotland and came over as a semi-pro soccer player. He was always interested in learning. He read every book in the library, and the library used to send away for new ones for him to read, up to the Catskill library system. He just couldn't get his hands on enough books, and he was so knowledgeable, I was in awe. But he was this quiet little Scottish man, and you'd never know it unless you started asking him, and then you couldn't keep him quiet. So when we were doing homework, we learned not to ask too many questions, because Dad could go on and on for quite a while for the answers . . . He did the New York Times *crossword puzzles every day and he finished them. He knew the Bible. He would proofread every newspaper and anything he picked up with his hands, he would say, "All these mistakes: spelling and grammar." He just knew everything. He was a printer.*

He became a supervisor at Lederle when it was Lederle Laboratories of American Cyanamid. He always wanted to learn more things too, but then supporting a family, he pretty much stayed in his job and did what he could do best.

My dad's mom had come over from Scotland with her five children alone, and she was blind and she did everything by herself. She cleaned house, she cooked, and she showed me how to bake. She had a garden. That whole thing just inspired me. I was so much in awe of her, and that she could do all this stuff and not see. We had started out living in the same house, a two-family house. She lived upstairs with my aunt and we lived downstairs. She was Hannah Quigley and then became Hannah Quigley Drummond, because I was a Drummond. So I grew up that way. Mom was great, too. Her family all came from Paris. My mom and dad just clicked and were married for over thirty years when he died. My mom and dad to the end were so close. There were squabbles and then he'd get the little grin, but it was a nice upbringing. . . . I had a wonderful family.

"I'll never be out of work again!"

Ted Hoffman had a family history with the water company (Figure 178). His mother worked for the water company in Weehawken during World War II, and his father, Frank Hoffman, went to work at the water works as a machinist in 1956, when Ted was 12 years old, and kept working there until he died in 1983. Ted's aunt and uncle also worked for the company. Frank's career and his dedication illustrate the on-the-job training and the work ethic that characterized most of the water works crew. While Ted never worked directly for the company, he went to the water works often and developed strong relationships with the men who worked there and a reverential respect for their work and the site.

Figure 178: *Ted Hoffman in the 1886 engine house, 2003. James Hogan*

My father worked as a machinist at the New Milford Plant for about twenty-five years, and I would frequently be in and out of the plant, but I never worked directly for the Hackensack Water Company. They had a rule that they would not hire relatives. . . . I think they wanted to keep the company as free from political intrigues and family intrigues as they could. . . . I guess they felt that they would have better control over the workers if they weren't connected in that way.

One day I went down and . . . I shaped up for a job as a laborer, and I wound up working for a contractor on one of the Hackensack Water Company projects. I almost fell off my chair! Not only did I wind up working for an outside contractor for a water company project, but they would pay me more than the water company

would pay, and the first plant that I worked on was a small induction plant off Saddle River over on Paramus Road around 1963. There was a drought and they needed water, so they were starting to put in these small induction plants to get as much water as they could. In 1963 or '64, I went up to Haworth and worked on the Haworth filtration plant for another construction job with the Kuchar Brothers, who were general contractors there. In 1964 I went down to Hirschfield Brook and we worked on another induction plant right behind the water company. We put in a balloon dam to actually collect as much water as possible for the drought condition; they were still looking for water. And then the last job that I had with the Kuchar Brothers was on the dam up at Old Tappan . . . in 1965 or '66.

My father was born and grew up in Union City. He went to Union Hill High School and actually aspired to be a doctor. The Depression came along and his funds were wiped out. He never trusted the banks after the Depression. I think he lost around $2,300, which he had saved. I think he graduated around 1938 and bounced around for a little while in the city, and worked for a courier service. The last name of the woman who ran that courier service was "Alfke," and her brother, Charles Alfke [see Figure 133], was a supervisor with the water company. My father put in an application with the water company but never followed through on it.

My mother starting working for the water company before they were married. . . . I believe she was in bookkeeping and she ran the addressograph, which would print the bills. She worked in Weehawken by the Weehawken Water Tower. In the early 1940s if you were female and you were married you could not work for the water company. Once you were married, you had to leave. The water company was very tough in terms of its rules. But it was also a good place to work. My parents had gotten . . . married in Mass-achusetts and they kept that a secret for a while so she could continue to work. In 1944 I was born, and at that point she had to leave. My aunt also worked for the water company as a secretary for one of the bosses in Weehawken, I think Mr. Alfke. My father's brother, my uncle, also worked for the water company for a while. A lot of my family, in one way or another, has been connected with the water company over the years.

Around 1938 my dad went to work at K&E, Keufel & Esser in Hoboken [Figure 179], and worked as a porter for a while, clean-ing out the machines. They were involved in optics and some of the men there, some of the old German precision machinists, took him under their wing and taught him his trade. He stayed with K&E until after the war and then went to work for Chicago Pneumatic and he became a finish machinist. Then he worked for Grumman Aircraft on landing gear for the jets that went into Korea off the carriers. When Chicago Pneumatic was moving out of Garfield in 1952, they wanted him to go up to their plant in Utica, but . . . he wouldn't go because he felt that if he was out of work up there he would not know anyone or be able to get into the job market.

After he was out of for a while, my mother said, "We've got to do something," so she went back to the water company looking for a position. I remember the night in 1956 we

got a call from a Mr. Stark at the water company. He wanted my father and I said, "Oh, you must really want my mother." He said, "No, no, I want your father. Is your father still around?" They offered him a job on his application, which he had put in back in 1938, and he said to my mother, "I'll never be out of work again!" They kept the application for seventeen years! They knew that he was a machinist and they were after machinists.

"every day when I get up and I walk into a shop, I learn something new"

Ted remembers his father's start at the water company and his approach to his work.

Figure 179: *Frank Hoffman at Keufel & Esser in Hoboken, c. 1945. Ted Hoffman*

When my father first went to work there I remember that for the first time he wasn't working at nights. I would get a chance to at least see him during the evenings when he'd get home. I remember there was an excite-ment of going there. I remember for the first time in a long time there was stability in terms of our financial situation. I can remem-ber going out to visit him frequently, especially in the summer. I can remember getting off the bus on Kinderkamack Road and walking down to the plant and in through the front gate. For me it was like going home. I got a chance to know the men and to know the place. It was always exciting for me to walk in there because I never knew what I was going to see or what they were doing. There was always something new and challenging in what they were working on, so it was always an interesting place.

When I think of what was being done there, it was creativity. I would say that my father could get a piece of steel to talk to you. It was just unbelievable what he could do and having the experience in the defense industry during the war, he had worked on periscopes and range finders and could take very, very small screws with very, very tiny threads, and use a jeweler's screwdriver and a magnifying glass and put things together on gauges and whatever. Or he could take a manhole cover, flip it up on a machine, and cut it down to wherever you wanted it to go. He had a wide range of abilities. He could deal with anything that he wanted to deal with, and he knew what had to be done.

One of the things he always said to me, and I think it stressed his involvement with knowledge and being able to do things, he said, "You know, in this world we have a lot of material objects, but they can be taken away from you very quickly." And I think that came back down to the Depression era and the bank account he lost! I don't think he ever got over working very hard and losing his savings. He said, "But there's one thing that no one can ever take away from you and that is your knowledge—the knowledge to do something. That is yours! No one can take that from you." I truly believe that he followed that rule. He got a great deal of knowledge. As he said to me, "I learned along the way" he said, "every day when I get up and I walk into a shop, I learn something new." At K&E, he learned to work with optics, with small tolerances and precision. When he got to Chicago Pneumatic, he understood fully what the finish cut was. If he screwed up the piece on the last run, you're talking maybe wasting $2,000, $3,000, or $4,000 on a ruined piece. He learned to really work a Warner Swayze No. 2 turret layer, to the point

where Chicago Pneumatic wanted to move him along with his machine up to Utica.

When he got to the water company, he brought all this knowledge with him. He had a way of holding a piston internally with a jig that he had made; an expanding jig that would come in and expand internally into that piston, so he could cut any tolerance he wanted on it, and they still have the jigs. They asked me if I would leave them there when he passed away and I did. His mind was always working. If he needed help, he would get one of the younger guys to give him a hand and move stuff in place, but my father actually did a lot of things by himself. I watched him jockey a lathe in place by himself with a series of levers and rollers. He was mechanical and managed to get wherever he had to go.

I think machinists have to have a self-reliant attitude. It's part of the personality, it's part of the creative drive that's usually in them because when you look at a piece of steel, what form do you see in it? Then you've got to put it in place and go to it. And a piece of steel may be very large or very small, so you'd better figure out how you're going to do this. They had a sense of mission. I think the war years gave them a sense of mission. When I look back, my father's war years were tough. The weeks that he spent down at K&E were long and arduous. In many ways, he sacrificed himself throughout the years working hard.

"he was always willing to accept the challenge"

Frank Hoffman's dedication and pride in his trade was evident at work and at home, as his son Ted recalls:

There were times during the summers when my father would be extremely busy, because the summers were the times when they *would pump a great deal of water and the pumps would run continually, everything was going. In the winters you didn't have that drain, that draw on the reservoir or the water supply, so the machines were not really working to full capacity. . . . Whenever it got to be very warm, then the machines were working at high capacities and in some cases they would start to break down. When you had a breakdown in the summer, then it was a serious thing, then you had problems. I think my father, internally, was always a nervous person. He . . . was always willing to accept the challenge, but always was a nervous person, being a precision person. There was always a drive to do and . . . get the job done right. I remember sometimes he would be stressed out. We would be talking at the table maybe over the weekend, and he would say, "Oh I've got a tough job coming up tomorrow." And I knew he had been thinking about it. Eventually he would figure it out and get in there and do what had to be done.*

He took care of his shop and he did what he had to do there. Whatever had to be done, get out of his way, and let him do it. That was his philosophy. He took pride in his work. When you looked at what he was doing, it was there. . . . He always said that his most valuable tool was the black mechanical pencil he always had with him. I asked him why and he said, "Well, this way I can keep track and I can verify what the paper mechanics are telling me. You'd be surprised—they give me these plans at times and the numbers don't line up," he said, "the fractions don't add up to where they should be." Paper mechanics, that's what he called them.

Machinists never made big money in terms of their skills and their labor time that it took to get to that degree of proficiency. They never made a great deal of money. As a matter of fact, it was one of the poorest paying . . . trades. I remember my father's one claim to fame as a machinist. He said, "I've been a successful

machinist over my life, and the reason I consider myself successful is," and he held up his hands, and he said, "I still have my ten fingers."

My father knew the place (New Milford Plant) was old and historic, because he had to repair everything that was in it. He used to say that the water company never buys anything new. They make you go back and take the old junk and put it back together again, but they don't spend money on new equipment. He was always talking about that. He told me that everything in the place leaked. He said, "It's like working with Public Service, there are lights all around but the bulbs are burned out. There isn't one thing that doesn't leak around here."

"a very, very close family atmosphere"

The nature of the work and the security of the job fostered close relationships and long-term employment. Jim Flynn went to work for the water company shortly after high school and stayed for thirty-four years.

When you went to work for the water company, you would come there and the old-timers would tell you if you stay here five years, you'll never leave. It's like a job for life, which it was. It was a family atmosphere, a very, very close family atmosphere. If somebody had an operation or was out sick for a while, a collection was taken up by the other employees. And if somebody was in the hospital for something, a lot of the guys would go to the hospital to see him. It's a little different today, I guess, than it was back then.

Barry Schwartz, who worked at the water company for 32 years, recalls various activities it organized for the workforce:

In the old days the water company had picnics during the springtime. They would bring all the employees up to Bear Mountain. Once in a while they would have a festivity at the plant if there was something new going on. There were some teams, bowling teams, back then. Every year the company held a service recognition dinner, where they would provide employees with an award for being there twenty, thirty, and forty years. It was held every year and still is. Employees that were there for twenty, thirty, and forty years would get a pin, and they would get some remuneration, normally stocks.

Miles Kuchar's father started contracting construction jobs for the water company in the 1930s. After Miles joined him in the business, he worked on Hackensack Water Company projects in five decades, from the 1940s to the 1980s (Figure 180).

They were fabulous people, everybody who worked for the water company. The people that worked there were first class. . . . They worked hard to make it a family organization and they all worked together. . . . I have a lot of respect for everybody there. It was a wonderful place to work. We always had a lot of fun and laughed, and we'd go out and eat and socialize and go fishing together. When it was time to work, we were working, when it was time to play, we played. Three times a year we'd go out to Montauk to go fishing. . . . We'd get on a small boat; the boat only took six people. We'd catch sometimes 500 pounds of fish in an hour out there and come home with 200 pounds after we cleaned it. We did nothing but laugh from the time we left the yard 'til the time we got back. That's the kind of people they were. They knew what they were doing. They worked together as a family. You couldn't want to work with nicer people. It's a shame most of them are all gone by now.

"they wanted it to be the best"

Dan Hoffman started at the water works after the service, stayed there for forty-eight years, and got to know every part of the company's supply and

Figure 180: *Miles Kuchar in front of the gate house and filtration house, 2003. James Hogan*

Figure 181: *Dan Hoffman, second from right, in the New Milford boiler house, c. 1980. The other men standing in front of the boilers are, from left to right, Paul Timkanic, Dick Hensch, and Frank Maritz, all of the engineering department.*
Pat Hoffman

distribution system (Figure 181). He was "the problem solver" people would call when anything came up, because he had worked on and studied all aspects of the system for decades. His wife, Pat Hoffman, recalls Dan's dedication to maintaining the water flow, a dedication that inspired many of his fellow workers over the decades:

> Dan Hoffman grew up in Oradell. There's a park in Oradell named after his brother, Robert Hoffman, who died in the war. The house that [Dan] lived in . . . is right near there, close to the plant. He had some family member [who] had worked there, and since he also lived so close, he was just really interested in the water company and the surrounding area, because that's where his family was from. He got involved there and . . . worked for the water company for forty-eight years. Aside from his family, the water company was his love. He would be there twenty-four hours a day if they needed him. He was so proud of the engines. The company was his pride, that's all he talked about. His face glowed when he talked about it. He got to know where all the mains were, what directions the water would flow, the speed. He knew everything, so everybody always went to him. He had this all in his head, memorized, and if he didn't, he found out everything. He really loved the water company.
>
> He started working when he was in his teens, and then he left for a year to go into the service because his brother was in the war, and he wanted to go find him, but he ended up finding out that his brother had died. . . . He started working with the steam and the boilers, and he said it was very noisy. He took such pride and everything had to be polished. Everything always had to stay clean, and they wanted it to be the best. Most of them that worked there had that idea. . . . That's how Dan was. He just took great pride in whatever he did, and he wanted to know the most about whatever he did so he always did schooling . . . he was always taking courses and doing things to learn more, and trying to learn more on the jobs. That was just in Dan himself, and working with the other people that had similar values helped.
>
> He started out learning the business from the men that worked there, but through schooling and experience he moved up, and he went for his Gold Seal license. He continually took more courses at Bergen Tech and Rutgers and different places. They actually wanted him to teach at Bergen Tech because he knew so much about the workings of the various pumps and things. He did

certain things for PSE&G. He earned his engineer's license. He got his Black Seal and he just always wanted to learn more, so he did. He took management courses; he just didn't want to sit back and say that was it. Until the day he died, he was trying to read up on everything and keep up on everything.

"he always wanted to know more and more about the company"

Dan Hoffman was totally dedicated to the plant and the people who worked there, as Pat remembers:

A lot of the bosses over him . . . went to Dan because he spent so many years there where the others hadn't, and a lot of the others came from colleges, where maybe you learn a lot from books, but you don't know from the experience, and you don't know the system because you come into a strange, new system. He just knew because he was a hands-on manager, and he always wanted to know more and more about the company and its operations. If any of the control operators had any problems or anything, they would call, and he just knew it. I don't know how he knew all this, but he did.

He was out there in the field all the time to see how it was going and to make sure things were right. All the well sites have pumping areas, so if anything went wrong with any of those, he was available. The well sites would break down and you had to keep repairing them to keep them going, or take pieces from other wells. Some of the well sites would be closed down and they would have to reopen them for various reasons, so they had to be worked on to get restarted. He knew how to do it because he had been involved in all these various things.

Dan was continually talking about various people at work, and they really were family. They all worried about each other. They got to be very close. When he became manager, he was very much concerned with his workers, and he didn't want anything happening to any of them. If they had a problem, it was his problem. He didn't want any of them to lose their jobs, and he would do anything he could to help them. He just took on all of them as his family, like he was going to watch out for them. So if there were any emergencies and they got called out, he was the first one to be there. He made sure he was with them. He was allowed to do just so much, because it was also union and you can do just so much, but he had to make sure that everything was going right so they weren't hurt. To a point you're limited, but he did as much as he was able to do and if nobody said anything, he would jump right in and help. The guys at the plant were really good together. The original New Milford crew was like a family and they would torment each other with practical jokes. Everybody liked each other a lot and they were always there for each other. That's one thing I liked. I thought that was a great thing, and I got to know all of them, and I really was happy that I did.

He talked a lot about the company because that was the only thing he was really involved with. He knew what was going on in the world. He kept up with all the news, but he was just twenty-four hours a day involved with what was happening at the water company. If there were any problems, that was his main thing that he was concerned with. He used to talk about the various pumps there and about how he would climb up on them and they'd be hot. Every so often he'd come out with little stories. He didn't say too much about himself, but he talked about the water company and the guys. I remember him talking about the noise and the different things that were hot when they went up, climbed up, but he didn't care, he was just so happy to be there.

"don't do anything to these walls!"

Dan Hoffman and his men knew the water works was historic and they wanted to keep it going, as Pat recalls:

When we were working at New Milford, all the guys that were there, they sensed that they were in a historic place. They all knew. . . . Dan and the other guys instilled it that this was historic and that they had better respect it. He knew it had historic significance right from the beginning. His attitude was "Don't do anything to these walls!" and he instilled pride in the workers and they all, for the most part, carried it through. I think they all had a special feeling about it. When they moved, they didn't have the same feeling over in Haworth. He was so sorry when the old equipment stopped. He was so proud of the old way and the old company, and he used to talk about it and he was just so sorry. . . . When they were going to close New Milford, it was like a heartbreak to him because . . . he kept asking them if they couldn't just keep so much water pumping out of there in addition to Haworth, the new plant. Eventually, it had to close, and a part of him went with it because that was his pride and joy.

He was always happy to see that things were going to go better. They told him they thought it was a change for the better, but he still didn't want to let go of the past. That was what he loved and he thought about the most, how it had been when he grew up there, because he spent so many years there. He grew up there in the sense that you mature as you're getting older and you're working on the job and you're learning new things, and he started out so young there and it just became his whole life.

You don't find the dedication as much now. Nowadays, people don't seem to stay in their jobs that long, not because of themselves but because most of these companies have moved them around, or they really had to keep moving, whereas he could stay in one company and he got to. I really loved the fact that this was, almost you could say, his *company, because he took such pride in it and he was so happy to work there.*

"Danny took care of his men"

As a contractor, Miles Kuchar worked with Dan Hoffman and George Haskew for many years. The examples they set and the bonds they formed remain vibrant in Miles' memory:

During the war his brother was lost out at sea, and Danny never finished high school. He joined the Navy to take his brother's place. Going back further, Danny was 8 years old when his father died and Danny had to go out and work to help put food on the table. And he went to work on a farm and he told me he worked so hard, harder than anyone else on the farm and they gave him a raise. That's the kind of a guy he was. And no matter who you talk to about Danny, they don't have a bad word because he never said anything bad about anybody else.

Dan started working at the water company shoveling coal. . . . When I first shook his hand I used to kid him that his hands were like leather and towards the end they were soft. But he worked his way up the ladder and became head electrician and head maintenance fellow. If he heard something breaking down in the middle of the night, he'd be down there fixing it. Danny really knew that plant. He knew every phase of it. His office was right there in the pumping station. And when they built the Haworth plant they used jet engines and they had problems at first, with [the engines] run-

ning at such high speed, if a bird or something got in there and broke the fins. Danny was remarkable . . . he could fix them and maintain them and all.

The former chief engineer, George Haskew, if he heard Danny was working down there he'd roll up his sleeves and get all greasy with Danny, helping him out. That was a big asset because George knew what had to be done and how long it would take to do it. They were both wonderful people who had a lot of respect for one another. You couldn't want nicer people. George was a fine business fellow. He had such a memory that you could talk about things that were done in the past and he'd remember the little things that everybody else had forgotten. He was very well liked. All those fellows were liked.

Danny took care of his men; if he saw there was any friction he would jump in there and stop it before it got too far. He would promote them when they deserved it and when they really worked for it, and consequently they had a tremendous amount of respect for him. He was just a fabulous guy, and to think he never had a high school education and climbing the ladder. . . . He worked hard for it.

As the careers of Pat Herman and Dan Hoffman intersected, Pat remembers the family atmosphere at the water company that helped bring them together:

When I was a sample collector in Spring Valley I'd bring the samples each day from Rockland County down to New Milford. Dan used to be up in Spring Valley for problems too, because he was the problem solver that got sent around, . . . so we did see each other. Dan always took it very seriously and he . . . got to know where all the mains were, their locations, the water flows and which direction they were coming . . . from in each main, whether they were from the wells. . . . [I]f there were problems . . . up in Spring Valley he would go up and try to help out. They usually called him and

they actually wanted him to work up there, but his office was down with the parent company, Hackensack Water, at the New Milford Plant. We knew of each other, but not anything more than that.

We got to know each other better when I would drop the samples off each day at New Milford. All the foremen under Dan, who was the manager down there, would say that I should talk to him, and they would push him out to see me because they had found that I had been a divorced mother, bringing up my kids myself, and he was a widower. They just thought that he needed somebody so they would continue, and . . . Walt Wilson and different ones were the cupids, and they did all different things to try and get us together . . . and sometimes I'd find flowers in my truck and different things. It just ended up where we did click and we did start seeing each other. We couldn't see each other very much, because I was always working. . . . I worked two jobs around the clock and he was always busy at the water company. But we did get together and it all just kept going, . . . and we had a wedding involving all the water company and all my family. The kids were all in it, so that they would be involved. I had two children, two daughters. We got married in 1992, and our wedding included my nephews and nieces and water company people for him. Everybody had a great time. We had a reception and all the foremen and all the different ones just hammed it up and had a good time. They tormented us.

Dan had quit high school to go into the service to find his brother, but the high school officials said that he would get his diploma. He had taken extra courses to make sure he would get it. He wanted it so bad. He had done all the work. . . . That was one of the sad things, because he kept calling them and they kept promising him that he would get this diploma in the mail, and as he got sicker he would call and then he would ask me to call, and the diploma arrived the day after I buried him.

Barry Schwartz and MaryFrances Schwartz shared a similar experience to that of Pat and Dan Hoffman, as MaryFrances recalls (Figure 182):[179]

There were several situations that led to marriage at the plant. It wasn't that unusual. Dating someone at the plant was okay if you were in different departments, but working in the same department was frowned upon because people were worried about favoritism. Barry and I happened to become divorced about the same time, and in talking with each other . . . we realized we had a lot in common. One day Barry offered to help with my camera to take some pictures and we started to realize we had more in common than just being a boss and employee. Then we started dating and

***Figure 182:** Barry Schwartz and MaryFrances Schwartz in the 1882 pump house, 2003. James Hogan*

at first we kept it quiet. But people would see us around Bergen County. We'd go bike riding in Van Saun Park and we would bump into somebody we knew so it wasn't kept a secret very long. We dated about a year and once we were married, and things were out in the open, there were problems with me working in Barry's department as an employee, so I transferred over to billing, which was then located in the Bergen Mall. We've been married 26 years and we have three kids.

"they were always proud of what they did"

Ted Hoffman began visiting his father, Frank Hoffman, at the water works when he was about 12 years old, and kept going there regularly for the next thirty years. Getting to know the water company and the men who worked there, and seeing their dedication to their jobs, made a strong impression on him, especially since the work was often hard and dangerous.

The water company functioned as an independent network. They had a maintenance crew . . . involved with maintaining boilers and another crew for the machinery. They had a chemical crew . . . applying the chemicals, moving the chlorine tanks and so on into place. They had their own police department; they had their own landscaping crews . . . they had their own chemistry department, their own engineering department, their own payroll department, their billing department; they had the meter reading services and the meter department. They also had construction crews digging up the streets 365 days a year, twenty-four hours at a time. You always felt sorry for those guys, especially during the winter.

When you look at the water company's financial history on the stock market for the number of years that it was on the big board, it never lost money. That was a blue chip stock. That family unit that they called the water company, people working together, not working against each other . . . they felt that they belonged there. They had a sense of mission and they had a . . . dedication that they were going to do the job . . . and that is reflected in the quality of the stock for all of those years.

When I first went to New Milford, Gus Carlson was the supervisor and the plant manager was a gentleman by the name of Meyers. Gus and I always got along well and anytime I was there, we'd stop in and see him. We'd talk and he would take me along wherever he was going and show me something. They were always proud of what they did and I wanted to know what they were doing and they wanted to show me what they were doing, . . . so in a sense I felt I was an adopted member of this place. It was a great place to work.

"the people there really made the difference"

Ted remembers the strong relationships that developed at the water works and how they affected his father and himself:

I think it was an enjoyable place to work for my father, with the young people, Joey Himes, Bobby Munson, Jesse Jones, and those people that he knew [who] had passed away, like Reineke and Meyer. Meyer was in the tool portion of the shop where they had a tool cage, and he was the tool keeper. If you needed equipment, you'd have to sign out with Hank Meyer. There were always jokes. . . . My father had picked up this old stereo unit he found in the garbage going to work one day, and took it in the shop and fixed it, so he had a little stereo music. He had his coffee pot. People would come there in the morning; it was sort of a rallying point. You never knew what was going to be discussed in the shop or who was going to be in that shop in the morning before they were sent out on a job and so on. It was a place that people constantly came in

and out of because they needed to pause or they needed advice, and so on. The place was sort of a meeting ground. . . . When I would walk into it, regardless of how old I was, I never knew what to expect. It was always exciting. Something new was happening in there, something different was going together.

For me the people there really made the difference, knowing not only the guy who worked in a trench, but the guy who worked on the top as well. I met Jules Von Scheidt [see Figure 133], the vice president of the company, sitting in my father's shop with his suit on, sitting in this old greasy chair talking with my father. Some of the supervisors would come in and they'd wonder what Von Scheidt was doing there. It's funny, the first time Gus Carlson was going to introduce Von Scheidt to my father, he said, "Oh, Gus, I've known Frank a long time." Gus Carlson couldn't understand how, and Jules Von Scheidt said, "I used to read the funny papers to him." It was like coming home, in many respects.

My father had a friend there that I feel honored to know and to have met. Back in the '50s, 1957 or '58, or I was in a physics course and I needed a project, and I . . . did one on water filtration, and he introduced me to the chemist at that time, whose name was Paul Tamer [see Figures 107 and 129]. Paul Tamer, along with George Spalding [see Figure 133], pioneered active carbon filtration in that plant. It was Paul Tamer who really came up with the idea of putting carbon into the coagulation basin. They had tried it on the filters first, and clogged up the filters. He was a young man at that time, in the '30s when they developed this, but by the time I met him, he was getting ready to retire. He was a very short man and he had emigrated here with his family from Russia; a very quiet man, but what a delightful soul, tremendous and bright.

He and my father knew each other from the old days, when my father's sister worked down in Weehawken. They would talk. Paul would take me down to the shop or they'd be up making coffee in the lab with the distilled water up there. My father said when you tasted the tea or the coffee from the plant water, you always got sort of a chlorine taste, . . . which they tried to get away from. Paul didn't believe in using chemicals to the greatest strength to purify water. He wanted to use the least amount of chlorine and chemicals he could use to make the water potable. He said there are other risks. I learned more about filtration from him and that project. . . than I could've read about. It was wonderful. It got to the point where I felt honored to meet Paul. . . . When Paul Tamer retired, Eddie Mullin [see Figure 161] became the chemist and the ritual continued. He would always be up in the laboratory with the distilled water and they'd have coffee up there.

"they were very proud of the function that they performed there"

The family atmosphere and the work ethic stand out in Ted's recollection of the water works.

Coming from my background, I think the work ethic had always been very, very important. When I [look] back, work was an important issue. An honest day's work for an honest day's dollar. That was something my father had always instilled in me, and I always have lived that. I remember the first time walking into the plant. My father introduced me to the people that he was going to be working with and . . . they would take an interest. They would want to show you what they were doing, especially if you were interested in it. . . . They would take their time to explain to you what was happening. Over the years, I got to know them to a point that I would feel that I was going home, that they were my family. I had the run of the place. . . .

I think when I look back, what I learned from those men was basically a sense of responsibility . . . I think they had a sense of pride in terms of what they did. They were very proud of the function that they performed there. They realized that water was an important commodity for the entire county and you couldn't say, "Well, I'm not going to get these pumps working for a couple of days. I'll take my time." Or, "I'll wait for the part to come in." They realized that there was a sense of urgency. That dedication stuck with me, and it still is with me. . . . I think when you look at doing a job, you do it to the best of your ability, or you don't do it. I think that was another philosophy I learned both from my dad and from the people who worked there.

The men there took me in as one of their family members. It was always interesting to get their opinion of higher education. They always . . . were interested in whether I was continuing with my studies and how I was doing in school and to stay in school and so on. They would say, "You don't want to be doing this. You don't want to get involved in what we're doing here." . . . They felt that in terms of the future, in terms of the work they did, they always wanted something better for their children. My father was not a college grad. Definitely he had the mentality for it, and never got there. But he definitely wanted me to get there and there was never a doubt in anyone's mind that the way out of where they were was through education.

"not an easy place to work"

Despite difficulties and hazards at the plant, the men that Ted Hoffman knew there stuck with their work and used their talents collectively to keep the water flowing.

I think when you looked at where they worked and what they did, . . . it was dangerous . . . it was dirty, it was something that many people wouldn't even want to get involved with. It was not an easy place to work. Whether you were dealing with chlorine or . . . asbestos or . . . coal or . . . cutting oil, it was a dangerous place to be. . . . I remember two incidents. My father fractured a vertebra . . . by grabbing something that had slipped. A man named Potter was cleaning out the coagulation basin in the winter when it was icy in there. It was difficult to hang on to the hose. You'd be slipping and sliding. Potter went out with the other men and the hose got away, and he slipped and fell and cracked his wrist in a couple of places. So it was a hard and dangerous place to be. You could lose your life there . . . very quickly. It was not a place you would aspire to stay in if you thought about the conditions.

But they did it and they worked at it on a continual basis. Many of them sacrificed their health there. Over the years, doing that work takes its toll on the body. I could actually see some of the men age in front of my eyes. You'd come back if you hadn't seen them for six or eight months, and all of a sudden . . . they looked old and they had been through a lot. It was a tough job, but I learned that sense of dedication, that sense of mission, that sense of obligation, that sense of work ethic. All of that was very, very important for my involvement in life.

When I think back and I look at some of the men I knew at that time, . . . they were common men and normal, everyday people, but collectively they were a talented crew. There wasn't anything that couldn't be done in that plant. They would come together and do it. I always thought of Gulliver's Travels, the Lilliputians, there were always big machines and there were all the little guys running around and working on them. They wouldn't let people in certain areas, but I always had the freedom to go anywhere in that plant. It felt like I was going home and I felt like I was part of the family there.

"I never stopped trying"

Jesse Jones worked for the water company for almost thirty-seven years, twenty-four of them at New Milford. He started there as a laborer and rose through a series of jobs that enabled him to work in all the different areas of the plant (see Figures 168, 169, and Figure 183).[180]

I started working at the New Milford Plant in August of 1966 as a laborer. My job included unloading chemical trucks and feeding the chemicals into the different places. I had a choice between being a letter carrier and working at the water company, and I chose the water company because I saw a better future there.

When I first walked into the plant and saw those steam engines, they were something I had never seen before and I was amazed by

Figure 183: *Jesse Jones in front of the waste gates by New Milford Avenue, 2003.* James Hogan

189

them. . . . I thought that I had chosen the right place to come and work. There was so much to learn, and I was so much interested in this place. I worked there a couple of months and I knew it was definitely the place I wanted to be, with the people and the atmosphere. The people I got introduced to over the first two or three months were very nice, very helpful. They were eager to help you learn. And from that I knew there was a great future.

As other jobs came up throughout the company, I applied for them, automatically. You had to have seniority for an upgrade job. If nobody in the company put up for it, you might have a chance before anyone else from outside. Some jobs I didn't get, but I never stopped trying. Finally I got a job in chemical treatment after about six years. That included working with the chemicals and the chemical equipment. As time went on, I became a leader of the maintenance people, in charge of the other maintenance people. At New Milford they had two sides, the maintenance side at the pumping station, and other side was the filtration plant, and I was working both sides. I worked with Ted Hoffman's dad [see Figure 179], who was a machinist, and he used to make parts for the steam engines that we had to use to maintain them.

The relations between the men were great. It used to be understood that some of the older guys didn't want to show you anything because they were a little afraid for their jobs. The old coal stokers and such were afraid of losing jobs because they were getting older and they feared they would get booted out by the younger generation. . . . But when I came I think the generation was changing. The newer guys were more energetic and willing to share thoughts and ideas. With me they were so willing to teach me. They weren't so afraid of losing their jobs to new people.

It was a really great time when I came. I heard someone say the building used to kind of rock and roll. Well in the boiler room, those guys that used to operate the boilers, they used to play their musical stuff on weekends when a supervisor wasn't around. They had little musical parties, and they would try to teach us how to play so that you could join in and there would be a real musical circle. There was a colored fella who was a musician. Another guy played a cello—he played Irish music, Irish gigs. The guys would be messing around, clowning around, like that. I never played—I just listened. Most of the other guys that were on shift work. They played during the night hours to help the time pass, to have a little party like. Mostly I miss the guys and the camaraderie. That was the best thing about working at New Milford—they become like your family.

When they closed New Milford, actually 90 percent of the guys didn't want to accept going to Haworth. They didn't want to leave New Milford. It was like leaving your home for the first time. Nobody really wanted to leave. Everybody could see the change coming, and now we had to go with the change. Follow the flow, you know. But it was hard to get used to Haworth, and it took a while. We used to work at Haworth sometimes when we were at New Milford, but home base was always New Milford and we missed it. I just retired from Haworth. Already I miss that plant too.

"it was inspirational and unforgettable"

Frank Vierling (Figure 184), a longtime Oradell resident and the Oradell Historian, grew up near the water works. His memories of the site from the 1930s include a childhood sense of wonder at its scale and complexity that many youths must have shared.[181]

There was no Little League and no television to keep small boys entertained in the 1930s. We made our own amusements. One

Figure 184: Frank Vierling in front of the boiler house, 2003. James Hogan

great source of enjoyment was our bicycles. I was about 9 years old when my friends and I first started bicycle tours of the towns surrounding Oradell. Haworth, Dumont, Harrington Park, Bergenfield, New Milford, and sometimes Paramus, Westwood, and Ridgewood made up our world of exploration. Our cycling often ended in New Milford. We'd stop at the Sattley Beverage Company, where they would treat us to a warm soda, right off the production line. Even when warm it was refreshing on a hot summer day. The Hackensack Water Company plant was usually our final stop. In all of our wanderings it was always the most exciting and interesting.

To small boys it was awesome. The memory still is awesome for me today, some seventy years later. . . . New Milford Avenue split the complex in two. South of the road was a long brick building

used to store the unending supply of coal needed to fire the steam boilers [see Figures 8, 18, and 24]. With the conversion from steam to electricity the coal storage building was razed. By the time we were making our inspections, the boilers had been moved across the street to the main plant. Early pictures show the boiler furnace smoke stack at the east end of the storage building [see Figure 19]. The coal arrived via the Erie Railroad to a siding at the foot of New Milford Avenue, probably the same railroad siding used earlier by the Van Buskirk mill, which once stood there on the west bank of the Hackensack River. By my day, the mill had been gone for many years. Watching the coal moved from railcar into the storage building was an extra adventure, which called for a special trip when word of that activity reached us. There was a large door on the west end of the coal building facing the river [see Figure 132]. From it, a railroad trestle descended across the river to a pit beneath a railroad siding. A coal car stood there in readiness to supply fuel for the hungry boilers. The building doors would swing open and a cable car would descend in some miraculous unseen way to the pit beneath the waiting railroad car. There, down in the pit, an unseen worker would open the car's hopper and fill the cable car. The car would then silently glide back into the black interior of the storage shed. We would eagerly await the car's emergence for another load. Until we discovered the man under the tracks, it all seemed to happen by magic. Car after car delivered their contents into that black interior.

From the storage building the coal was pushed in miniature coal cars on narrow railroad tracks across New Milford Avenue into the boiler room. There, stokers spread the coal across a moving grate that carried the fuel into the flames. Some years later the little cars were eliminated when a conveyor carried the coal under the road and onto the moving grate. The abandoned tracks remained across the road for many years. In earlier days the coal storage building had also been the steam generating plant. Steam, instead of coal, was delivered to the pumps by a pipe over New Milford Avenue [see Figure 19]. By far the most exciting part of our stops was to look in the doors of the main pump house. In summer the doors were always open wide [see Figure 25], an open invitation for us to "come see." It was always an awesome sight. The giant machines with their great turning flywheels, their shiny pistons riding up and then plunging down, and the hissing steam were all exciting and thrilling, and at the same time a bit scary to little boys. The workers encouraged us to come in, but we never ventured more than a few feet into the vast plant. Around back we could enter the boiler room to see the coal fed slowly into the white hot fires that generated the steam power. It was too hot to linger there very long.

Years later, on school field trips, we were formally introduced to the working of the whole plant. It was inspirational and unforgettable. We were guided throughout the plant and learned of its progressive growth as the demand for pure water grew, from the first 1882 pump house to the giant pumps of the day. We were taken through the laboratory, where purification was explained, and told of the advancements that were developed right there in that laboratory. I remember a bell jar filled with chlorine gas used in the purification process. "There is enough gas in that jar to kill thousands," explained one of the technicians. The filtration beds were demonstrated to show us how they trapped out any impurities through successive layers of stones, gravel, and sand. And how carbon was used to control the odor and taste.

These scenes remain vivid in my memory today, some seventy years later, as I'm sure it does for my contemporaries, and the many generations of school children that followed.

Chapter 8

A Rare Surviving Example of Early Water Treatment and Distribution

When United Water Resources closed the New Milford Plant in 1990 it examined various options for the future of the site. In 1991 it hired Sheffield Archaeological Associates to undertake a preliminary historic survey of the water works. The Sheffield group surveyed the extensive documentation of the plant at the site (Figure 185) and in the water company's engineering office, and it examined the historic significance of the buildings and machinery. Because of their significance and because of environmental considerations, the water company decided that the future of Van Buskirk Island and the water works would best be addressed at the public level. In 1993 United Water donated the island and its historic structures plus some adjacent land along the Hackensack River, a total of approximately 47 acres, to the citizens of Bergen County for public benefit uses, along with $1 million to help the county address the site.[182]

After considering private redevelopment proposals for the site, the county and the Borough of Oradell in 1996 endorsed the concept of a passive park on Van Buskirk Island and the restoration of a portion of the historic water works. The county assembled a task force to examine the potential characteristics of the proposed park and the partial restoration. To assist this process the county commissioned an historic structure report for the water works complex.

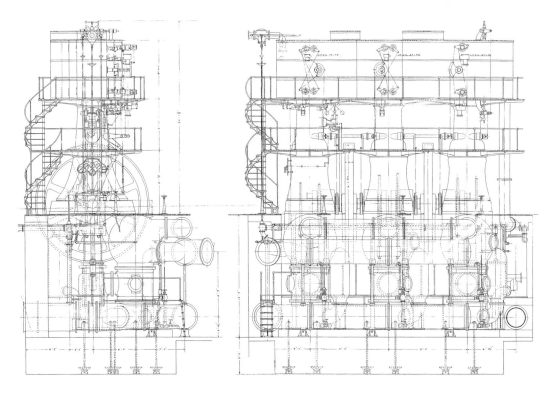

Figure 185: *"General Drawing, 18 Million Gallon Pumping Engine, Hackensack Water Company, 12/11/01." The No. 6 Allis-Chalmers VTE pumping engine installed in the 1898 engine house (see Figures 32–34). Numerous other original drawings of the historic pumping engines in the pumping station office that were documented by the 1991 Sheffield Report have unfortunately disappeared. Allis-Chalmers Co., Edw. P. Allis Works, Milwaukee, Wisconsin. Water Works Conservancy*

Because of its gradual deterioration and the lack of a preservation plan, Preservation New Jersey designated the water works as one of the state's Most Endangered Sites for 1996. In designating the site, Preservation New

Jersey reported: "An impressive group of structures, the Hackensack Water Company is considered an American engineering marvel for its historic architecture, steam pumping equipment, and its role in the development of modern water purification." In September 1996, a group of concerned citizens in Oradell and the surrounding area formed the Water Works Conservancy to advocate for the full preservation of the water works under the umbrella of the nonprofit Oradell Arts and Business Coalition, Inc. The Conservancy organized and in 1997 submitted a nomination prepared by Albin Rothe Architects-Planners of Mahwah of the New Milford Plant to the New Jersey Register and the National Register of Historic Places. In 1997 the county and the Conservancy collaborated on an application to the New Jersey Historic Trust for a preservation grant to undertake preliminary restoration work on the plant.[179]

In 1998 John Bowie Associates of Media, Pennsylvania, and Jane Mork Gibson of Norristown, Pennsylvania, completed the historic structure report, which documented the evolution of the pumping station from 1882 to 1918 through its existing elevations and layout (Figure 186), and the existing equipment and the adjacent piping network (Figure 187). The report documented the evolution of the filtration plant from 1905 to 1955 through its existing elevations and layout (Figure 188), and it illustrated the filtration process of the original filter house (Figure 189).

"a testament to . . . New Jersey's role in the development of our nation"

In 1998 the New Jersey Historic Trust awarded the county a grant from the New Jersey Historic Preservation Bond Program for the water works,

Figure 186: *"Pumping Station." The ground floor plan, top right, shows the evolution of the engine house (1A-original 1882 section; 1B-1886 addition; 1C-1891 addition; 1D-1898 addition; and 1G-1911 addition) and the boiler house (1E-1898 original section and 1F-1906 addition). John Bowie Associates and Jane Mork Gibson, "The New Milford Plant of the Hackensack Water Company, Historic Structures Report," 1998*

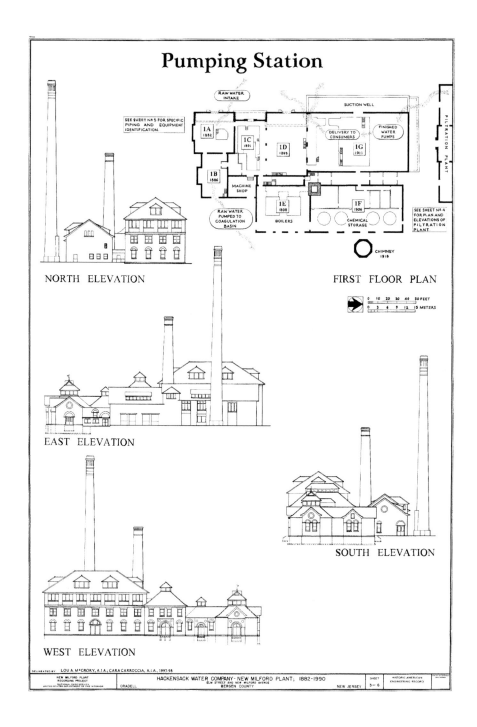

Pumping Station

NORTH ELEVATION

FIRST FLOOR PLAN

EAST ELEVATION

SOUTH ELEVATION

WEST ELEVATION

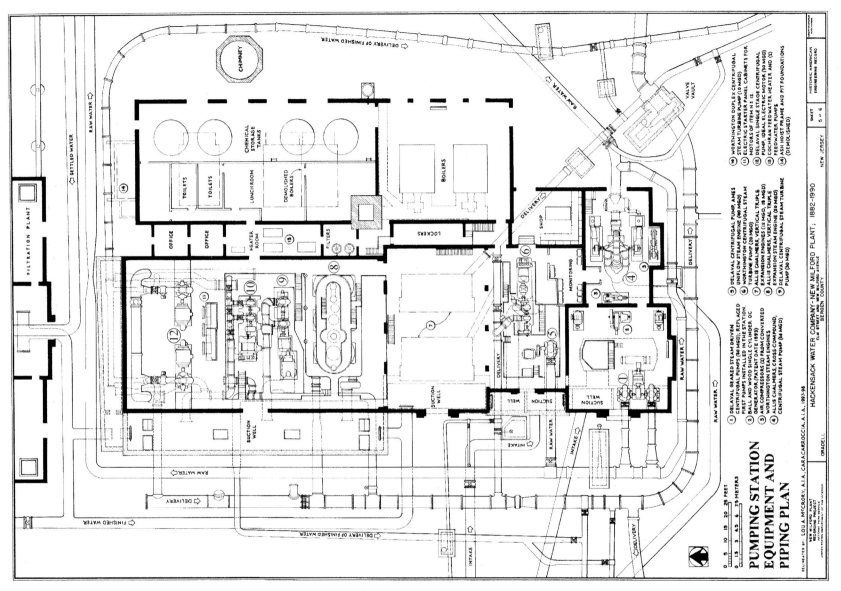

Figure 187: *"Pumping Station Equipment and Piping Plan." The notes on this plan correlate to the water company's historic pump numbers as follows: 1-Nos. 1 & 2 DeLaval pumps, 1948; 4-No. 3 Allis-Chalmers pump, 1915; 5-No. 4 DeLaval pump, 1937; 6-No. 11 Worthington pump, 1941; 8-No. 7 Allis-Chalmers VTE pumping engine, 1911; 9-No. 10 DeLaval pump, 1929; 10-No. 12 Worthington pump, 1941; and 12-Nos. 13 and 14 DeLaval electric pumps, 1956 and 1959. John Bowie Associates and Jane Mork Gibson, "The New Milford Plant of the Hackensack Water Company, Historic Structures Report," 1998*

195

citing it as "an unusually well preserved complex of handsome industrial buildings and structures built in the Industrial Romanesque Revival style." The Historic Trust noted that "The facility houses a substantial amount of original equipment, many of which are rare surviving examples of early water treatment and distribution technology." In 1998 the county proposed a plan that called for the demolition of most of the historic buildings, structures, and machinery; partial preservation of some buildings and machinery, and creation of a passive park on the remainder of the island. The Historic Trust informed the county that this new proposal for partial demolition might jeopardize its preservation grant.[184]

In January 1999 the Oradell citizens group incorporated the Water Works Conservancy as a nonprofit corporation to undertake the preservation of the water works by restoring and adapting it for programs and exhibits that would improve the public's understanding of the historic importance of the site and of water conservation.

In designating the Hackensack Water Works as an "American Treasure" in 2000, the Save America's Treasures Program, a coalition of the White House Millennium Council, the National Park Service, and the National Trust for Historic Preservation, noted that "All the components of this industrial complex, including its collection of engineering masterpieces, remain intact as a testament to the toil and struggle of its civic workers and of New Jersey's role in the development of our nation." In June 2001 the New Jersey Department of Environmental Protection entered the water works into the State Register, noting that "The New Milford Plant of the Hackensack Water Company is a rare surviving example of early water treatment and distribution." The National Park Service subsequently entered

Figure 188: "Filtration Plant." The evolution of the plant is illustrated in elevations, bottom; and in a plan, top: Section 2A-1905; Section 2B-1912; Section 2C-1934; and Section 2D-1955. The plan corresponds with the east elevation at the bottom. John Bowie Associates and Jane Mork Gibson, "The New Milford Plant of the Hackensack Water Company, Historic Structures Report," 1998

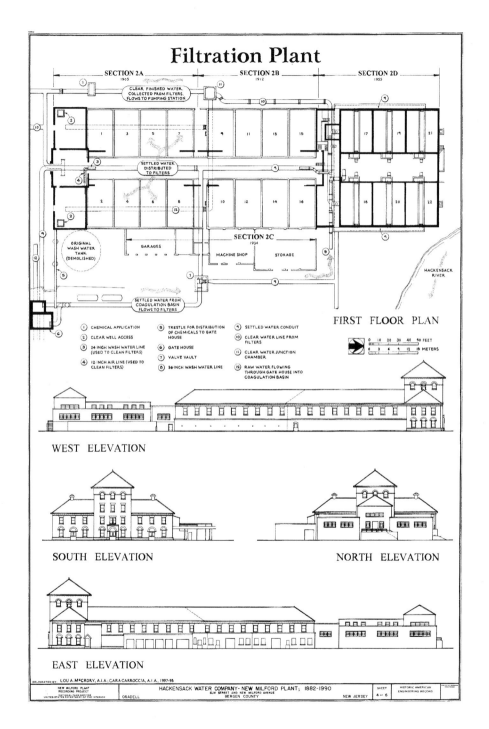

196

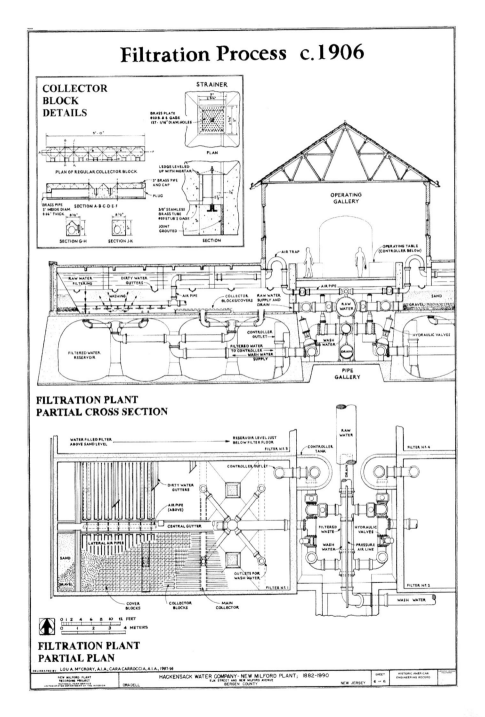

the site into the National Register. The state designation requires the approval of the New Jersey Historic Sites Council for any work that a public agency in the state proposes to undertake that would affect the site's historic significance. State and federal regulations require that projects affecting designated historic properties must comply with the Secretary of the Interior's Standards for Historic Properties.[185]

In the fall of 2001 the county submitted a plan for state approval to redevelop the site in keeping with the earlier partial demolition/passive park proposal. The plan proposed the demolition of most of the complex and the preservation of parts of it for park, office, and exhibition space. It called for turning the No. 7 Allis-Chalmers steam engine, built in 1911, into an open-air exhibit, and planting gardens within fragments of the old brick walls of the engine house. In response to the county's proposal, Preservation New Jersey and the National Trust for Historic Preservation formed the Save the Water Works Coalition.

While recognizing the county's financial and flood concerns, the New Jersey Historic Sites Council cited examples of historic properties being successfully preserved through public-private partnerships and historic buildings being successfully occupied in floodplains, including New Bridge Landing in River Edge, just south of Oradell, and Harper's Ferry in West Virginia. In rejecting the county's proposal, the council noted that the walled garden plan did not follow the U.S. Department of the Interior's Standards for Historic Properties, as required by state law. In its resolution of February 21, 2002, the council instructed the county to develop a preservation plan for the site that preserves the historic significance of its buildings and structures.

Figure 189: "Filtration Process, c 1906." The plan of a filter and a portion of the pipe gallery is at the bottom; a section through a filtered water reservoir (or clear well), a filter, and a portion of the operating gallery is in the center; and the design for the collector blocks at the bottom of the filters is at the top left. John Bowie Associates and Jane Mork Gibson, "The New Milford Plant of the Hackensack Water Company, Historic Structures Report," 1998

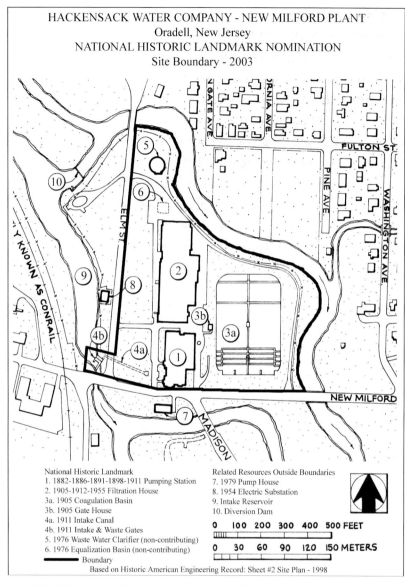

HACKENSACK WATER COMPANY - NEW MILFORD PLANT
Oradell, New Jersey
NATIONAL HISTORIC LANDMARK NOMINATION
Site Boundary - 2003

National Historic Landmark
1. 1882-1886-1891-1898-1911 Pumping Station
2. 1905-1912-1955 Filtration House
3a. 1905 Coagulation Basin
3b. 1905 Gate House
4a. 1911 Intake Canal
4b. 1911 Intake & Waste Gates
5. 1976 Waste Water Clarifier (non-contributing)
6. 1976 Equalization Basin (non-contributing)
■■■ Boundary

Related Resources Outside Boundaries
7. 1979 Pump House
8. 1954 Electric Substation
9. Intake Reservoir
10. Diversion Dam

0 100 200 300 400 500 FEET

0 30 60 90 120 150 METERS

Based on Historic American Engineering Record: Sheet #2 Site Plan - 1998

Figure 190: *"Hackensack Water Company New Milford Plant, Oradell, New Jersey, National Historic Landmark Nomination, Site Plan, 2003." The boundaries of the proposed National Landmark district include the portions of Van Buskirk Island with historic buildings and structures associated with the water works. Water Works Conservancy*

In the fall of 2001 the Water Works Conservancy commissioned a nomination of the Hackensack Water Works to the National Landmark Program of the National Park Service (Figure 190). In the spring of 2002, the National Trust for Historic Preservation in Washington, D.C., designated the Hackensack Water Works as one of its Eleven Most Endangered Historic Sites for 2002. In 2002 the New Jersey Historical Commission awarded the Water Works Conservancy a grant for the preparation of this book, and in 2003 it awarded the Conservancy a grant for its publication.

The Hackensack Water Works is nationally significant as the oldest example of large-scale American mechanical filtration, and as a rare, intact water supply and purification facility from the late nineteenth and early twentieth centuries. It has statewide significance as a monument to New Jersey's historic leadership in supplying and purifying water (Figure 191).

Figure 191: *1905 filtration house, 1997. The brick exterior of this landmark purification plant remains virtually untouched since its 1905 design by the engineering firm of Hering & Fuller of New York. Chip Renner, "The New Milford Plant of the Hackensack Water Company," National Register Nomination*

It is locally significant as the water plant that enabled Bergen County to develop as a major suburb of New York City and Hoboken to grow between 1882 and 1923. With its role in purifying water and protecting the Hackensack River watershed, the water works also represents one of the earliest environmental efforts in New Jersey—the quest for clean water.

As illustrated in historic documents and oral accounts, people associated with the Hackensack Water Company throughout its history understood the importance of the water works. The early owners invested substantial funds and hired top engineers, contractors, and staff to design, build, and operate a facility that immediately became a local monument to American engineering and enterprise (Figure 192). When water quality became a major concern, the water company's directors commissioned the country's leading engineers to design a state-of-the-art filtration plant with numerous innovations, and they hired a leading sanitary engineer to operate it. Throughout the twentieth century, the water company continued to engage top-quality directors, staff, and consultants in the operation and development of the water works. Over time, company employees developed a reverence for the plant's historic significance. As Dan Hoffman said, "Don't do anything to these walls" (Figure 193). Recognizing its historic and environmental importance, the Hackensack Water Company donated the water works to the citizens of Bergen County in the belief that public stewardship would generate the greatest public benefit.

Today this legacy of substantial private investment, superb engineering, and corporate and employee stewardship has produced an historic site of remarkable integrity, with museum-quality machinery, buildings, and

Figure 192: 1882 engine house, 1999. The oldest section of the engine house survives remarkably intact from its original construction. Chip Renner

Figure 193: 1906 boiler house, left; 1911 engine house, left center; 1905 filtration house, right; 1997. The Hackensack Water Company's New Milford pumping station and filtration plant constitute one of the best-preserved historic water works in America. Chip Renner, "The New Milford Plant of the Hackensack Water Company," National Register Nomination

structures (Figures 194 and 195). The plant's landmark achievements and significant integrity warrant its preservation as one of New Jersey's premier industrial heritage sites. The water works' tangible resources, history, and location present a unique opportunity to combine preservation with environmental and educational objectives. The proper adaptive reuse of the water works will include indoor and outdoor space for exhibits, programs, and visitor services, plus natural areas that respect and enhance the environment of Van Buskirk Island and the adjacent Hackensack River corridor.

The design and scale of the water works buildings make them suitable for adaptive reuse. The pumping station buildings include intriguing spaces and historic machinery, particularly the No. 3 and No. 7 Allis-Chalmers steam pumping engines in the 1886 and 1911 sections of the engine house. The buildings provide authentic settings and artifacts for exhibits on the evolution of steam technology and water supply (Figures 196 and 197). With the removal of nonhistoric machinery and materials, other portions of the engine house can be used for additional long-term and changing exhibits, and for programs and events as well (Figures 198 and 199). When restored, the original open areas of the boiler house will provide space for multiple purposes, including traveling exhibits, classrooms, programs and events, and support facilities.

The filtration house is well suited for restoration and adaptive reuse as an authentic setting for hands-on historic exhibits and current activities focusing on water quality, including watershed protection and water conservation. The 1905 coagulant house at the southern end of the filtration house has a number of interesting spaces that be can be used as classrooms, for exhibits, and as support facilities (Figure 200). The 1905–1912 filter gallery (see Figure 148 and Color Plates 26 and 27) will provide a unique and engaging space for exhibits, programs, and events, while the 1955 filter gallery (Figure 201 and Figures 140 and 141) can be restored and adapted as a setting for educational activities and visitor services.

Figure 194: 1911 engine house, 1997. The last section of the engine house retains its original combination of traditional architectural details with early twentieth-century innovations. Chip Renner, "The New Milford Plant of the Hackensack Water Company," National Register Nomination

Figure 195: 1898 boiler house, center; 1898 engine house roof, left; coagulation basin and gate house, right; 1997. The remarkable survival of late nineteenth- and early twentieth-century features throughout the site reflects the Hackensack Water Company's appreciation of its early history. Chip Renner

Figure 196: *1911 engine house, 1998. Two stories of windows and dormer windows fill the cavernous space of the last section of the engine house with daylight, and the No. 7 Allis-Chalmers pumping engine is an obvious and rare monument to water works engineering. A. Pierce Bounds, "The New Milford Plant of the Hackensack Water Company, Historic Structures Report."*

Figure 197: *No. 7 Allis-Chalmers VTE pumping engine, 1997. The flowing lines and massive construction of the machine age gives No. 7 the appearance of industrial sculpture within the 1911 engine house. The basement story of the pumping engine is visible at the bottom. Dave Frieder*

The coagulation basin (Figure 202), the first structure of its kind for a large-scale mechanical filtration plant, provides a unique opportunity to combine the interpretation of its historic function with an educational use focusing on Hackensack River ecology. The gate house on the west embankment provides a focus for interpreting the coagulation basin's original design and use (see Figure 46). Removal of the 1937 interior partitions

Figure 198: 1882 engine house, 1998. Windows around the roof turret flood the oldest section of the engine house with daylight. A. Pierce Bounds, "The New Milford Plant of the Hackensack Water Company, Historic Structures Report."

and breaching of the coagulation basin's embankments in one or more areas will create a two-acre bowl, providing a unique setting for plants, wildlife, and environmental programs (see Figure 118).

The open spaces of Van Buskirk Island around the plant are ideally suited for passive recreation within the natural setting of the Hackensack River Corridor, as Bergen County has proposed. These spaces should include trails, indigenous plants, and educational markers and a minimum of new facilities like parking. The 1911 cast-iron and wrought-iron sluice and waste gates northwest of the intersection of New Milford Avenue and Elm Street, are historic artifacts of the industrial era, and they provide a focal point for

interpreting the use of river water for public supply from the late nineteenth century to the present (see Figures 89, 91, and 183, and Color Plate 30). The 1892 Elm Street Bridge, which Bergen County has recently considered replacing, and the 1906 New Milford Avenue Bridge should be preserved and interpreted as period transportation components that contribute significantly to the unique historic character of Van Buskirk Island. The 1959 electric substation west of Elm Street and the 1979 engine house south of New Milford Avenue are not historic features and should be removed, although the latter could be adapted for visitor or support services.

As recommended by the Historic Sites Council, the restoration of the water works buildings, structures, and artifacts should follow the Secretary of the Interior's Standards for Rehabilitation, which provide some flexibility for adaptive reuse. The design of exhibits and interpretive components within the buildings and throughout the island should complement the site's historic character and natural environment. The insertion of modern requirements like parking and lighting should also respect the historic and environmental character of the site.

As with all historic sites in flood zones, such as Harper's Ferry and New Bridge Landing, the adaptive reuse of the Hackensack Water Works and Van Buskirk Island must incorporate design and use that is appropriate for public safety and the preservation of the buildings, structures, and artifacts in times of flooding. Exhibits should be designed to be waterproof or located above the flood plain. While flooding of the site usually occurs with adequate warning, special procedures need to be planned for evacuation and preparation of the site when flooding occurs.

2003 is the one hundredth anniversary of the Hackensack Water Company's start of work on its landmark filtration plant on Van Buskirk Island, and issues of water supply and quality are often in the news and on people's minds in many parts of the world. With memories of the 2002 drought along the mid-Atlantic coast still fresh, many New Jersey residents are concerned about increasing demands on limited supplies of fresh water, and the state

Figure 199: 1898 engine house, 2002. The clear span of the Hackensack Water Company's in-house design provided the enormous space needed for the pumping station's first vertical triple expansion pumping engines (see Figure 34). Dave Frieder

Figure 200: *1905 coagulant house, 1998. The fourth floor of the chemical house tower retains its original Otis elevator, left, within the old "mixing room." A. Pierce Bounds, "The New Milford Plant of the Hackensack Water Company, Historic Structures Report"*

Figure 202: *Coagulation basin, 1996. Looking northward from the west compartment. The 1905 embankment is visible on the left, the 1937 compartment partition is visible on the right, the 1937 baffle wall frames are visible in the center, and the pre-1937 skimmer wall is visible in the rear. The overall basin covers about 2.3 acres. Dave Frieder, "The New Milford Plant of the Hackensack Water Company," National Register Nomination*

Figure 201: *1955 filter house, 1997. This view toward the southeast shows the open filters, bottom, on the west side of the filter gallery, center. A portion of the 1912 filter house is visible in the right center. Dave Frieder*

government has elevated water supply into a prime consideration for future development in its quest to control sprawl. In the spring of 2003, Governor James McGreevey designated conservation zones around several drinking water sources in the state, including the Oradell Reservoir built by the Hackensack Water Company. The New Jersey Department of Environmental Protection also announced the Governor's intention to include Woodcliff Lake and Lake Tappan, two other Hackensack Water Company reservoirs, in future designations. Many observers predict that the focus on water quality and supply will only increase as the twenty-first century unfolds. All this makes the preservation of the Hackensack Water Works even more compelling, both as a monument to the ingenuity and dedication of our predecessors and as an authentic setting for water conservation activities.

In June of 2003, Department of Environmental Protection Commissioner Bradley Campbell adopted the Historic Sites Council's resolution of February 21, 2002, requiring a preservation plan for the Hackensack Water Works "to assure the integration of preservation and interpretation of the buildings with the development of the park, in order to anticipate and resolve any potential conflicts," including those that could arise between the preservation of the historic buildings and the conservation of the environment on and around Van Buskirk Island. In his decision, Commissioner Campbell recognized the national significance of the Hackensack Water Works and its eligibility for "National Historic Landmark designation."[186]

In concurring with the commissioner's and the council's assessment that "the Hackensack Water Company facility on Van Buskirk Island is a historic site with national significance worth preserving," Bergen County Executive Dennis McNerney in August of 2003 accepted the Historic Sites Council's preservation conditions for the development of Van Buskirk Park, and agreed "to develop a preservation master plan to be implemented in phases." The county executive noted that "the first phase (is) for stabilizing and preserving the structures identified in the (National Register) Nomination as the Pump House, the Filtration Plant, and the smaller gatehouse associated

with the Sedimentation and Coagulation Basin. This first phase will prevent further deterioration of the structures, decorative elements, trim, and interior machines that comprise the facility. Subsequent phases will address the restoration of the various buildings and the design and implementation of Van Buskirk Island Park. . . . Once complete, the Hackensack Water Company will become a jewel in the Bergen County park system."[187]

With the budget constraints of the current economic climate, the public officials responsible for the long-term stewardship of the Hackensack Water Works should consider the opportunities presented by public/nonprofit partnerships. Noteworthy examples of highly successful public-private collaborations on nationally-significant historic sites include Ellis Island in New York Harbor and Historic Morven in Princeton, New Jersey. The county and state governments can contribute resources to the preservation and adaptive reuse of the site and the nonprofit partner can leverage these with private donations of funds, materials, and in-kind services. Volunteer efforts in restoring historic equipment at the Pump House Steam Museum at the historic water works in Kingston, Ontario, provide an inspirational model for the pumping engines at the New Milford Plant. Collaborations among public agencies, nonprofits, and private individuals and businesses offer tremendous potential to develop significant educational exhibits and programs at the water works for schoolchildren and adults.[188]

Hundreds of individuals dedicated their efforts to creating, developing, and operating the Hackensack Water Works on Van Buskirk Island as a national leader in supplying municipal water over a 110-year period. Their legacy is one of New Jersey's finest historic industrial complexes. 2003 marks the tenth anniversary of the water company's donation of the site to the citizens of Bergen County, and while delays in resolving its future have taken a toll, the historic buildings and structures remain remarkably intact. The Water Works Conservancy, Preservation New Jersey, the National Trust for Historic Preservation, the New Jersey Department of Environmental Protection, and many individuals deserve tremendous credit for halting the proposed demolition of the water works. As this book goes to press, the critical next phases in preserving this national historic resource are on the horizon: stabilization, restoration for public use, and interpretation. The cultural significance of the Hackensack Water Works as a monument to American ingenuity, skill, and dedication warrants the finest preservation possible, and our collective responsibility to preserve the meaning of this American treasure for succeeding generations demands it (Figure 203).

Figure 203: *Hackensack Water Works, April 2002. 1905–1912 filtration plant, left; 1911-1898-1891-1882 engine house, right. Frank Vierling*

Appendix: New Milford Pumpage and Existing Pumping Engines

New Milford Pumping Station
Pumpage 1883–1990

Year	Milestones	Average Gallons per Day
1883	Opening of water works, 1882	3,862,863
1890	Engine house addition, 1886	5,496,579
1899	Engine house additions, 1891, 1898	10,471,055
1905	Opening of filtration plant	18,900,000
1910		23,200,000
1915	Engine house addition, 1911; filter house extension, 1912	28,800,000
1920	End of WWI, 1918	35,800,000
1925	Hoboken contract ends, 1923	31,000,000
1930	Suburban development	37,000,000
1935	Great Depression	33,800,000
1940	WWII	35,000,000
1945	WWII ends	40,100,000
1950		41,900,000
1955	Suburban development; filter house addition	52,900,000
1960		62,900,000
1965	Drought; Haworth Plant opens	61,110,000
1970		50,338,000
1975		56,800,000
1980		58,091,000
1985	Ozone experiments	59,283,000
1990	Haworth Water Treatment Plant, 1989; New Milford Plant closed, May 1990	49,666,000

1883–1899: Figures reported by D. W. French to Allen Hazen.
1905–1960: Figures reported by Peter Pallo, Hackensack Water Company.
1965–1990: Figures reported by United Water Resources.

Existing Pumping Engines 1998

No.	Date	Bldg	Pump Type	Power	MGD*	Water
1	1948	1A	DeLaval Centrifugal	Steam	40	Raw
2	1948	1A	DeLaval Centrifugal	Steam	40	Raw
3	1915	1B	Allis-Chalmers Cross Compound Centrifugal	Steam	36	Raw
4	1937	1C	DeLaval Centrifugal, Ideal Motor	Electric**	40	Raw
7	1911	1G	Allis-Chalmers Vertical Triple Expansion	Steam***	20	Filtered
10	1929	1G	DeLaval Turbine Driven Duplex Centrifugal	Steam	30	Filtered
11	1941	1C	Worthington Turbine Driven Duplex Centrifugal	Steam	20	Filtered
12	1941	1G	Worthington Turbine Driven Duplex Centrifugal	Steam	10	Filtered
13	1956	1G	DeLaval Centrifugal, Ideal Motor	Electric	30	Filtered
14	1959	1G	DeLaval Centrifugal, Ideal Motor	Electric	30	Filtered

* Millions of gallons per day.
** Originally steam powered; converted to electricity in 1958.
*** Only nonoperational steam pump in 1990 when plant closed.
From: "The New Milford Plant of the Hackensack Water Company, Historic Structure Report," John Bowie Associates and Jane Mork Gibson, 1998.

Notes

Preface – One of the Great Pioneering Plants

[1] Martin Melosi, *Sanitary City: Urban Infrastructure in America from Colonial Times to the Present* (Baltimore: Johns Hopkins University Press, 2000): 130.

[2] Adrian Leiby, *The Hackensack Water Company 1869–1969* (River Edge, N.J.: Bergen County Historical Society, 1969): 134.

[3] When the water works was begun, Van Buskirk Island was part of the village of New Milford. In 1894 the island became part of the new Borough of Delford. In 1920 the Borough changed its name to Oradell.

Chapter 1 – "Give Our People a Good Supply of Water"

[4] Leiby, 11.

[5] Ibid., 30–31.

[6] Ibid., 33.

[7] Ibid., 36.

[8] Leiby pointed out that the Hackensack River is brackish at New Bridge, but he surmised that back in the 1870s the surface of the water may have remained fresh during certain tides and that was when pumping most likely took place. Ibid., 43.

[9] Ibid., 45–46.

[10] Ibid., 49–50.

[11] By the fall of 1879 Voorhis had declared personal bankruptcy, and with his fortune and reputation ruined, committed suicide. As a fellow lawyer and Bergen native, Leiby was very sympathetic to Voorhis's troubles and detailed his many accomplishments as well as his failures. Ibid., 51–56.

[12] Ibid., 60–61.

[13] Ibid., 61–64.

[14] Ibid., 65–66.

[15] Louis Tribus, "Memoir of Charles Benjamin Brush, M. Am. Soc. C. E.," *Transactions of the American Society of Civil Engineers* 84 (1931): 818–819.

[16] Ibid., 818–819; *Index to Transactions, Volumes I to LXXXIII* (New York: American Society of Civil Engineers, 1921): 143.

[17] Leiby, 89; a later handwritten note on two of the engine house drawings reads "Detail Plans, Engine and Boiler Houses, New Milford, Architect Withers 1883." The note appears to refer to the prominent New York architect Frederick Clark Withers, who designed some important company structures in Weehawken in 1883, but the draftsmanship on the New Milford and Weehawken drawings is dissimilar and Withers' name is prominent on the latter. No other reference to Withers as the architect at New Milford has appeared. Although Leiby cited no documentation for his acknowledgement of Brush as the architect, it may have appeared in company papers to which he had access.

[18] Leiby, 69; "Works for Hackensack, N.J.," *American Contract Journal* (17 June 1882): 205.

[19] The original foundation plan, probably supplied by the Worthington Company, shows the precise construction required to support the engine over the pump well. Worthington listed the Hackensack and Weehawken engines in its 1884 catalog.

[20] George Haskew, correspondence with author, 13 July 2002.

[21] Francis R. Kowsky, *The Architecture of Frederick Clark Withers and the Progress of the Gothic Revival in America after 1850* (Middleton, Conn.: Wesleyan University Press, 1980): 140–141.

[22] *Engineering News* 16 (November 1886): 292–294.

[23] "High Service Tower of the Hackensack Water Company at Union Hill, N.J.," *Carpentry and Building, A Monthly Journal* 7, no. 1 (October 1885): 181.

[24] Leiby, 70; *Hudson Dispatch* (17 December 1936).

Chapter 2 – A Promising Field

[25] M. N. Baker, *The Quest for Pure Water: The History of Water Purification from the Earliest Records to the Twentieth Century* (Baltimore: American Water Works Association, 1948): 380.

[26] George W. Fuller, "The Filtration Works of the East Jersey Water Company, at Little Falls, New Jersey," *Transactions of the American Society of Civil Engineers* 50 (1902): 453.

[27] Baker, 363.

[28] Ibid., 345.

[29] Ibid., 380.

[30] Leiby, 74.

[31] Ibid., 78.

[32] William B. Yereance and Y. W. Demarest, "Test of the Hackensack Water Company's Pumping Station at New Milford, New Jersey, April 1888." In the archives of United Water Resources, Harrington Park, New Jersey.

[33] Melosi, 135.

34 Baker, 169–171.

35 Melosi, 130.

36 Albert Ripley Leeds, "Water Analysis: Certificate of Dr. Albert R. Leeds, as to Analysis of Samples of Water Submitted by the Hackensack Water Company, Reorganized, 1887–1900." In the archives of United Water Resources, Harrington Park, New Jersey.

37 Ibid.

38 Ibid., May 13, 1887.

39 Ibid., July 28, 1887.

40 Ibid., July 28, 1887.

41 Baker, 381.

42 Egyptians, Greeks, and Romans all filtered water through porous earthen vessels. A medical text from India around 400 A.D. noted, "Impure water . . . may be purified by filtration through sand and course gravel." In his 1627 book, *A Natural History of Ten Centuries*, Sir Francis Bacon "repeated the notion that by digging a pit on the seashore, fresh water could be obtained from salt water by percolation through the sand." In 1685 an Italian physician named Luc Antonio Porzio published "the first known illustrated description of sand filters," with separate designs for a floating filter, one on land and one for well water. Porzio noted that "his plan was an imitation of Nature's method of passing water through the 'Bowels of the Earth'"; Ibid., 128.

43 Ibid., 133.

44 Allen Hazen, *Clean Water and How to Get It* (New York: John Wiley & Sons, 1907): 68.

45 Leeds, March 25, 1889; October 10, 1889; December 7, 1889.

46 Ibid., January 20, 1890; March 7, 1890. The emphasis is Leeds'.

47 Ibid., May 9, 1890.

48 Ibid., July 16, 1890.

49 Ibid., March 7, 1891.

50 Ibid., March 24, 1891.

51 Leiby, 81–82.

52 Ibid., 83–84.

53 Ibid., 86, 89–90.

54 *Hackensack Republican* (3 September 1891).

55 Cornelius C. Vermeule, letter to Chief Engineer Charles B. Brush, Hackensack Water Company Reorganized, New York, 24 June 1892: 1. A handwritten note on the letter reads, "French's Copy," referring to Superintendent D. W. French. In the archives of United Water Resources, Harrington Park, New Jersey.

56 Ibid., 11.

57 Ibid., 11–12.

58 *Bergen County Democrat* (27 May 1892).

59 "The Hackensack Water Company," *Scientific American* 46, no. 14 (2 April 1992): 213–214.

60 Ibid., 214.

61 Leeds, Oct. 30, 1891.

62 Ibid., Feb. 20, 1892.

63 Ibid., March 3, 1892.

64 Ibid., Oct. 11, 1892; Nov. 14, 1892.

65 Leeds, July 19, 1893; Baker, 380–381.

66 Leiby, 89.

67 Leeds, July 11, 1895.

68 Baker, 140.

69 Ibid., 173.

70 Ibid., 233.

71 Baker, 235–236; Hazen, 73.

72 Leeds, Jan. 18, 1897; March 20, 1897.

73 Tribus, 819; Leiby, 89.

74 The main drawing included "General Conditions" for bidding most of the "Carpenter Work" on the job, including "the Slate and Tin Roofing (and) Painting Outside Work." A handwritten note, "Agreed to Sept. 15, 1898, Cooper & Demarest," indicates that this partnership, which ran a lumberyard adjacent to the site, contracted for this work. For a view of the Cooper & Demarest yard, see the lower right on the back cover, and *Oradell Centennial 1894–1994* (Oradell, N.J.: Borough of Oradell, 1994): 40.

75 Louis C. Hunter, *A History of Industrial Power in the United States, 1730–1930* (Charlottesville: University Press of Virginia for Hagley Museum and Library, 1985): 578, 586.

76 Leeds, Nov. 12, 1899; Melosi, 136.

77 "The Typhoid Record," *Engineering News* (30 March 1999).

78 George Warren Fuller, "Report on the Investigations into the Purification of the Ohio River Water for the Improved Water Supply of the City of Cincinnati, Ohio" (Cincinnati: Cincinnati Commissioners of Waterworks, 1899): 20, 402.

79 Leiby, 96; Allen Hazen, letter to President R. W. de Forest, Hackensack Water Company, 25 January 1900, New York: 1. In the archives of United Water Resources, Harrington Park, New Jersey.

80 Allen Hazen, "The Albany Water Filtration Plant," *Transactions of the American Society of Civil Engineers* 43 (1900): 293, 314–315.

81 Ibid., 316–317.

82 Hazen, letter to R. W. de Forest: 1–3, 21.

83 Ibid., 4.

84 Ibid.

[85] Ibid., 3, 5–8.

[86] Ibid., 8–10.

[87] Ibid., 11.

[88] Ibid., 12–13.

[89] Ibid., 13–15. Hazen suggested that a short canal or tunnel could connect reservoirs on the second and third sites.

[90] Allen Hazen, letter to Hackensack Water Company, 20 June 1900, Hoboken, N.J.: 1.

[91] Ibid., 7.

[92] Leiby, 114.

[93] George Warren Fuller, "The Filtration Works of the East Jersey Water Company, at Little Falls, New Jersey." *Transactions of the American Society of Civil Engineers* 50 (1903): 396–400.

[94] Leiby, 103–104.

[95] Ibid., 104.

[96] Ibid., 102–103.

[97] Ibid., 107.

[98] Fuller, "The Filtration Works of the East Jersey Water Company," 438, 439; Leiby, 110.

[99] Rudolph Hering, letter to Hackensack Water Company Reorganized, 3 February 1903, Weehawken, N.J.: 2–4. In the archives of United Water Resources, Harrington Park, New Jersey. Born in Philadelphia, Hering had studied bridge engineering in Germany, and after working on bridge and sewer projects in his hometown, had devoted his career to sanitary engineering. While his main expertise was in sewerage, his studies on new sources of water supply and filtration for Philadelphia and many other cities made him exceptionally well-qualified to write the Hackensack report for Hering & Fuller, the partnership between two of the leading sanitary engineers that existed from 1901 to 1911. Hering probably authored the Hackensack report because of its emphasis on water storage, while the actual design of the New Milford Filtration Plant primarily reflected Fuller's research and innovations. Colleagues called Hering the "Dean of Sanitary Engineering" in America, and the Sanitary Engineering Division of the ASCE established the "Rudolph Hering Medal" for best contributions in the field to its *Transactions*. Fuller, George Warren, John Trautwine, Jr., and Charles Whiting Baker, "Memoir of Rudolph Hering," *Transactions of the American Society of Civil Engineers* 87 (1924): 1350–1354.

[100] Hering, 8, 10.

[101] Ibid., 13, 17.

[102] Ibid., 17.

[103] Ibid., 18.

[104] Ibid., 19.

[105] Ibid., 20–21.

[106] Ibid., 21–22.

[107] The "Ransome method" of concrete construction would have required paying royalties to the Ransome Company, which Hering suggested could be avoided to save money. Ibid., 22–23.

[108] Ibid., 24–25.

[109] Fuller, "The Filtration Works of the East Jersey Water Company," 400.

[110] Ibid., 445–447, 451.

[111] Ibid., 452–453, 459.

[112] Ibid., 453, 455.

[113] Ibid., 457.

Chapter 3 – A Perfect Model in Every Sense

[114] "Memoranda Regarding Design of Mechanical Filters Plant for the Hackensack Water Company at New Milford, Following Discussions in the Office, April 20–23, 1903": 2. In the archives of United Water Resources, Harrington Park, New Jersey.

[115] Ibid., 1, 2, 4, 9.

[116] Leiby, 111.

[117] "The Mechanical Filters of the Hackensack Water Company," *Engineering Record* 50, no. 20 (12 Nov. 1904), 572; 50, no. 21 (19 Nov. 1904): 592.

[118] Ibid.

[119] Ibid.

[120] Leiby, 136–137.

[121] Ibid., 572.

[122] Ibid., 572–573.

[123] Glen Abplanalp, "Little Falls Treatment Plant—1902 to Present," Unpublished paper. Passaic Valley Water Authority, Passaic, N.J., 1970: 7.

[124] "Hackensack," *Engineering Record* 50, no. 20 (1904): 572.

[125] Ibid.

[126] Hazen, "The Albany Water Filtration Plant," 258.

[127] "Hackensack," *Engineering Record* 50, no. 20 (1904): 572–573.

[128] Ibid., 572.

[129] Ibid., 573.

[130] Ibid., 573. William B. Fuller, on the Hering & Fuller team, was probably involved in developing the concrete designs, as his discussion of the Little Falls plant indicates that he was quite interested in and knowledgeable about concrete construction. See Fuller, "The Filtration Works of the East Jersey Water Company," 453–455.

[131] "Hackensack," *Engineering Record* 50, no. 21 (1904): 591–592.

[132] Ibid.

133 Hazen, "The Albany Water Filtration Plant," 276.

134 "Hackensack," *Engineering Record* 50, no. 21 (1904): 592.

135 Ibid., 591–592.

136 "Hackensack," *Engineering Record* 50, no. 20 (1904): 573–574.

137 Ibid., 573, 575.

138 Hazen, *Clean Water and How to Get It*, 78.

139 "Hackensack," *Engineering Record* 50, no. 21 (1904): 592.

140 Fuller, "The Filtration Works of the East Jersey Water Company," 419.

141 "Hackensack," *Engineering Record* 50, no. 21 (1904): 590.

142 Ibid., 591–592.

143 Ibid., 590.

144 Ibid., 592.

145 Ibid.

146 *Hackensack Water Company Filtration Plant, New Milford, N.J. 1906* (Weehawken, N.J.: Hackensack Water Company): 3. In the archive of United Water Resources Archives, Harrington Park, New Jersey.

147 Ibid., 5.

148 Ibid., 7.

149 Ibid., 11.

150 Ibid., 12.

Chapter 4 – The Height of American Steam Engineering

151 Leiby, 148.

152 Baker, 337.

153 Leiby, 143.

154 Cornelius C. Vermeule, letter to Superintendent D. W. French, Hackensack Water Company, 23 December 1910, Weehawken, N.J.: 1.

155 Ibid., 2–4.

156 Leiby, 146.

157 Sheffield Archaeological Consultants. "Historical Study and Evaluation of the Hackensack Water Company," Hackensack Water Company, Harrington Park, N.J., 1991: 63.

158 Leiby, 165–166.

159 George R. Spalding, "Activated Char as a Deodorant in Water Purification," *Journal of the American Water Works Association* 22, no. 5 (May 1930): 646.

160 Leiby, 175–176; Anderson, Kenneth. *Not a Drop to Drink* (New York: Carlton Press, 1962): 34–43.

161 Hering & Fuller, "Improvements to Coagulating Basin, General Plan, 3/8/37." Drawing in archives of United Water Resources, Harrington Park, New Jersey.

162 Leiby, 188.

163 Ibid., 193–194.

164 *Pure Filtered Water for Four Hundred Thousand People in Bergen and Hudson Counties.* (New Milford, N.J.: Department of Filtration-Sanitation, Hackensack Water Company, 1938): 8–9. Archives of United Water Resources, Harrington Park, New Jersey.

Chapter 5 – That's Why We Did It That Way

165 Miles Kuchar, Oral history interview with author, May 2002. Water Works Conservancy.

166 Leiby, 202–210.

167 Ted Hoffman, Oral History interview with author, June 2002. Water Works Conservancy.

168 George Haskew, Oral History interview with author, June 2002. Water Works Conservancy.

169 *Water: How the Hackensack Water Company Serves 700,000 People.* Hackensack Water Company (1960): 1–2, 7, 9–10.

170 Ibid., 219.

171 Ibid., 220–221.

172 George Haskew remembered Adrian Leiby: "Mr. Leiby was a very interesting man. He was interested in history and photography. The photographer that he mentions in his book was an old friend of his and worked with him in making any pictures that Leiby wanted. He lived in Bergenfield, in an historical house. He and his wife were members of the old sandstone church in Bergenfield, and were completely tied to its whole history. His historical interests prompted the business of writing a book, I'm sure. He wasn't very tall, but he was kind of patrician, in some ways, with his office in New York at a prestigious law firm. He was always pleasant and a gentleman, certainly." Interview with author, June 2002. Water Works Conservancy.

173 Jim Flynn, Oral History interview with author, June 2002. Water Works Conservancy.

Chapter 6 – The Consumer Is the Best Indicator of Water Quality

174 Barry Schwartz, Oral History interview with author, June 2002. Water Works Conservancy.

175 MaryFrances Schwartz, Correspondence and interview with Maggie Harrer, 11 June 2003. Water Works Conservancy.

176 Pat Hoffman, Oral History interview with author, June 2002. Water Works Conservancy.

177 Barry Schwartz described the testing process in the photograph: "The men are using what is known as a Seechi Disk to measure the clarity of the treated water and to determine the effectiveness of the coagulation/flocculation treatment. The Seechi Disk is divided into four quadrants with alternate black-and-white quadrants. You would lower the disk into the water and measure, in feet, the depth at which you could no longer discern the quadrants. The greater the depth, the clearer the water. It was actually a field measurement of turbidity. Today automatic samplers and continuous monitors are used." Correspondence with author, 1 April 2003.

[178] Fred Schelhas, Correspondence and interview with Maggie Harrer, 19 July 2002. Water Works Conservancy.

Chapter 7 – *If You Stay Here Five Years, You'll Never Leave*

[179] MaryFrances Schwartz, Interview with Maggie Harrer, 3 April 2003. Water Works Conservancy.

[180] Jesse Jones, Interview with Maggie Harrer, 10 March 2003. Water Works Conservancy.

[181] Frank Vierling, Correspondence with author, 23 July 2002; *Oradell Centennial 1894–1994* (Oradell, New Jersey: Borough of Oradell, 1994): 13.

Chapter 8 – *A Rare Surviving Example of Early Water Treatment and Distribution*

[182] Sheffield Archaeological Consultants, "Historical Study and Evaluation of the Hackensack Water Company," Hackensack Water Company, Harrington Park, New Jersey, 1991.

[183] PreservationNJ.org., "New Jersey's 10 Most Endangered Historic Sites, 1996, Bergen County, Hackensack Water Company."

[184] "New Milford Plant, Hackensack Water Co.," New Jersey Historic Preservation Bond Program, Matching Grant Awards, Project Profile, New Jersey Historic Trust, Trenton, New Jersey, 1997.

[185] Richard Moe and Bobby Greene. Save America's Treasures, National Trust for Historic Preservation, Letter to Bradley Campbell, Commissioner, New Jersey Department of Environmental Protection (9 April 2002). Water Works Conservancy; Wild, Cari J., Letter to William Schuber (22 June 2001) listing the New Milford Plant of the Hackensack Water Company on the New Jersey Register of Historic Places. Files of Historic Preservation Office, New Jersey Department of Environmental Protection, Trenton, New Jersey.

[186] Bradley Campbell, Commissioner, New Jersey Department of Environmental Protection, Letter to Dennis McNerney, Bergen County Executive (20 August 2003). Files of Historic Preservation Office, New Jersey Department of Environmental Protection, Trenton, New Jersey.

[187] Dennis McNerney, County Executive, Bergen County, Letter to Bradley Campbell, Commissioner, New Jersey Department of Environmental Protection (20 August 2003). Files of Historic Preservation Office, New Jersey Department of Environmental Protection, Trenton, New Jersey.

[188] For the Pump House Steam Museum in Kingston, Ontario, see: www.marmus.ca/marmus/pumphouse.html

Bibliography

Abplanalp, Glen. "Little Falls Treatment Plant—1902 to Present." Unpublished paper, Passaic Valley Water Commission, Totowa, New Jersey, 1970.

Anderson, Kenneth. *Not a Drop to Drink*. New York: Carlton Press, 1962.

Baker, M. N. *The Quest for Pure Water: The History of Water Purification from the Earliest Records to the Twentieth Century*. Baltimore: American Water Works Association, 1948.

Bishop, Gordon. "Pollution on Tap," *Newark Star Ledger* (15 May 1988).

Bowie Associates, John, and Jane Mork Gibson. "The New Milford Plant of the Hackensack Water Company, Historic Structures Report," Bergen County Archives, Hackensack, New Jersey, 1998.

Brush, Charles B. "Remarks on the Aeration of Water." *Transactions of the American Society of Civil Engineers* 15 (1886): 139.

"The Construction of the Water Purification and Softening Works at New Orleans." *Engineering News* 59, no. 14 (3 April 1909): 447–451.

"A Conversational History of the Cincinnati Water Works." Unpublished paper, City of Cincinnati, Ohio, Department of Water Works, 2000.

DeLaval, Carl George. *Centrifugal Pumping Machinery*. New York: McGraw Hill Publishing Company, 1911.

Engineering News 13 (January–June 1885).

Engineering News 16 (November 1886): 292–294.

Forwell, Prescott. *Water Supply Engineering: The Designing, Construction and Maintenance of Water Supplies*. New York: John Wiley & Sons, 1912.

Fuller, George Warren, John Trautwine, Jr., and Charles Whiting Baker. "The Filtration Works of the East Jersey Water Company, at Little Falls, New Jersey." *Transactions of the American Society of Civil Engineers* 50 (1903): 394–472.

———. "The Improved Water and Sewer Works of Columbus, Ohio: Discussion." *Transactions of the American Society of Civil Engineers* 57 (1910): 419.

———"Memoir of Rudolph Hering." *Transactions of the American Society of Civil Engineers* 87 (1924): 1350–1354.

———. "Progress in Water Purification." *Journal of the American Water Works Association* no. 25 (October 1933): 1566–1576.

———. "Report on Appraisal of Hackensack Water Company, 1915." Unpublished report, Rutgers University Library Special Collections.

———. *Report on the Investigations into the Purification of the Ohio River Water for the Improved Water Supply of the City of Cincinnati, Ohio*. Cincinnati, Ohio: Cincinnati Commissioners of Waterworks. In archives of City of Cincinnati, Department of Water Works, 1899.

Galishoff, Stuart. "Triumph and Failure, the American Response to the Urban Water Supply 1860–1923." In *Pollution and Reform in American Cities* 1870–1930. Edited by Martin Melosi. Austin: University of Texas Press, 1980.

Gregory, John H. "The Improved Water and Sewer Works of Columbus, Ohio." *Transactions of the American Society of Civil Engineers* 57 (1910): 235–255.

Grubb Archaeological Associates. "Cultural Resource Survey, Little Falls Water Treatment Plant Upgrade." Unpublished report, Passaic Valley Water Authority, 2001.

"The Hackensack Water Company." *Scientific American* 66, no. 14 (April 1892): 213–214.

Hackensack Water Company Filtration Plant, New Milford, N.J. 1906. Weehawken, New Jersey: Hackensack Water Company. Pamphlet in the archives of United Water Resources, Harrington Park, New Jersey.

Hackensack Water Company, Serving 600,000 Customers in Bergen and Hudson Counties. Hackensack Water Company, c. 1954. Brochure in the archives of United Water Resources, Harrington Park, New Jersey.

Hackensack Water Works. Oral history interviews: George Haskew, Ted Hoffman, Miles Kuchar, Barry Schwartz, Pat Hoffman, Jim Flynn. In archive of Water Works Conservancy, Oradell, New Jersey, 2002.

Hazen, Allen. "The Albany Water Filtration Plant." *Transactions of the American Society of Civil Engineers* 43 (1900): 245–352.

———. *Clean Water and How to Get It.* New York: John Wiley & Sons, 1907.

———. Letter to R. W. de Forest, New York, 25 January 1900. Archives of United Water Resources, Harrington Park, New Jersey.

———. Report to Hackensack Water Company, Hoboken, N.J., 20 June 1900. Archives of United Water Resources, Harrington Park, New Jersey.

Hering, Rudolph. Letter to Hackensack Water Company, Reorganized. Weehawken, N.J., 3 February 1903. In the archives of United Water Resources, Harrington Park, New Jersey.

"High Service Tower of the Hackensack Water Company at Union Hill, N.J." *Carpentry and Building, A Monthly Journal* 7, no. 1 (October 1885): 181–182.

Historic water works documented by the Historic American Engineering Record, National Park Service, Washington, D.C.: "Brandywine Pumping Station" (DEL, 2-Wilm, 38-2); "Chestnut Hill High Service Pumping Station" (MASS, 13-Boston, 75-4); "Chestnut Hill Low Service Pumping Station" (MASS, 13-Boston, 81-1); "Cincinnati Water Works" (OH-29); "Fairmount Water Works" (PA-51, Phila., 328); "Louisville Pumping Station, Louisville, Kentucky" (KY-56, Louvi 72); "McNeil Street Pumping Station, Shreveport Water Works" (LA-2); "Youngstown City Water Works" (OH-118).

Hunter, Louis C. *A History of Industrial Power in the United States, 1730–1930.* Charlottesville, Virginia: University Press of Virginia for Hagley Museum and Library, 1985.

Index to Transactions, Volumes 1-83, 1867–1920. New York: American Society of Civil Engineers, 1921.

Leeds, Albert Ripley. "Water Analysis: Certificate of Dr. Albert R. Leeds, as to Analysis of Samples of Water Submitted by the Hackensack Water Company, Reorganized, 1887–1900." Unpublished log in the archives of United Water Resources, Harrington Park, New Jersey.

Leiby, Adrian. *The Hackensack Water Company, 1869–1969.* Hackensack, New Jersey: Bergen County Historical Society, 1969.

"Louisville Water Company Pumping Station." National Landmark Nomination, National Park Service, Washington, D.C., 1972.

Manual of American Waterworks. New York: *Engineering News*, 1888.

Mason, William. *Water Supply.* New York: John Wiley & Sons, 1896.

"McNeil Street Pumping Station." National Landmark Nomination, National Park Service, Washington, D.C., 1980.

"The Mechanical Filters of the Hackensack Water Company I." *Engineering Record* 50, no. 20 (12 November 1904): 572–575.

"The Mechanical Filters of the Hackensack Water Company II." *Engineering Record* 50, no. 21 (19 November 1904): 590–592.

Melosi, Martin. *Sanitary City: Urban Infrastructure in America from Colonial Times to the Present.* Baltimore: Johns Hopkins University Press, 2000.

"Memoranda Regarding Design of Mechanical Filter Plant for the Hackensack Water Company at New Milford, following Discussions in the Office,

April 20–23, 1903." Unpublished memo in the archives of United Water Resources, Harrington Park, New Jersey.

Metcalf, Leonard. "The Groined Arch as a Cover for Reservoirs and Sand Filters." *Transaction of the American Society of Civil Engineers* 43 (1900): 37.

Metz, Jennifer. "Monroe Avenue Water Filtration Plant." National Register Nomination, National Park Service, Washington, D.C., 2002.

Milster, Conrad. Letter to Henry H. Baxter on the Colonel Ward Pumping Station, Buffalo, New York, Files of Conrad Milster, Pratt Institute, 7 July 2001.

———."An Operating Exhibit at the Phillipsburg Pumping Station." *Live Steam* (September 1979): 24–27.

———. "Remarks on the Hackensack Water Works." Unpublished remarks presented to New Jersey Historical Sites Council meeting in Hackensack New Jersey, December 20, 2001. Files of Conrad Milster, Pratt Institute.

Moe, Richard, and Bobby Greene. Save America's Treasures, National Trust for Historic Preservation, Letter to Bradley Campbell, Commissioner, New Jersey Department of Environmental Protection, 9 April 2002. Water Works Conservancy.

Murphy, Cullen. "Engines of the Gilded Age." *Preservation* (May/June 1999): 70–74.

New Milford Plant, Hackensack Water Company. Documents and drawings in the archives of United Water Resources, Harrington Park, New Jersey, 1882–1900.

"New Milford Plant, Hackensack Water Co." New Jersey Historic Preservation Bond Program, Matching Grant Awards, Project Profile, New Jersey Historic Trust, Trenton, New Jersey, 1997.

"New Milford Plant of the Hackensack Water Company." Bergen County Historic Sites Inventory (No. 0238-D, 0244-D1). Unpublished survey report in files of New Jersey Historic Preservation Office, Trenton, New Jersey, 1981.

"New Orleans Waterworks." *Municipal Journal and Engineer* 24, no. 19 (6 May 1908).

"New Waterworks for the City of Cincinnati." Drawings in the archives of the Cincinnati Water Works, Cincinnati, Ohio, 1898–1907.

Oradell Centennial 1894–1994. Oradell, New Jersey: Borough of Oradell, 1994.

"Performance of the 12-MGD Allis Pumping Engine at Hackensack, N.J." *Stevens Institute Indicator* (October 1900).

Pitts, Carolyn. "Fairmount Water Works." National Landmark Nomination, National Park Service, Washington, D.C., 1976.

PreservationNJ.org. "New Jersey's 10 Most Endangered Historic Sites, Bergen County, Hackensack Water Company, 1996."

Pure Water for Four Hundred Thousand People. New Milford, New Jersey: Department of Filtration-Sanitation, Hackensack Water Company, 1934. Archives of United Water Resources, Harrington Park, New Jersey.

Pure Filtered Water for Four Hundred Thousand People in Bergen and Hudson Counties. New Milford, New Jersey: Department of Filtration-Sanitation, Hackensack Water Company, 1938. Archives of United Water Resources, Harrington Park, New Jersey.

Reynolds, Terry. "Shreveport Water Works Company, McNeill Street Pumping Station." Unpublished report of the Historic American Engineering Record, National Park Service, Washington D.C., 1980.

Rothe, Albin. "New Milford Plant of the Hackensack Water Company." National Register Nomination, New Jersey Historic Preservation Office, Trenton, New Jersey, 1998.

Sheffield Archaeological Consultants. "Historical Study and Evaluation of the Hackensack Water Company." Hackensack Water Company, Harrington Park, New Jersey, 1991.

Spalding, George R. "Activated Char as a Deodorant in Water Purification." *Journal of the American Water Works Association* 22, no. 5 (May 1930): 646–648.

Tribus, Louis. "Memoir of Charles Benjamin Brush, M. Am. Soc. C. E." *Transactions of the American Society of Civil Engineers* 84 (1921): 818–819.

Turneau, Frederick E., and Harvey Russell. *Public Water Supplies.* New York: John Wiley & Sons, 1924.

Tuttle, Arthur S. "Memoir of George Warren Fuller." *Transactions of the American Society of Civil Engineers* 100 (1935): 1653–1660.

"The Typhoid Record in Philadelphia." *Engineering Record* (30 March 1899).

Vermeule, Cornelius C. Letter to Mr. Charles B. Brush, Hackensack Water Company, Reorganized. New York, 24 June 1892. In the archives of United Water Resources, Harrington Park, New Jersey.

———. Letter to D. W. French, Hackensack Water Company. Weehawken, New Jersey, 23 December 1910. In the archives of United Water Resources, Harrington Park, New Jersey.

"Water Filtering and Softening Works at Columbus, Ohio." *Engineering Record* 53, no. 8 (24 February 1906): 202–208.

Water: How the Hackensack Water Company Serves 600,000 People. Weehawken, New Jersey: Hackensack Water Company, c. 1957. Pamphlet in the archives of United Water Resources, Harrington Park, New Jersey.

Water: How the Hackensack Water Company Serves 700,000 People. Hackensack Water Company, 1960. Pamphlet in the archives of United Water Resources, Harrington Park, New Jersey.

Waterman, Earle L. *Elements of Water Supply Engineering.* New York: John Wiley & Sons, 1938.

Water Works: A History of the Louisville Water Company. Louisville, Kentucky: Louisville Water Company, 1999.

Whipple, George C. "The History of Water Purification." *Transactions of the American Society of Civil Engineers* 85 (1922): 476–481.

"Works for Hackensack, N.J." *American Contract Journal* (June 1882): 205.

Vogel, Robert. Letter to Planning Board, Borough of Oradell, New Jersey, in the archives of the Water Works Conservancy, Oradell, New Jersey, 11 September 1996.

Vopasek, Frank J. "The Oradell Pumping Station." *Live Steam* 18, no. 5 (May 1984): 30–33.

Yereance, William B., and Y. W. Demarest, "Test of the Hackensack Water Company's Pumping Station at New Milford, New Jersey, April 1888." Report in the archive of United Water Resources, Harrington Park, New Jersey.

Zink, Clifford W. "The Hackensack Water Works." National Landmark Nomination, National Park Service, Washington, D.C., 2003.

———. "The Hackensack Water Works: Sparkling History, Cloudy Future." *New Jersey Heritage* 1, no. 2 (Spring 2002): 16–29.

Index